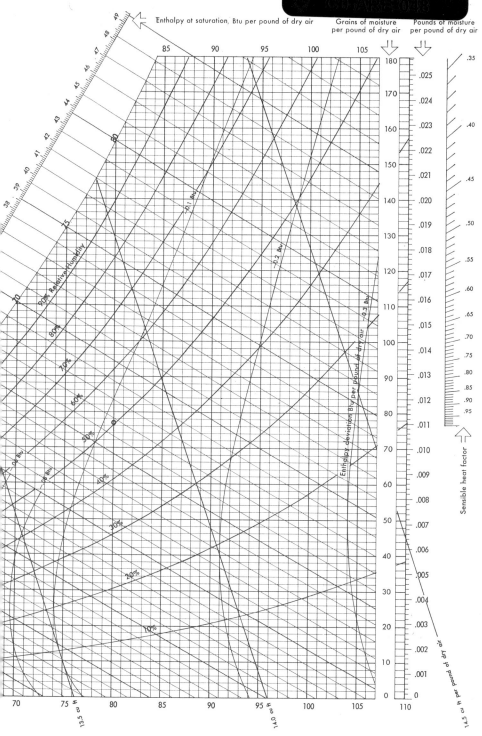

Coffee Processing Technology

Volume Two
Aromatization — Properties — Brewing —
Decaffeination — Plant Design

Coffee Processing Technology

Volume Two

Aromatization—Properties—Brewing—Decaffeination—Plant Design

by MICHAEL SIVETZ, M.S.

Chemical Engineer, Consultant in Soluble Coffee Plant Design, Construction and Operation, Research and Development in Coffee Flavors.
Formerly:

Technical Director, Cafe Soluble, S.A., Managua, Nicaragua;
Technical Director, J. A. Folger Co., Houston, Texas;
Project Leader, General Foods Res. Lab., Hoboken, New Jersey;
Project Engineer, Argonne National Laboratory, Argonne, Illinois;
Field Engineer, Coca-Cola Export Corp., New York, N. Y.

WESTPORT, CONNECTICUT

THE AVI PUBLISHING COMPANY, INC.

1963

Printed in the United States of America
BY MACK PRINTING COMPANY, EASTON, PENNSYLVANIA

Preface to Volume II

In Volume I of this work, we have attemped to present the technology of coffee (with a brief glance at its history) from its beginning, first as seed, then as ripe fruit on the coffee tree to its ultimate destination in the cup of the consumer. We have touched only lightly on the huge field of coffee horticulture because this has been very competently presented by others and it would otherwise have swelled this book beyond reasonable bounds. Chapters 3 through 6 deal with the harvesting and processing of the fruit until it has reached the dry green coffee stage. The central theme here is how to preserve the high quality which it has as ripe fruit, to prevent deterioration which so easily takes place, and to do it at the lowest cost.

Having reached this relatively stable condition, the coffee must then be freed from various imperfections and be stored and transported, while again guarding against deterioration, to the roaster in the coffee consuming country. This is dealt with in Chapter 7. The art and technology of roasting are the subjects of Chapter 8. More than 80 per cent of all roast coffee goes to the consumer in this form. The remainder is extracted and most of the extract is dried to form soluble or instant coffee. This operation requires a high degree of chemical engineering skill if a high-grade product is to result. The extraction or percolation step is the subject of Chapters 9 and 10. The removal of water from the extract is described in Chapters 11 and 12. The chief problem in the manufacture of instant coffee is how to retain the flavor and aroma. A great deal of progress has been made in this field and the latest developments are presented. The progress has come about by determining the exact chemical constituents of coffee flavor and aroma and studying their properties. This points the way to future developments.

In order to deliver the coffee either roasted and ground or as soluble powder to the consumer in a fresh, potent condition, exacting standards of packaging are required. Chapter 13 deals with this.

The above is covered in Volume I.

Volume II continues with an elaborate study of the aromatization of instant coffee in Chapter 14; the chemical, physical, and physiological properties of coffee in all its forms are presented in the next three chapters.

Returning to the manufacture of instant coffee, the control of process and product, and plant design with cost studies are discussed in Chapters 18 and 20. Chapter 19 deals with four subjects, (1) decaffeination which is an important segment of soluble coffee production, (2) brewing on a large scale and in the home, (3) vending machines for coffee, and (4) additives, substitutes, synthetic flavors, and, perhaps most interesting, the possibility of getting a full measure of real, natural but controlled coffee flavor into the cup of instant coffee.

August, 1963

MICHAEL SIVETZ
2666 Las Gallinas Avenue
San Rafael, California

Table of Contents — Volume One

To make this two-volume book most useful, we list here the complete table of contents for both volumes. Chapters 1 through 13 constitute Volume I on Fruit—Green, Roast, and Soluble Coffee. Chapters 14 through 21 and the three Appendices are in Volume II on Aromatization—Properties—Brewing—Decaffeination—Plant Design. Each volume has its own index.

VOLUME I. FRUIT—GREEN, ROAST, AND SOLUBLE COFFEE

Table of Contents — Volume Two

To make this two-volume book most useful, we list here the complete table of contents for both volumes. Chapters 1 through 13 constitute Volume I on Fruit–Green, Roast, and Soluble Coffee. Chapters 14 through 21 and the three Appendices are in Volume II on Aromatization–Properties–Brewing–Decaffeination–Plant Design. Each volume has its own index.

VOLUME II. AROMATIZATION–PROPERTIES
DECAFFEINATION–BREWING–PLANT DESIGN

x

CHAPTER 14

Aromatizing Soluble Coffee

INTRODUCTION

Since aroma is an essential component of soluble coffee, this chapter will be devoted to an analysis of the properties of coffee aroma and flavor, as well as the various methods described in patents and published articles for their recovery, retention, and storage without change.

Aromatizing instant (soluble) coffee means preserving or restoring the characteristic aroma of roast coffee in the preparation of the water soluble powder. Ever since coffee processing machinery has been in operation, inventors have endeavored to isolate, retain, or restore the coffee aroma. The patent literature is therefore full of objectives and claims in this direction. Yet, the elusive and fugitive character of the aroma has defied capture and definition to this very day. The aroma and flavor are such transient entities that progress in their isolation, analysis, and chemistry has been slow.

Therefore, in order to aromatize instant coffee, the chemical and physical nature of the volatile aroma must be known. This means that a knowledge of the odor potency of each volatile constituent, and the odor impression of each combination of volatile constituents are needed. The problem is further complicated by the unbalance in coffee aroma, readily brought about by oxidation, volatilization, and diffusion, as well as by chemical reactions.

In the past decade, significant progress has been made in isolating and fixing coffee aroma. Future progress is expected at an accelerated pace. A comprehensive history of this field is to be found in the patents and periodical literature. After these are reviewed, an explanation of the part played by the colloidal matter in brewed coffee flavor and the reasons for change of flavor in instant coffee extract will be presented. With the idea that retention of the coffee volatiles is preferable to their restoration to the final instant coffee powder, freeze concentration of extracts and distillates will be covered. Since coffee oil, extracted or expelled from roast coffee, has come into prominent commercial use, the methods for its recovery and reapplication will also be discussed. In addition, as coffee aroma is composed of volatile chemical substances, the techniques for their recovery will be investigated together with the sources of the aroma which include grinder gas, vacuum distillation from roast and ground (R & G) coffee, dry vacuum aroma (DVA), atmospheric distillation from R & G coffee, and distillation from coffee extracts.

1

Finally, incorporation of the recovered coffee essence into the coffee extract or into other media such as gelatin, gums, molten carbohydrates, and capsules will be explained.

In summary, aroma and flavor can be added to instant coffee in numerous ways. Present commercial methods for aromatizing coffee will no doubt change as more dependable and acceptable techniques of flavor retention are developed. The methods used at any time depend not only on technical feasability but also on successful advertising and the costs of the operation. Every aromatization technique involves special equipment and analytical methods. It is not inconceivable that instant coffee fortified with flavor will evolve when suitable fortifiers have been determined. Analogous developments concerning aromas and flavors in dairy products, fruits, tobacco, bakery products, vegetables, smoke, and other industries influence the coffee flavor field. Scientific research in coffee aroma and flavor will find the answers sooner than trial-and-error experiments. As the gap between commercial taste identities of green coffees and trained tasting associated with the chemical constituents of coffee aroma and flavor becomes smaller, a basic definition of coffee flavor that is acceptable and valuable will be forthcoming. Because of the fundamental nature of flavors in chemistry as well as in human responses, these problems offer an exciting and possibly lucrative field of endeavor.

A REVIEW OF PATENTS

Until 1957 soluble coffees were processed as indicated in earlier chapters of Vol. I by percolation and spray drying, often with much loss in flavor resulting from only fair to poor practices at each process stage. There had been no significant instant coffee flavor improvement until about 1952 when the larger hollow bead particles with better coffee flavor and physical properties was marketed as 100 per cent coffee. Instant coffee still lacked the delectable aroma of roast coffee. The phenomenal growth rate of instant coffee sales in the early 1950's was not maintained and, as sales competition increased, the industry recognized that coffee aroma had to be introduced into the instant coffee jar in order to stimulate consumption.

Expelled and Distilled Coffee Oil

The industry's largest research resources were directed to that end. Cole's U.S. patent 2,542,119, assigned to General Foods Corporation, was applied for in 1948 and issued in 1951. It dealt with separation of coffee aroma volatiles by film distillation from coffee oil. Canadian patent 572,026 issued in 1959 to Clinton and Pitchon and assigned to General Foods Corporation dealt with "aromatizing the head space of a jar of soluble coffee"; this patent was applied for in the United States in 1954. This was followed by U.S. patent 2,875,063 and 2,947,634 (five-fold coffee oil concentration) to Feldman *et al.* for General Foods Corporation in 1959. U.S. patent 2,931,728 issued in 1960 to Franck and Guggenheim and assigned to General Foods Corporation refers to extraction of oil from roast coffee.

In 1957 Maxwell House commercially prepared and marketed an expelled-oil-coated instant coffee which had aroma in the jar and was packed in inert gas. Thus the needed coffee aroma was added back to the conventionally prepared powder. The aroma volatiles were, however, quickly lost, and the instant coffee flavor staled within a day or two. Much of the coffee aroma in the jar never appeared in the cup except for an oily, smoother texture in the cup taste. Other soluble coffee firms since 1957 have made similar aroma additions by means of coffee oil add-back to powder. A 1950 U.S. patent by two Swiss workers, Schaeppi and Mosimann, expelled coffee oil and sprayed it back on instant coffee powder. In 1960, a U.S. patent by Barch and Reich of Standard Brands (Chase & Sanborn) proposed fatty acid addition to reduce foam formed when mixing instant coffee powder in the cup; fatty acids can also hold coffee aromas. Gilmont's 1949 application for U.S. patent 2,563,233, issued in 1951, uses solvent extraction of coffee oil. Solvent is stripped in a molecular still to fractionate the most aromatic coffee oil fraction which is sprayed back over the instant coffee powder. Kellogg has five U.S. patents dated 1926, 1942, 1944, 1945, and 1951, which deal with aspects of expressed coffee oil add-back to dry coffee solubles. It has often been observed that a novel idea is likely to be put into practice about 20 years after the original principles are defined in a patent or otherwise published. This frequently holds for instant coffee developments.

Petroleum Solvents

Trigg *et al.* had a 1919 U.S. patent, 1,292,458, that used petroleum jelly or mineral oil to capture coffee aromas. By solvent transfer these aromas are placed on the instant coffee powder. There were two more Trigg patents in 1921. One refers to lactose as a coffee aroma adsorber. The other uses petroleum ether extraction of aqueous coffee condensate to remove coffee aromas and add them back to the instant coffee powder. Use of petroleum ether as a transfer medium for coffee aromas is not greatly different from using coffee oil for the same purpose.

Kato (1903) adds back solvent-extracted coffee oil to the dry soluble coffee powder. Vietinghoff (1916) also mixed fat residue with the soluble coffee powder. Comparable patents usually can be found in British, Swiss, and other European countries, and these will be covered separately.

In 1938, Sylvan's Swedish patent extracted R & G coffee with petroleum ether and then transferred the flavorful portion to alcohol extract of ether and then to instant coffee in a process not unlike Trigg's 1919 patent using enfleurage into petroleum jelly.

Coffee oil add-back to powder was neither a new approach nor the only way to transfer coffee aroma onto the instant coffee powder and into the jar. Since this was the method chosen by a leading producer of instant coffee, it will be covered first. Thereafter, other and possibly better aromatizing methods will be discussed.

Powder Aroma Retention

The procedure already outlined in Chapter 12 for retaining greater coffee aroma and flavor volatiles through spray drying powder particles with a lower ratio of surface to weight is a direct method with no complicating side processes. More complicated processes entail greater plant investment, higher operating costs, and make oxidation, deterioration, and loss of coffee volatiles more likely.

Roast Coffee Contact

Two aromatizing U.S. patents, Heyman (1935) 2,022,467 and Meyer and Haas (1931) 1,836,931, use R & G coffee to contact soluble coffee powder and thus transfer coffee oil and aroma to the soluble coffee powder. It is of interest that the Chock Full O' Nuts instant coffee marketed in the New York City area in 1961 added about 1 per cent fine ground coffee to its instant product. This was packed in a can under vacuum to protect the natural coffee aroma and flavor from oxidation.

Spray Drier Techniques

Blench has two interesting patents. The earlier one (1956) aromatizes instant coffee powder by countercurrently cascading it against rising aroma-laden gases. The 1959 patent adds petroleum ether to coffee extract before spray drying and claims marked coffee flavor retention that effects better retention of volatiles through spray drying.

Polar Solvent Transfer

Only a step away from the method of using direct contact of R & G coffee with soluble coffee powder is to transfer aroma by means of solvents. This is done by polar solvents such as liquid carbon dioxide or sulfur dioxide as explained in Brandt's (1944) U.S. patent 2,345,378, or by ethylene oxide reviewed in Brandt's (1942) U.S. patent 2,286,334. Solvent extracted coffee oil is also dispersed over soluble coffee powder by vibration. Etaix of Paris in U.S. patent 1,251,359 of 1917, does an aroma transfer from R & G coffee to soluble coffee powder by cold nitrogen gas recirculation. It is claimed that moisture is needed to effect transfer. This does not transfer coffee oil as do the methods outlined in Brandt's patents. Methylene chloride and Freon are also polar solvents for aroma and oil transfer. In 1930, I. G. Farben Industrie took out a French patent for liquid ammonia extraction of R & G coffee (especially for alkaloids); evaporation of the ammonia left a water soluble coffee with good aroma and flavor. The similarity between this method and the later Brandt (1944) patent using liquefied polar solvents should be noted.

Alcohol Solvents

Another class of instant coffee aromatization patents is based on R & G coffee extraction with alcohols or aldehydes. These patents are of interest because they show that petroleum solvents that remove coffee oil do not remove all the coffee flavor from the R & G coffee. Further, since the coffee volatiles identified to date contain many aldehydes, a carbonyl solvent probably has merit. Alcohol extractions of R & G coffee are covered in U.S. patents by Musher (1950); Cohen (1950); and Anhaltzer (1921). Musher had some earlier U.S. patents in 1939, 1940, and 1942. In 1948 Medial Laboratories acquired a British patent using a three-step extraction of R & G coffee with three solvents (petroleum ether, alcohol, and water) which is similar to Cohen's 1950 U.S. patent. Medial Laboratory has a 1949 Swiss patent using alcohol extraction of R & G coffee, followed, in turn, by chilling the solution to remove fats and then its addition to coffee powder with alcohol evaporation. The Schott Swiss patent 277,290 (1951) uses alcohol extraction of R & G coffee and is similar to the Medical Laboratory 1949 patent and Cohen's 1950 patent. *

Distillation

The patents discussed so far have more or less referred to coffee oil transfer as this is the technique widely used today. There are, however, many patents for adding aroma and flavor to instant coffee through recovery of coffee volatiles by steam distillation with heat or under vacuum. These should be considered even though their commercial application is not yet as wide as coffee oil add-back. Coffee aroma gases and especially the steam distillates have been a major source of coffee flavor recovery. As pointed out in the percolation section (Chapter 10), the return of vent gas condensate is a notable contribution to coffee flavor in the instant coffee powder.

---

* Mysher patents, Addenda to list A. p. 60: 2,198,206/40, 2,278,463/42, 2,278,473/42, 2,282,802/42, and 2,493,080/50.

Patents assigned to Hills Bros. by Nutting and Darling relate to steamed R & G volatiles recovery. In 1956, Hills Bros. was one of the first companies to process and sell an aromatized instant coffee that was so markedly different from others that, in the following years, its flavor was altered to conform to its competitors. Other steam distillation patents are owned by Wendt (1939) and Heyman (1947). The Bonotto patent (1959) steam distilled R & G coffee by collecting and concentrating the aromatics on silica gel. These are then driven off by steam and reincorporated into instant coffee. This patent is assigned to McCormick and Company. Bacot's (1950) U.S. patent also relates to pre-steam distillation of aromatics before water extraction of R & G coffee. These are only a few of the patents that use steam distillation of coffee volatiles. They are listed here to indicate continuing interest in this method of coffee flavor recovery. Such persistence over the years is usually an indication of merit.

Lemonnier (1954) was granted a patent for dry vacuum distillation (DVA) of coffee volatiles to be added back to the powder. Johnston (1942) has a similar patent for an atmospheric recovery system for grinder gases. Two 1949 Swiss patents deal with recovery of R & G coffee distillates with reincorporation into the extract. A French patent by Laguilharre (1950) concentrates volatiles from the first part of the distillate from coffee extract. Thereafter, the extract is dried with concentrated volatiles restored. In 1950, a Swiss patent similar to the Lemonnier dry vacuum aroma (DVA) recovery was taken out by Schott, followed by two more Swiss coffee patents in 1951.

Some of the percolation patents mentioned (see p. 335) also aromatize. For example, Barotte (1890)[1] and Whitaker and Metzgar[1] (1915) used steam distillation prior to extraction of R & G coffee and reincorporated the volatiles into the extract.

Extract Distillation

Milleville's patents (1948 and 1950) made a marked contribution to fruit flavor concentration from fruit purées, juices, and jellies. Fruit flavor volatiles are more stable than coffee aroma volatiles, and this work is not entirely applicable to coffee. See pp. 341, 342, and 351.

Molten Carbohydrates

A process related to fruit flavor recovery is the incorporation of the flavor into a molten carbohydrate which is immediately cooled to form a protective powder. Patents[1] by Turkot (1957 and 1959), Eskew (1960),

---

[1] See Chapter 10, Vol. I, and Appendix I patents.

Dimick (1959), Makower (1959), and Epstein (1948) relate to this process, which has not, however, been successful with coffee aroma or flavor even though some of these patents refer to coffee applications. Similar patents for coffee have been taken out by Chase and Lee (1958), Lorand (1932), G. Washington (1924), and others. A 1944 British patent covers mixing R & G steam distillate and absorbing non-condensables in corn syrup. Roaster gases are similarly collected and all are mixed into coffee extract which is vacuum dried in thin layers. The residue is 50 per cent each of coffee solubles and carbohydrates.

A British patent by Nyrop in 1950 introduced up to 2 per cent hexose sugars with phosphoric acid, claiming the spray dried product had better coffee flavor retention. Girardet has a 1951 British patent similar to Nyrop's, pointing to the addition of carbohydrates and gelatin to help retain flavor achieved through spray drying. Girardet also has a 1950 Swiss patent on coffee flavors. In 1948, Nestlés Afico, S.A., obtained a Swiss patent for adding a quantity of polyhydric alcohol to coffee extract equal to the amounts of solubles obtained in spray drying to give a low hygroscopic powder with aroma retention. A 1956 British patent 744,757 fixes extracted coffee flavor in a carbohydrate melt. Since soluble coffee use has not grown in Europe (except for England) as quickly as in the United States, fewer patents and less research work have come from Europe. Patent details are listed in Appendix I.

A 1947 British patent by Kestner, 687,106, extracts green coffee, and dries and heats or roasts the extract residue making soluble coffee.

COFFEE FLAVOR CHEMISTRY

European soluble coffee patents go back to 1925 with Staudinger, followed in 1926 and 1928 by a Swiss firm, International Nahrungs und Genusmittel. All three are British patents. With Staudinger's analyses of coffee aroma in the 1920's and the patents for synthetic coffee by Swiss firms at about the same time, knowledge of coffee chemistry was then more advanced in Europe than in the United States. Since World War II, however, the United States has taken the lead as a result of research sponsored by the Coffee Brewing Institute, a branch of the National Coffee Association in New York City, supplemented by private research in the field of flavor and aroma of instant coffees. See chapter 19 and Appendix I.

In the food industry most flavor developments result from trial-and-error tests rather than scientific research directed toward gaining basic knowledge. The application of gas chromatography and mass spectroscopy and other analytical instruments has made investments in coffee chemistry studies more basic and sound. After knowledge is accumulated about coffee chemistry and flavors, it is often years before such information is commercially used. The study of coffee flavor is not without its parallels in other flavored products such as smoked meat and fruit flavors. *Freeze concentration* and *locked-in flavor* preparations are discussed later in this chapter.

Means of Aromatizing

A very satisfactory aromatized instant coffee can be prepared in many ways. Tastes may differ yet each type retains much of the pleasurable aroma sought from the original R & G coffee. Aromatization involves two basic steps (1) recovery of the flavor portion in some concentrated form, and (2) its reincorporation into or onto the instant coffee powder. Placing fugacious and unstable volatiles like coffee aroma *on* the powder is of questionable value.

Difference Between Roast and Instant Coffee

Data offered in Chapter 10 have shown that the hydrolysis products deviate in flavor from regular coffee; the higher the hydrolysis yields of solubles, the greater the deviation in flavor. A second point is that aroma is low in instant coffees. The lower it is, the less it tastes like brewed coffee.

The third point is all-important. Even if hydrolysis yields of solubles are low and as much aroma as necessary has been added, instant coffee still will not taste like brewed coffee as it has no brew colloids. While the colloidal portion of a cup of brewed coffee contributes 5 to 10 per cent oil to the solubles portion, instant coffees have only a few tenths per cent petroleum ether solubles at most before spray drying and less than 1 per cent after coffee oil add-back.

Coffee Brew Colloids

Colloids give a tactile sensation of smoothness to the cup and also increases opacity which can be measured by the amount of transmitted light. Since these colloids contribute so much in appearance, taste, and flavor to brewed coffee, it is desirable to understand what part brew colloids play in coffee flavor before attempting to define the term "aromatizing." "Aromatizing" is often understood to mean making instant coffee resemble regular brewed coffee. To explain brew colloids is best done by describing their properties. It will then be possible to understand why brew colloids do not exist in instant coffee, to evaluate how their absence affects it, and to determine whether it is worthwhile to attempt to place them in instant coffee. Most of the physical properties of brew colloids can be ascertained by relatively simple brewing and bench top tests.

Filtration of Brew Colloids

Passage of a coffee brew through a paper filter removes practically all colloidal particles. The amount removed will depend on the porosity of the filter paper and the method of preparation. True colloids, less than the size of about 1 mu, will pass through the paper; hence it appears that the brew colloid particles are larger than 1 mu and may be considered as pseudo-colloids. In other words, their colloidal properties are real only in so far as the life of the brewed cup of coffee is concerned. Further evidence that brew colloid particles are not true colloids is that some rise to the top as a fatty layer and some fall to the bottom as sediment. This separation is noticeable as soon as brewed coffee cools to room temperature.

Coffee passing through filter paper has no "brew flavor." In fact, the flavor of the filtered brew has a striking resemblance to the percolator coffee extract diluted to cup strength. This resemblance, at times, can be used as an index of the kind of extract cup that will be obtained from some coffees. Care must be taken that the filter paper used has not absorbed foreign odors (especially when paper is stored in a coffee aroma area) and is rinsed with boiling distilled water to remove any residual foreign flavors before use. Removal of the brew colloid leaves a harsh, typically acid, instant coffee flavor; the colloids give a smooth taste texture to the cup. Gravity funnel filtration is more effective than Buchner pressure filtration in removing the brew colloids.

Rinsing the colloid collected with hot distilled water washes away considerable coffee flavor; hence the particles are ad- or absorbers of coffee flavor constituents. Transferring the filtered colloids from the paper to a cup of instant coffee imparts an appreciable brew flavor and turbidity. The instant coffee flavor is then weaker and the taste texture is smoother. Colloid ad- or absorption also gives a less acid cup (0.05 pH) as noted by taste and pH measurements. This type of phenomenon is consistent with the general properties of colloidal substances.

Filtration removes most, but not all, of the colloids. The addition of $^1/_{10}$ to $^1/_{20}$ of a cup of brewed coffee or the filtered out colloids from this quantity of brewed coffee to a cup of instant coffee is enough to give a perceptibly smoother and less acid cup.

Yield of Brew Colloids

If brew colloids can be transferred to instant coffee, it is of interest to know how much is perceptible in taste and how much is made available under different modes of brew preparation. For example, some obvious preparation factors are roast, grind, and the ratio of water to R & G coffee.

Darker roasts and finer grinds release more colloids as is evidenced by greater turbidity of the cup. The addition of a brew solution equivalent to $1/2$ to 1 gm of R & G coffee will impart perceptible brew flavor to a cup of instant coffee. But since each cup of instant coffee originates from about 6 gm R & G coffee, this is 8 to 16 per cent of the R & G coffee which is a significant fraction. Brew colloids will result in water to R & G coffee ratios from normal brew strength (about 20 water to 1 R & G or 1.1 per cent solubles) to much stronger ratios (about 5 to 1 ratio or 7 per cent solubles). The greater-than-proportional strength in the second case results because the R & G coffee absorbs water selectively, i.e., in preference to the solubles. Hence, the higher the coffee to water ratio, the more accentuated is the solubles concentration, but the less the solubles yield.

The water to R & G coffee ratio, however, does not seem to influence the yield of brew colloids. This might follow from the fact that the colloidal particles come from the surface of the R & G coffee, and the roast and particularly the grind are more important factors. The water to R & G coffee ratio does influence the solubles content of the resulting extract; hence, it influences the pH and the electrolytic density (electrical conductivity) of the solution. Colloidal phenomena are sensitive to pH and electrolytic density and therefore will appear different under such changed conditions. For example, the 5 to 1 water to R & G coffee ratio may result in a pH of about 4.90 whereas the 20 to 1 household brew ratio may show a pH of 5.0.

Nature of Brew Colloids

It is a common observation that the hydrolyzed solubles cause turbidity. About one-fourth of the solubles hydrolyzed are from proteins. Addition of alkali will dissolve these colloids which are in acid solution suspension at about pH 4.0. The brew colloids are oily in nature, but they behave like proteinaceous oils which show increased turbidity at pH values below 5.0. Texts on colloid and protein chemistry such as those by McBain (1931), Jirgensons (1958), Fox and Foster (1957), Hartman (1939), Conant (1939), and others, elaborate on such phenomena as protein solubility with pH. Hartman (1939) points out that proteins adsorb acids, a process which certainly occurs with coffee brew colloids. Different proteins have minimum solubilities or isoelectric points at different pH's, mostly between pH 4.7 and 5.2. Some proteins can act as acids (carboxylic groups) or bases (amino groups) depending on the solution in which they exist. These are described as amphoteric. Some proteins are soluble only in alkali, such as corn zein. It is beyond the scope of this text to discuss protein chemistry, but it is apparent that proteins play an important part in brew colloid stability and in hydrolysis solubles from which tars are formed.

Freezing usually causes colloid particles to coalesce and they cannot be restored to their original condition on thawing. This is partly true for coffee brew colloids; however, it depends on the degree of colloid coalescence, rate of freezing, and, hence, the size of ice crystals. For example, quick frozen brew colloids that are freeze dried will reconstitute practically to their original colloidal condition.

The colloidal nature of coffee brew is not limited to brewing with boiling water; room temperature extractions of R & G coffee yield good brew flavor and cup turbidity.

Repeated boiling of brewed coffee breaks down the colloidal stability, with oil coalescing to droplets and rising to the surface. Brew colloids that collect as cream on the top of a cooled, quiet brew show on evaporation a separation of oil droplets and a black, tarry protein residue that is insoluble in water.

Centrifuging Brew Colloids

Since the brew colloids are not true colloids, because they separate out on standing, the process of separation can be accelerated by centrifuging. For example, by taking 10 ml of a strong Silex brew (40 gm fine grind roast coffee with 400 ml water) and placing it in a laboratory centrifuge, depending on blend and roast, about 1 per cent of tan colored buttery oil and a few per cent of sediment will result. The middle portion will be a clear solution tasting similar to instant coffee but without hydrolysis flavors. The oil-emulsion colloid portion has excellent and strong coffee flavor. The sediment has strong brew flavor when added to a cup of instant coffee. The potency of coffee flavor of the "cream" and the sediment portions is such that either one at a 5 to 10 per cent level from original brewed cup imparts a characteristically noticeable brew flavor to a cup of instant coffee. The sediment may carry some R & G fines (fiber) and a slight amount of carbohydrates and oil (petroleum ether solubles), but is otherwise protein.

Conant points out that proteins are divided into simple proteins which yield only amino acids on hydrolysis, or conjugated proteins in which some other component is linked to the protein. The non-protein portion is called a prosthetic group. Casein from milk is classed as a phosphoprotein and contains phosphoric acid as the prosthetic group; the protein of coffee colloids appears also to be a phosphoprotein.

The composition of the floating, buttery or creamy portion will depend on the degree of coalescence of the colloidal oil-protein. The greater the coffee oil content, the greater the colloid coalescence will be. For example, petroleum ether extraction of the "cream" can yield from 15 per cent down to a fraction of 1 per cent of oil. The portion insoluble in petroleum ether is a black tar containing protein and phosphorus.

Lecithin

Hartman (1939) points out that phospholipids (substituted fats containing phosphoric acid and proteins such as lecithin, cephalin, and sphingomyelin) are found in seeds of plants. Lecithin is obtained commercially from soybeans and is a mixture of the diglycerides of stearic, palmitic, and oleic acids linked to the choline ester of phosphoric acid. It contains about 4 per cent phosphorus. Commercial lecithin has about 2.2 per cent phosphorus according to the Merck Index. Its importance is that it is insoluble but swells in water, forming a colloidal suspension. It is soluble in fatty acids but insoluble in vegetable oils. These properties make lecithin a very effective surfactant and emulsifier and it is used for these purposes in the food industry.

The brew colloid particles appear to be in the range of 1 to 10 mu, varying with the degree of coalescence. The fact that the brew colloids are not entirely stable means that a major fraction of the colloids coalesce to particles larger than 1 mu which then may rise to form a creamy emulsion film. Heating this emulsion on a steam bath causes emulsion breakup into a clear, almost tasteless yellow oil and black tarry deposit. The oil has a flavor that is bitter and similar to that of fatty acids in vegetable oil. The black-brown deposit is probably the protective colloid (phosphoprotein) layer that surrounds the minute oil particles. The emulsion has a physical texture like dairy cream and a rich coffee flavor with a note of unsweetened chocolate.

Test for Phospholipids

Lecithin colloid with coffee oil gives instant coffee smoothness and body. Without this ingredient, its flavor is flat. Brew colloids give positive tests for phospholipids as follows: (1) acetone precipitates colloids; (2) methyl acetate precipitates colloids (result: upper layer clear green; lower layer clear brown); (3) cadmium chloride precipitates brew colloids using ethanol; and (4) ethyl and petroleum ether emulsify in colloids.

The brew colloid has its natural characteristics only if it is not concentrated. If colloids have an opportunity to coagulate, the tactile taste and basic brew flavor properties are lost. There is separation of free vegetable oil and proteinaceous tarry sediment. Concentration of the brew colloids may be effected in several ways: (1) percolation to solubles concentrations over 15 per cent and especially 20 per cent; (2) evaporation of water by any means, e.g., still or spray drying. As already pointed out, concentration of the colloidal emulsion either by evaporation or centrifuging simply coalesces the colloidal micron-sized particles until they become larger and larger. This simultaneously reduces their production of a smooth, tactile sensation. An emulsion exists until water solubles are perhaps 15 to 25 per cent, but the emulsion particles are then coalescing irreversibly.

Freeze Dried Emulsion

If the brew colloid solution were freeze dried as a means of reintroducing some noticeable brew flavor into spray dried instant coffee, there might be some merit in concentrating the brew colloids to a certain degree to minimize evaporation costs of freeze drying. On the basis of adding only about 5 per cent of freeze dried brew flavored instant coffee to 95 per cent spray dried instant coffee, it will be more like brewed coffee. Colloidal proteins will precipitate in the rising acidity with increased solubles concentration and electrolytic density. Brewed coffee has characteristically a pH of 5.0 and contains about 1 per cent solubles. Hence, the electrolytic density or conductivity of the coffee solution is relatively poor. Since the protective oil-protein colloid is sensitive to breaking down in more acid environments, the pH range is an important consideration in colloid stability. Percolator extracts with high solubles concentrations coagulate brew colloids.

Turbidity is no assurance of brew flavor, but without turbidity there is neither brew taste sensation nor flavor. Also, where brew colloids are spray dried they cannot survive the solubles concentration without losing stability; hence, spray dried powders have no brew character. But since freeze drying, with prior quick freezing, prevents gross coalescence of the brew colloid, subsequent ice sublimation from interstitial voids may produce soluble coffee powders with brew taste character. Some brew colloidal taste character can be produced through spray drying by using high pressure atomization as for cream, whole milk, egg whites, egg yolk, whole eggs, coffee oil emulsion in gum, and other food products.

Atomization at 3,000 to 5,000 psig of brew tasting coffee extract (several per cent solubles) can bring some brew flavor into the powder. But because of the fine atomization, practically all the coffee flavor volatiles are lost. This indicates a need to balance blended powders to achieve a desired coffee flavor and taste texture effect. With milk and eggs there are not many significant volatile flavors that can be lost. The colloids in brewed coffee are delicate, and homogenization of brewed coffee may coagulate the colloid.

Simulation of Colloidal Oil

This can be done by homogenizing at about 5,000 psig, for instance, one part of coffee oil with one part of a 25 per cent solution of gum arabic and atomizing at high pressures (3,000 psig). This results in a coating of gum arabic around micron-sized oil droplets. Lecithin does not have to be used but may be desirable. In the cup of instant coffee containing $1/2$ to 1 per cent of homogenized oil, a smooth tasting cup with brew flavor is achieved.

Coffee oil does not homogenize with coffee extract and cannot be spray dried even at high atomization pressures without having oil separation.

The high pressure atomization of cream is used to prepare dry cream powders. The protein protective layer around the oil must be conserved for restoration of tactile emulsion sensations on reconstitution. The oil droplets produce a powder with a sugar-protein coating.

Review of Brew Colloids

In summary, brew colloids are micron-sized oil droplets (in a protective protein-phosphate medium) that are unstable in acid media, high electro-lytic media, and in concentrated solutions. These droplets break down the emulsion to liberate free oil and protein-phosphate tars. The colloids are buffers, adsorbing acids, to give a less acid and harsh tasting cup of coffee with a smooth tactile sensation. The oils help carry coffee flavor and aroma. The colloids are unstable at elevated temperatures and concen-trated solutions such as occur in spray drying. High pressure atomization spray drying brings some brew colloids through but hardly any volatile flavors. Freeze drying brings many brew colloids into a powder form. Brew flavor colloidal effect is simulated by emulsifying coffee oil in gum arabic and freeze or spray drying at high pressures.

FREEZE CONCENTRATION OF COFFEE SOLUBLES

The less water in the extract sent to the spray drier, the less has to be evaporated. Also, the greater the percentage of water retained in the powder, the greater is the retention of volatile flavors. Furthermore, as the higher extract concentrations are more viscous, they give thicker walled particles with less surface per unit weight; and their water evapor-ation occurs by diffusion more than by flash evaporation. Thus the theo-retical and practical evidence is all in favor of freeze concentration.

No one freeze concentrates coffee extract commercially. Strongly sup-porting this statement is the fact that extract solubles concentrations of over 30 per cent are readily obtained by normal percolation. With inter-column heating of extract 40 per cent solubles can readily be obtained. However, these higher concentrations of solubles are obtained at the price of coffee flavor loss caused by high percolator solubles inventories or percolator residence time.

The best tasting percolator extracts with minimum hydrolysis flavors are made with the highest water flow throughputs at the lesser extract concentrations of about 20 per cent solubles. These concentrations are too low to carry much volatile coffee flavor through spray drying. Therefore, freeze concentration of the lower extract concentrations improves instant coffee powder quality.

Cost.—There are some limiting technical features to freeze concentration. Investment is not one. The cost of freeze concentration equipment is approximately the same as for expelling oil, spraying it back on the powder, and finally inert gas packaging. Freeze concentration of orange

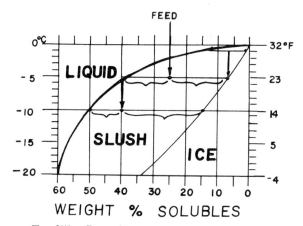

FIG. 251. PHASE DIAGRAM FOR COFFEE EXTRACT

juice has been the technique used to obtain a far superior flavored orange juice concentrate. Assuming the removal of 2 lb of water per pound of coffee solubles, the basic electrical cost for cooling and freezing water adds about 0.1 cent per pound of solubles. The cost of equipment for freezing, centrifuging, etc., would be about $300,000 for a plant producing 3,000,000 lb of soluble coffee per year, amortized over 10 years at $30,000 per year or about 1 cent per pound of soluble coffee. One difficulty is that there is no "off-the-shelf" equipment to buy, and an installation would require some development work, although this would be nominal. There are numerous patents and articles on freeze concentration for fruit juices, vinegar, and other foods, and there are several plants doing freeze concentration of these items commercially. The reduced cost for overseas shipment of vinegar, with most of the water removed by freeze concentration is an example.

Viscosity, the Limiting Factor.—The physical factor limiting freeze concentration is the increased viscosity of coffee extracts at solubles concentrations of over 50 per cent at the freezing temperature, about 14 F (−10 C), required to separate out ice crystals. Figure 251 shows a schematic phase diagram for ice and coffee solubles. It can be seen, for example, that at 23 F (−5 C), the equilibrium mixture is about 6 per cent coffee solubles in the solid phase and 40 per cent solubles in the liquid phase. This means that the ice phase must go to another stage of freezing out ice for higher concentrations of solubles. When the rejected ice has only a few per cent solubles, it would be practical to vacuum evaporate the dilute solution to recover these solubles. Figure 252 illustrates such a batch countercurrent freeze concentration process. The process of freeze concentration should be protected with inert gas to avoid oxidation of

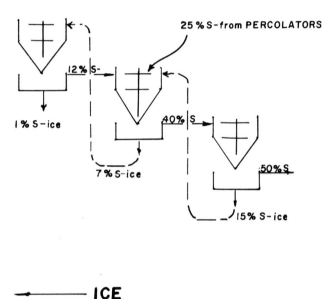

FIG. 252. COUNTERCURRENT MULTI-STAGE FREEZE CONCENTRATION

coffee flavors as cited in many of the Union Carbide patents. The freeze concentration process has the advantage of coagulating the tarry coffee substances between the ice crystals. The resulting extract has a markedly reduced hydrolysis flavor and taste.

Ice Crystal Growth.—While published references to freeze concentrations are listed, patents and articles are not covered in detail. Several articles are directly pertinent to coffee extract. The enthusiasm for the flavor carry-through in these articles is justified. Sharp separation of ice and more concentrated coffee extract is obtained with large ice crystals which entrain little extract in centrifuge separations. The growth of ice crystals takes time as studied specifically by Adams and Lewis (1934), Badger and McCabe (1936) and others. This literature on water ice crystal growth is surprisingly meager. Recent work has been done on saline water purification by the Carrier Corporation. Large crystals make for efficient separation of ice from the concentrated coffee solution.

Good-sized ice crystals can be grown from refrigerated metal surfaces, but as they grow out, the rate of heat transfer diminishes. There is hardly any literature on the growth of ice crystals in suspension. This process would be analogous to evaporator crystallization as used in the sugar and salt crystal industries. Companies like Swenson Evaporator and Struthers-Wells, prominent in this type of crystallizer equipment manufacture, have few requests for ice crystallizers. This situation may change as greater flavor retention (and less weight of water) for fruit juices and other beverages is sought. For example, it is now common practice for a soft beverage bottler to reconstitute orange and fruit juice concentrates for local consumption. Even beer is now concentrated at the factory for local reconstitution and distribution.

Freeze concentration requires a turbulent flow of extract around the freezing surfaces so that as ice crystals grow, the adjacent concentrated extract layers are removed. Quick freezing of the extract is not suitable for ice crystal separation because only small ice crystals form. Small crystals grow in a rotary film freezer (such as is used for ice cream, and final concentrated orange juice) as manufactured by Girdler Corporation, Cherry-Burrell Corporation, or Creamery Package Company. Work on saline water purification shows that the growth of ice crystals in a chilled suspended medium is feasible.

Batch Freezing of Ice.—Preparation of commercial 100-lb blocks of ice uses a center air bubbler to mix the concentrating solubles in the water. Coffee extract can also be frozen in the same way with brine at about 18 F (−8 C) circulating outside the can. However, after ice crystals 2 in. thick have formed, the rate of ice growth is very slow. It is better to have an immersion freezing plate with extract circulating around it, and to remove the plate with about 1 in. of ice crystals. The ice crystal growth rate is high up to that thickness. The cooling rate depends on the coolant temperature. The concentration of coffee solubles influences extract viscosity and the rate of heat transfer. The ice crystals also occlude extract. Thus, the growth of free ice crystals in a turbulent fluid extract solution with the cooling from a side stream of the extract is more attractive. A pure 1 in. thick ice crystal can be grown in about 24 hr from a chilled wall at 18 F (−8 C).

Example I.—A 25 per cent solubles concentration extract (3 lb water per pound solubles) can be concentrated to 55 per cent solubles concentration extract (0.8 lb water per pound solubles). This removes about four times the final water content associated with the solubles. The water removed from solubles, when drying these extracts to 3 per cent moisture, are respectively 100/1 and 26/1. Hence, retention of volatile flavors is improved at least four times. The thicker particle wall factor may actually increase volatile flavor retention in spray drying to as much as ten times. Particles spray dried from such high extract solubles concentrations are dark, shiny, and beady, have good fluidity, and excellent water solubility without much foaming. The ice crystals on chilled plates can be thawed off the plate and placed into a basket centrifuge for recovery of coffee solubles. The ice phase can be discarded or the ice can be further recrystallized, depending on the solubles content of the ice. The phase diagram, Fig. 251, shows a 25 per cent extract feed concentration with a tie-line at 40 and 6 per cent solubles; the phase weight distribution is, respectively, 55 to 45 and shows 85 per cent of the solubles in concentrated extract phase.

Preparation of Phase Diagram.—By taking several coffee extract solubles concentrations and cooling them, the rate of temperature fall alters slope when ice has formed. This gives the liquid-slush equilibrium temperatures point at that concentration. Further cooling gives a falling slope again. When the latent heat of ice has been absorbed, the solution is solid, and this is the solid-slush equilibrium temperature point. This is somewhat more difficult to determine exactly. The temperature transition readings become more difficult to determine with higher extract concentrations. Since mechanical separation of ice crystals and extract is the commercial objective, phase data over this range are easily obtained. The phase diagram is similar to that obtained from sugar water compositions of fruit juices, Olive (1948).

Example II.—Continuing with the separation of phases at 14 F (−10 C), the 35 weight parts of 50 per cent solubles extract and 10 parts of 15 per cent solubles gives a separation respectively of 95 per cent solubles in the concentrate and 5 per cent solubles in the ice phase. Ice crystals should be at least 2 mm in size for effective centrifuge separation of extract and ice. Ice crystals 1 mm long can be grown in about an hour.

Volatile Flavor Protection.—Some deterioration of extract flavor occurs in freeze concentration. It is best to set aside the volatiles condensed from the percolator vent and to return them to the freeze concentrated extract just before spray drying. This minimizes the deterioration of the delicate volatile flavor portion. Freeze concentration of brew colloids in extract causes coalescence of the colloid, oil release and loss of brew taste character in the resulting concentrated extract, and hence also in the spray dried powder. Significant volatile flavor deterioration is noted in freeze concentrated extract in the form of a heavy coffee flavor similar to that obtained by pre-wetting R & G coffee and leaving it in air. The spray dried powder from high concentration extracts usually has a strong natural coffee aroma and flavor in the cup.

Centrifuging.—The separation of extract from ice can be carried out in a few minutes in a basket centrifuge operating at a few thousand revolutions per minute. The process is similar to the separation of sugar crystals from molasses.

Rotary Chilled Freezing Tube.—This type of unit will produce 3,000 lb per hr of an extract slush containing about 50 per cent of ice crystals by chilling a 33 per cent solubles extract from room temperature to 14 F (-10 C) with a refrigeration consumption of 240,000 Btu per hr or a rating of 20 tons per day. With a 165 Btu per hr per sq ft per deg F heat transfer rate, about a 30 F (17 C) mean temperature difference (refrigerant at -14 F or -26 C) and about 48 sq ft of freezing tube surface will be required. An ammonia refrigerated 20 ton compressor (60 hp) condenser system with each of six cylinders driven by a 10 hp motor, would cost about $25,000. The small ice crystals formed are useful only if they can be grown to larger crystals.

Freeze Concentrating Volatiles Distillate.—Since the freeze concentration of coffee extracts is limited by the increased viscosity of the ice crystal extract mixture at lower temperatures, an alternative procedure for concentrating coffee flavor volatiles may be preferable. The coffee extract can be concentrated in a vacuum film evaporator, and the distillate can be frozen immediately. The distillate containing about 0.6 per cent of acetic acid (depending on initial extract concentration and fraction distilled) and lesser amounts of homologous carboxylic acids, aldehydes, and other volatiles, can be freeze concentrated. Figure 253 shows the phase diagram for acetic acid. This can be used as a guide when freezing coffee distillates. For example, a separation of equal parts by weight of ice crystals and concentrated acetic acid, starting with 0.6 per cent acetic acid, will yield about 1.2 per cent acetic acid with hardly any acetic acid in the ice crystal phase. A second stage separation of equal weight ice crystal to acid solution separation will again almost double the concentration of the acid. The ice crystal phase at these low acid concentrations has hardly any acid. After three such freeze concentration stages, seven-eighths of the original distillate water will have been removed, (see Fig. 253).

Evaporation of Extract.—Coffee extract can be concentrated by vacuum evaporation from 25 per cent solubles (3 lb water to 1 lb solubles) to 50 per cent solubles (1 lb water to 1 lb solubles). Then, the 2 lb of distilled water are freeze concentrated to $1/4$ lb and returned to the extract. The water now to be evaporated in spray drying is about one-third of its original content in the 25 per cent solubles extract.

Freeze concentration of the evaporated distillate is efficient because the distillate has water-like properties. Therefore, freezing, crystal growth, and phase separations are easy. However, such handling of the flavor volatiles often is accompanied by oxidation, deterioration, and loss. Further, the aroma of less desirable hydrolysis volatiles (furfural, furan, acetone, etc.) becomes more prominent.

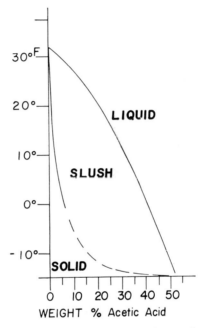

Fig. 253.   Phase Diagram for Acetic Acid

Elimination of Hydrolysis Volatiles.—This is desirable before freeze concentrated distillate is returned to the evaporator concentrated extract. The concentration of the aldehyde volatiles in the evaporator distillate may be undesirable because in the distillate the volatiles can react among themselves. Such reactions throw down a yellow to reddish and then black colloid which eventually precipitates. By excluding air, however, and keeping temperatures below 32 F (0 C) these reactions can be reduced. Evaporation of the flavor volatiles gives the extract residue a caramelized flavor; restoration to the extract of the stripped volatiles largely restores the original flavorful cup (without caramel flavor). This procedure is like taking away the overtones of dominant coffee flavor to reveal the sub-flavor, and then replacing the dominating coffee flavor tones to eliminate the sub-flavor.

Other Distillates.—The freeze concentration of coffee extract distillates can also be carried out with percolator vent gas distillates, R & G coffee steam distillates, and dry vacuum aroma distillates. All have considerable water associated with the volatiles. These distillates will be discussed below.

COFFEE OIL

Solvent Extraction

Coffee oil can be extracted from R & G coffee with numerous solvents and with various results. The properties of the extracted oil vary because each solvent is selective in what it extracts. The selectivity of the solvent will depend on its nature. For example, the solvent may be a pure hydrocarbon such as butane or hexane; or it may be a polar chlorinated hydrocarbon, e.g., chloroform, Freons, carbon tetrachloride, etc. The solvent may also be polar such as carbon dioxide, sulfur dioxide, or ammonia. What is extracted from the roast coffee will naturally depend on the affinity of the solvent for constituents in the roast coffee. Therefore, these solvents will remove coffee oil to varying degrees and with varying amounts of aromatics and waxes. The aroma and taste character of the resulting oil after evaporating the solvent will also vary, as will its aromatizing effect on the instant coffee powder. Furthermore, the removal of the solvent from the oil may not be complete in some cases. Any residual solvent in the coffee oil will affect the subsequent taste and aroma of the "aromatized" instant coffee. Solvent extraction is influenced by blend, roast, and grind. Time of solvent contact, temperature, and ratio of solvent to R & G coffee are also factors influencing the quality and quantity of coffee oil removed from the roast coffee. Solvent extraction of the R & G coffee should be done within a few hours after roasting. In order to avoid loss of volatiles, no water quench should be used.

Polar Solvents.—The compounds SO_2, CO_2, and NH_3 are polar (ionized) solvents soluble in water. They are gases at atmospheric pressure and room temperature. When these gases are compressed and cooled, however, they become useful as liquid solvents. For example, CO_2 in the gas phase is a solvent for oils. This accounts for the contamination of manufactured CO_2. See Sivetz (1947) on purification of CO_2 gas in soft drink bottling industry. As CO_2 gas pressures are increased, the solvent effect is greater, and is at a maximum for liquid CO_2. Since NH_3 and SO_2 are likely to leave a pungent residue after coffee oil extraction, and are more irritating to work with, they are less useful as solvents for coffee oil.

SO_2, however, does have the advantage of being a reducing agent and thus it allows the solvent extraction of coffee oil without an oxidizing atmosphere. Purity of the solvent can be checked by evaporating it from a neutral sugar powder, e.g., dextrose and instant coffee. One solvent may not yield a wholesome coffee oil-aroma residue after evaporation. Then a mixture of (low boiling) solvents can be used to obtain more wholesome tasting coffee oil and aroma extraction. Other polar solvents not previously mentioned are: nitrous oxide, bp −130 F (−90 C); methane, bp −258 F (−161 C); ethane, bp −128 F (−89 C); propane, bp −44 F (−42 C); methyl chloride, bp 75 F (24 C); methylamine, bp 45 F (7 C).

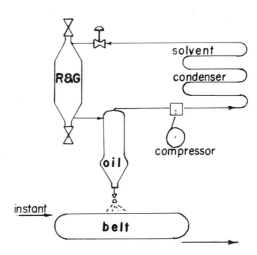

Fig. 254. Closed Cycle Aromatizing of Instant Coffee from Solvent Extracted Roast Coffee

Liquid CO_2.—Brandt's patents (1942 and 1944) outline the means for transfer of coffee oil with aroma from roast coffee to instant coffee powder. Liquid CO_2 is very volatile at room temperature.[2] It is ideal for use as an aroma transfer medium. Carbon dioxide is non-flammable, non-toxic in foods, and relatively inert chemically; it excludes oxygen in its use, and is relatively cheap. There are other solvents that approach the performance of CO_2 but are flammable. Figure 254 illustrates a system used by some firms for aromatizing their instant coffee. The solvent can be CO_2, SO_2, ammonia, low boiling chlorinated hydrocarbons (Freons) or even low boiling hydrocarbons (pentane). When the solvent extracted oil carries aroma and flavor properties that differentiate high grown premium

---

[2] The vapor pressure of CO_2 at 77 F (25 C) is 938 psia (48, 523 mm Hg).

quality coffees from others, the transfer process is sensitive. Faithfulness of aroma and flavor transfer can only be achieved with pure solvents. The extraction system must be clean and the coffee oil transfer must be complete for a balanced coffee flavor.

Coffee Oil Yield.—Top quality coffee should be used as the source of coffee oil. Roast coffee has about 10 to 12 per cent of coffee oil. Aromatic coffee oil yields of over 5 per cent are readily attainable. If only $1/2$ per cent coffee oil is sprayed on the instant coffee powder then only $1/10$ the oil times $1/2.5$ (solubles yield) or $1/25$ of the roast coffee percolated will have oil extracted. Recovery of a costly solvent in a closed cycle system is essential to make this type of coffee oil extraction process economical. Otherwise solvent costs would be too high. A recycle system of solvent compression and condensation also assures that the aromatics of the coffee are held in a closed system free of air. Once coffee volatiles are in the oil, they are relatively secure and stable.

Solvent-Extracted R & G Coffee.—This coffee must be stripped of its solvent residue before water extraction. Thus low boiling solvents, like CO_2, are advantageous. CO_2 leaves neither residual odor nor taste. If there is a solvent residue, then the R & G coffee may be heated under vacuum or may be steamed to remove noticeable traces of the solvent. Normally such a procedure is feasible but undesirable.

Solvent-extracted R & G coffee with its oils removed is noticeably lighter in color. Brewed solvent extracted R & G coffee is lower in coffee flavor and aroma; some coffee flavor remains but coffee aroma is mostly depleted. The solvent-extracted R & G coffee makes a much darker brew.

Solvent-extraction of R & G coffee does not degrade the ground coffee particles as is the case in oil expelling. Solvent extractions of roast coffee make subsequent water extraction easier. If CO_2 is used as the solvent, the coffee oil after solvent evaporation is left in an inert atmosphere.

Coffee Oil Stability.—The coffee oil with aroma, whether extracted or expelled, is quite stable chemically. It shows no rapid tendency to stale or deteriorate in a sealed brown bottle or tin can. Keeping the oil refrigerated helps extend its period of freshness.

Once the coffee oil is spread on the instant coffee powder it stales noticeably in air at 80 F (27 C) during the first day and to an objectionable level within the first week. In air at less than 40 F (4 C), the coffee oil on instant coffee powder remains fresh for at least a month.

Cleanliness of Extraction System.—Acetone-ethanol mixtures effectively clean coffee oil residues. Equipment used for handling solvents and coffee oil must be kept scrupulously clean. A little residual stale oil in the system may contaminate coffee oil subsequently prepared. New piping systems can contribute contamination from pipe sealing compound and machining or lubricating oils. Flanged connections are more sanitary than screwed pipe threads.

Oil Add-Back.—Coffee oil add-back, at more than 0.6 per cent of instant coffee powder, releases oil droplets. These appear as oil slicks on the cup and give a heavy oil taste. Coffee oil additions make a cup of instant coffee taste smoother and more like natural coffee in taste and aroma. The coffee aroma in the jar is especially good and desirable. Consumer testing of the fresh coffee oil sprayed onto instant coffee powder will usually show a significant preference over the untreated instant coffee powder. This is due to the initial coffee aroma from the jar and the small enhancement in flavor in the cup. The addition of coffee oil can sometimes mean the difference between consumption or rejection of instant coffee. With oil add-back, undesirable taste and odor caused by hydrolysis are diminished. The R & G coffee used to prepare the coffee oil carries its aroma and taste qualities to the cup of instant coffee. The aroma is usually more noticeable at some distance from the cup when the powder is dissolved in boiling water.

Hydrocarbon Solvents.—The solvents discussed have been very volatile. They mostly require pressurized systems at room temperature to maintain the solvent in liquid condition. Some solvents, however, do not need pressurized systems. These solvents can be useful for extraction of coffee oil, and yet can be successfully evaporated from the coffee oil and the roast coffee. The hydrocarbons pentane, bp 97 F (36 C) and hexane, bp 136 F (58 C) extract oil from R & G coffee efficiently in a Soxhlet extractor. The solvent evaporates from the coffee oil under mild stripping conditions, yet leaves most of the coffee aroma in the oil. Carbon disulfide, bp 115 F (46 C) is an excellent coffee oil solvent but is highly flammable. Chlorinated solvents such as ethylene dichloride, bp 183 F (84 C); trichlorethylene, bp 189 F (87 C); carbon tetrachloride, bp 171 F (77 C); and chloroform, bp 142 F (61 C) are good extractors of coffee oil but may leave an undesirable residual odor and taste.

Columnar Extraction System.—The chemistry and physical properties of coffee oil will be covered in Chapter 17 but it is pertinent to describe here some of the equipment and operating variables in solvent extraction of coffee oil from freshly roasted and ground coffee. Soxhlet extraction of coffee from R & G coffee is satisfactory for small samples. But columnar solvent extraction of larger amounts of R & G coffee is more efficient and more rapid and gives high coffee oil yields. A bank of extraction columns, as used for percolation, works well with hexane solvent, to give an example. The size of the columns depends on the rate of processing desired. Hexane at 80 F (27 C) will extract from a single R & G coffee column about half the coffee oil in 15 min. With multiple column extraction, the full coffee oil yield can be obtained in a 15-min cycle time. Figure 255 shows a generalized profile of hexane-coffee oil drawoff plotted vs time or relative bed volume. Figure 256 shows the relation between specific gravity of the hexane-coffee oil solutions as taken by hydrometer or balance vs. the weight per cent of coffee oil at room temperature. Similar coffee oil concentration—specific gravity curves can be prepared for any solvent being used.

The generalized curves (Figs. 225 and 256) are for a R & G coffee column several inches in diameter and several feet high. Note that about 80 per cent of the oil yield is in the wetting part of the curve; the overall

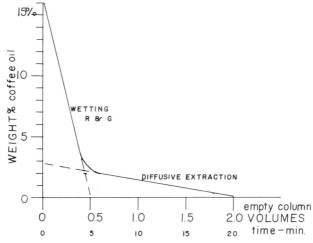

FIG. 255. COFFEE OIL CONCENTRATION PROFILE FROM COLUMNAR EXTRACTION OF ROAST COFFEE

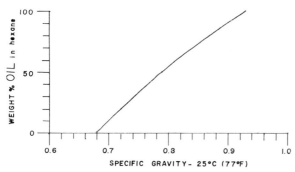

FIG. 256. COFFEE OIL CONCENTRATION IN HEXANE vs SPECIFIC GRAVITY

coffee oil yield in this case is only about 10 per cent. Hexane occupies about two-thirds of the empty column volume, but only about one-third of the empty column volume of hexane drains off freely. Note the similarity in hexane concentration profile to percolation water solubles concentration profile. The initial steep slope is the ground wetting with solvent while the oil concentrates in the free solvent. The later shallow slope is the slow diffusion of coffee oil out of the particle into the passing solvent.

Perforated tube entrances and exits may be used in these percolation columns with hole sizes depending on the grind size being processed. The solvent filled oil is drained from the spent coffee ground column. The R & G coffee is then steamed free of solvent. The immiscible layers of water and solvent in the distillate are separated and the solvent is reused.

Independent Extraction Variables.—(1) *Temperature:* This is an important variable since it governs vapor pressure and volatility of the solvent from both flammability and stripping viewpoints. Although hexane can be stripped from coffee oil, pentane is easier to strip, and butane is easier still. The temperature of extraction governs the amount of waxes removed with the solvent.

(2) *Particle size:* Finer grinds release their oil more readily. Higher coffee oil yields are obtained faster, but more color is extracted.

(3) *Moisture:* The R & G coffee must be low enough in moisture not to interfere with wetting of the particles by the hydrocarbon. Moistures between 2 and 10 per cent are suitable. About 5 per cent is optimum.

(4) *Ratio of solvent to R & G coffee:* Extraction is so rapid (as shown in Fig. 255) that large amounts of solvent are needed only in exhaustive oil removal.

(5) *Construction materials:* For protecting the coffee oil, especially the fatty acids, all materials such as vessels, pumps, and piping should be free of iron and copper. Stainless steel or glass are best for this service.

Dependent Extraction Variables.—These variables include yield and quality of coffee oil, rate of extraction, and concentration of the oil in the effluent solvent. The degree of roast governs the amount of fatty acids in the oil. Coffee oils after roasting have about 5 per cent fatty acids; after percolation hydrolysis they have 12 to 15 per cent fatty acids. The coffee oil content of fresh dark roast coffee is 10 to 12 per cent, but after percolation it is 15 to 20 per cent. The fresh R & G coffee oil has the fresh aromatic coffee volatiles, but the coffee oil from R & G coffee after percolation has none. If higher-than-room temperature is used for solvent extractions, waxes and fatty acids settle out from the coffee oil.

Expelled Coffee Oil

Since 1957, major coffee processors have expelled coffee oil from freshly roasted coffee beans and then sprayed it on instant coffee powder which is packed in a jar with CO_2 atmosphere containing only a few per cent of oxygen. Figure 257 (A and B) shows a photo, and a sectional view of the V. D. Anderson oil duo-expeller used. There are about 25 of these

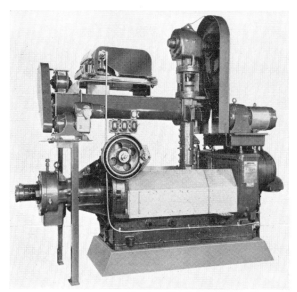

Courtesy The V. D. Anderson Company

Fig. 257A.   Coffee Oil Expeller

coffee oil expellers in use by firms such as Nestlé, Kroger, Standard Brands, and others. The unit on top of the expeller is a Sharpless Super-D-canter centrifuge for immediate clarification of the expelled oil. The French Oil Machinery Company of Piqua, Ohio, also makes oil expellers. Similar types of expellers can also be used to squeeze water out of percolated spent grounds reducing moistures to about 55 per cent.

Expeller Operation.—The entering R & G coffee may be steam heated, 150 psig–375 F (190 C) by the entering screw jacket or moistened to help soften the coffee. A motorized choke valve on the discharge end of the expeller controls the back pressure (50 tons) on the extruded expelled cake. An ammeter control on the main driving motor (about 50 hp), if overloaded, reduces the vertical rate of coffee feed. The expelled cake can be extruded into strings and cut into pellets for reintroduction into the percolators with the normal R & G coffee. Because of the great amount of frictional heat developed during the expelling process, the central shaft of the expeller is water cooled. A series of short replaceable blades rotating at 20 rpm compresses the coffee as it is pushed and pressed forward. The coffee oil comes out of peripheral slots that are only a few thousandths of an inch wide. The coffee oil is hot, about 180 F (82 C) when it leaves these slots and is then immediately cooled. Centrifuging away "foots" makes the aromatic coffee oil more stable, and it can be stored at room temperature when it is clear. These expellers, depending on accessories, cost about $20,000 each. A molecular still has been used according to the Cole patent (1951) to strip volatiles and to concentrate them in a lesser amount of coffee oil. The coffee oil carries a sulfurous portion of the coffee aroma as well as phenols which stain the hands yellow and have a barbecue odor.

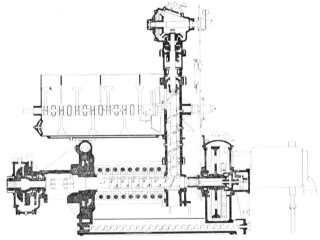

Courtesy The V. D. Anderson Company

FIG. 257B.   COFFEE OIL EXPELLER

Oil Yield.—Roast coffee is a very hard material as compared to palm kernels. The duo-expeller will reduce palm kernel oil from 50 to 15 per cent in the vertical squeeze and from 15 to 5 per cent oil in the horizontal squeeze. Roast coffee contains about 12 per cent coffee oil. At a rate of roast bean coffee feed of 500 lb per hr and a residual 5 per cent oil left in the expeller cake, about 35 lb per hr of oil can be produced. If a 7 per cent coffee oil yield is obtained from 7 per cent of the percolated roast coffees, the overall coffee oil yield is $1/2$ per cent of the original R & G coffee. This is about 1.3 per cent of the instant coffee. About 3 per cent moisture in the roast coffee also helps to soften the granular structure.

Expeller Construction Materials.—All expeller oil contacting surfaces should be stainless steel or nickel. Copper or bare steel will react with fatty acids, dissolve, and result in subsequent deterioration of the coffee oil aroma. Some expellers are also run with an inert gas blanket.

Oil on Powder.—The coffee oil can be sprayed onto the instant coffee powder as shown in Fig. 258. The powder takes on a darker, "wet snow" or "sandy" appearance with poor fluidity. When "plated' correctly, several tenths of 1 per cent coffee oil on the instant coffee powder imparts

Courtesy The Johnson-March Corporation

Fig. 258A. Coffee Oil Spray Equipment for Instant Coffee Powder

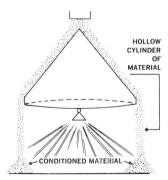

Fig. 258B. Coffee Oil Spray Equipment for Instant Coffee Powder

a taste texture, and cup smoothness. This retains aroma volatiles and reduces foaming in the cup. Some dark roast (espresso) instant coffees have about 1 per cent coffee oil, as normally percolated and spray dried. Similar coffee oil contents result from percolation of fine grind coffee. The dark roast oils on instant coffee powder stale more slowly than oils from lighter roast coffees.

Nature of Oil.—In general the chemical, physical, and yield properties of the coffee will vary with the type of original coffee. Robusta coffee oil emulsifies easily with extract while good mild coffee oils hardly emulsify. Combining lime with the fatty acid emulsifiers can break an emulsion. The coffee extract pH rises and color darkens, producing a disagreeable taste.

COFFEE VOLATILES RECOVERY

Aroma Sources

Most coffee patents are concerned with recovery of the volatiles which produce the aroma so enjoyable in coffee preparation. There are also the pleasant, naturally liberated coffee aromas from coffee roasting and grinding, and from the freshly opened (vacuum or inert gas packed) tin can. Each of these aroma sources has been investigated with varying results. Coffee aroma also can be induced: (1) by placing a vacuum over the fresh R & G coffee; (2) by wetting and/or heating the roast coffee; and (3) by distilling coffee extract. An inert gas stream, steam, or vacuum may carry the liberated volatiles to condensers.

Coffee Aroma Essence

The nature of the coffee volatiles will be described in Chapters 15, 16, and 17. Without knowledge of their chemical and physical properties, it is scientifically impossible to evaluate their performance in the phases of liberation, collection, stability aromatization, and pleasure.

The first work of real merit was done in about 1925 by Staudinger, a chemist, who isolated the coffee aroma essence in a series of cold traps. See U.S. patent 1,696,419 (1928). He then identified many of the individual chemical compounds. Considering the nature of the analytical equipment and the methods available at that time, the results were good and many aroma constituents were identified. These have been duplicated, confirmed, and improved upon since then by other workers with better equipment and methods. The British patent 246,454 (1926) assigned to International Nahrungs und Genussmittel Aktiengesellschaft of Schaffhausen, Switzerland, is informative. It describes a series of coffee aroma condensers: ice water, dry ice in solvent, and liquid nitrogen, at respectively 32 F (0 C), —112 F (—80 C), and —292 F (—180 C). Similar aroma recoveries have been made by other workers. Not until Zlatkis and Sivetz (1960), has the coffee aroma been confirmed and isolated as "an extremely powerful essence that is a clear, yellow-green liquid that floats on water at 0 C." The coffee aroma and flavor essence is so volatile and in such low concentrations in the roast coffee that its isolation was even doubtful until these results were reported.

Essence Composition.—The above reference together with Rhoade's[3] two publications (1958 and 1960) report qualitative and quantitative composition of aroma volatiles from roast coffee. Before that time quantitative data on coffee aroma constituents were largely lacking. Most of the earlier work reported was qualitative, and some was incorrect. The availability of gas chromatography for qualitative and quantitative volatiles identification supplemented by infra-red and mass spectroscopy identification has produced reliable and confirmed knowledge about coffee aroma for the first time (1960). Also, work done by Merritt and Proctor[4] (1959) at the Armed Services Food and Container Institute at Natick, Mass., has provided further confirmatory knowledge about coffee aroma composition. Now there are more sensitive gas chromatographic ionization detectors that can perform even better analyses than those used in the papers mentioned above. Furthermore many more persons in the flavor and chromatographic fields are prepared to do these analyses on a more routine basis.

An examination of the coffee aroma-flavor volatiles shows that there are about 400 ppm of these substances in roast coffee. They are discrete chemicals, mostly aldehydes and ketones, but also sulfides, furans, esters, and alcohols. The aldehydes are predominant in quantity, but the sulfides are often predominant in taste and aroma influence. Many of these components boil at room temperature, which accounts for the difficulty in their isolation. Also, these components are more volatile than water and are only partly recovered with water in an ice water cooled condenser.

Substances Less Volatile than Coffee Essence

These substances boil in the temperature range of water or higher. Zlatkis and Sivetz (1960) cover these compounds also. They are primarily the homologous acids: formic, acetic, propionic, butyric, and valeric. Acetic acid is dominant at about 0.35 per cent in roast coffee and about 0.5 per cent in the water portion of percolated extract. Percolator vent condensate might have up to 1.4 per cent acetic acid before

---

[3] Listed under "Analytical Chemistry."
[4] Listed under "Aromatized Instant Coffee."

the R & G coffee becomes wet with water. Under vacuum and/or heating of extracts or R & G coffee, some higher boiling esters, aldehydes, and alcohols as well as furfurals may be distilled.

Dry Vacuum Aroma

Dry vacuum aroma (DVA) corresponds to the coffee volatiles driven off with enough water so that they are soluble in the water condensate or aqueous phase. These are differentiated from coffee essence which is more volatile and potent with limited solubility in water. Such distillates are usually about 99 per cent water. The major portion of the organics are homologues of acetic acid with only about tens to hundreds of parts per million of coffee essence volatiles.

This aqueous condensate of volatiles is very unstable. It is clear on collection and turns clear yellow within an hour with the development of a sickening tobacco-like odor. It turns colloidal reddish in a few hours and becomes colloidal black overnight at room temperature. The black colloid after coagulation will settle out and appears to be a phenol-formaldehyde or furan precipitate. It would require specific study to determine the chemical reactions occurring here. This might lead to an explanation of staling and coffee flavor loss by chemical interaction. The precipitate is a polymer because in more concentrated solutions (such as ethyl ether extracts with ethyl ether evaporated) containing about 25 per cent water, a solid black gel develops in storage at room temperature (less rapidly at lower temperatures). These lesser coffee volatiles are not as readily lost as the essence in the spray drying of instant coffee.

TECHNIQUES OF AROMA AND FLAVOR RECOVERY

Numerous patents describe methods for the recovery of coffee volatiles. They refer to ice water or chilled brine, dry ice in solvent, and liquid nitrogen condensers. Most of these aroma collections were more qualitative than quantitative. The reason is that much of the earlier work was done by chemists, and their laboratory equipment was largely for qualitative results, not for complete recovery of volatiles. The difference between collecting coffee aroma volatiles qualitatively and quantitatively lies largely in design of the condensers, cooling methods, construction materials, mainly gas throughput rates and temperatures of collection of coffee essences. Even low effluent gas temperatures from a condenser do not assure complete condensation. There may be entrainment of water condensate droplets with effluent gases. One may cool with liquid nitrogen at −292 F (−180 C) and have little heat transfer surface in the condenser; but when the condenser surfaces collect ice in the process of essence collection, the heat transfer rate decreases. The surface in contact with the condensing essence then may be far above liquid nitrogen temperatures.

Volatility of Coffee Essence Aroma

The most volatile constituent, hydrogen sulfide, boils at −76 F (−60 C). Methyl mercaptan, the next most volatile constituent, boils at 45 F (7 C). The rest of the volatiles boil at higher temperatures. Since H_2S is not an important part of good, fresh coffee aroma, it need not be collected. But if one chooses to collect it, the effluent gas temperature from the last condenser must be less than −76 F (−60 C). In practice, with effluent gas temperatures of −50 F (−45 C), the effluent condenser gas has no odor other than the pungency of carbon dioxide. This gas effluent temperature establishes the performance required from the last condenser.

Solid CO_2 Coolant

With carbon dioxide coolant at −109 F (−78 C), liquid nitrogen coolant is not needed in an adequately designed and sized heat exchanger for essence recovery.

Dry ice can be used to cool many liquid media to −108 F (−78 C) or to some higher temperatures if eutectic ices form. Examples of liquid media are isopropyl alcohol, Cellosolve, and the Freon-11 or Genetron-11 chlorinated hydrocarbons.

Evaporation of CO_2 gas circulates the coolant to effect a uniform temperature. Pump circulation of the coolant is more positive and may have to be used in some designs. Care must be taken to seal the cooled liquid media from atmospheric water condensation. This causes ice and fouls media, pumps, and strainers. Usually a desiccant in the liquid medium suffices to absorb small amounts of moisture. The advantages of the Freon-11 type medium are that it is not flammable and ice floats to its surface. The CO_2 has good solubility in Freon-11. However, CO_2 volatilizes and separates from the coolant when warm. Such dry ice coolant systems are suitable for temporary testing.

Refrigerant Coolant Systems

For permanent coolant installations, it is more economical to have a two- or three-stage refrigeration system. This may operate, for example, at −60 F (−51 C) or −100 F (−73 C) (Freon-22). A closed cycle coolant system loses no refrigerant and is always under operating control. At these temperatures, no CO_2 gas from aroma sources will freeze out as dry ice snow in the trap as will occur with a liquid nitrogen coolant.

Assuming a CO_2 flow of 8.8 lb/min, a three-stage Freon-22 system would have the following operating characteristics:

	Aroma Temperature, CO_2 Gas				Refrigerant Temperatures at Suction		Refrigeration Cooling Load	
	In		Out					
Stage	F	C	F	C	F	C	Tons	Motor hp
1	200	93	35	2	30	−1	1.0	1.5
2	35	2	0	−18	−25	−32	0.5	1.0
3	0	−18	−50	−46	−80	−62	0.4	15.0

Note the high horsepower requirement at the lower temperature compressor stage. Actually, a two-stage system will work if the final heat exchanger is made large enough. A desirable feature in the coolant system would be a refrigerant gas at 100 F (38 C) to defrost ice in the cooling tubes. All condensate lines, valves, fittings, heat exchangers, etc, should be of stainless steel construction to withstand the thermal stresses at these low temperatures. A No. 4 metal finish helps in cleaning. All low temperature surfaces should have 8 in. of polystyrene foam insulation.

Aroma Condensing Sequence.—Ice water or brine can be used instead of the 30 F (−1 C) refrigerant in the shell of the first gas condenser. Condensate from the 35 F (2 C) effluent gas can be separated by a cyclone receiver. The aqueous condensate should be frozen and/or added back to the extract just before drying. The primary condenser gas outlet temperature is 35 F (2 C) so that considerable water removal will occur without ice forming on the cooling surfaces. The second stage series condenser may cool the exit gas to 0 F (−18 C). This removes almost all the water vapor. It may even be desirable to use a larger heat exchanger and a colder gas outlet temperature such as −20 F (−29 C) to assure that the least possible amount of water vapor carries over into the coldest condenser collecting the coffee aroma essence. The less water associated with the coffee essence aldehydes, the easier it is to isolate the essence.

The boiling temperature at atmospheric pressure of the coffee aroma volatiles must be noted. Most of the aroma volatiles will be recovered in the intermediate condenser cooled to −25 F (−32 C). The most cooled condenser is a scavenger to assure (by the odor of its effluent gases) that no odorous coffee substances escape. With this in mind, the aromatic coffee essence is condensed at −20 to −30 F (−29 to −34 C) effluent gas temperatures from the second condenser. No third condenser is needed. Effluent gas temperatures from each trap can be recorded to monitor aroma collection performance. If ice buildup shows rising effluent gas temperatures, then either the trap can be thawed and its contents recovered, or an alternate clean trap can be placed in line. The gas line should have a flowmeter. A gas flow recorder is desirable until condensation effectiveness is established. Essence condensation can also be effected at higher condensation temperatures and pressures, however, this is not usually practical.

This type of aroma trapping system may also be used for grinder gas, percolator vent gases, and steamed gases from R & G coffee.

Essence Stability.—The collected coffee essences can be stored safely at temperatures below 20 F (-7 C) as long as there is no free water to allow its chemical deterioration.

Small Condenser Heat Load.—The first gas condenser has the major heat load of condensing water. This can be estimated as saturated moisture in the entering CO_2 gas at the entering temperature. The heat load for condensing coffee essence in later condensers is very small, and most of it may be caused by inadequate insulation. The cooling loads and the heat exchangers are small in size; hence the overall coffee essence recovery equipment needs only a small investment. It does require special engineering, however, which adds to the equipment cost.

Quality and Potency of Condensates.—It is convenient to use a micro-syringe to measure out hundredths of a milliliter into a cup of instant coffee, or larger brew batch, to gain insight into the aroma, potency and taste properties of the recovered volatiles. The person recovering the coffee essence must not do the tasting for two reasons: (1) the condenser operator or unloader is saturated with essence (including hands and clothes) so that he becomes insensitive to cup evaluations, and (2) the person collecting essence may be so involved in the research effort that he becomes biased. An independent yet objective group of tasters should evaluate the aroma and flavor merits of recovered coffee essences.

Recovery of Roaster Gases.—These gases are, as a rule, impractical to recover because their properties represent more of what is occurring chemically in the roasting process than the final volatiles composition of the roasted coffee bean.

Recovery of Aromatics from Coffee Oil.—Recovery of essence by molecular or any other type of distillation or separation from coffee oil is not practical because the coffee aroma constituents are tenaciously held and are well protected in their natural habitat. Concentrating the aromatics from coffee oil is of dubious value since not all the coffee flavor volatiles are in the oil. They do not pass from coffee oil to water to improve cup flavor.

Coffee Aroma Recovery from Grinder Gas.—There are several patents on the recovery of coffee aromatics from grinder gas, such as Johnston (1942) of Standard Brands and Clinton (1959 and 1962) of General Foods. In some cases, the roast coffee bean grinder is placed in an inert gas atmosphere to eliminate air oxidation as well as moisture. The grinder gases are rich in coffee aroma and CO_2 gas, but the portion of coffee volatiles liberated is only a small fraction of that available in the rest of the coffee bean. For example, a regular grind may only release about one-third of its CO_2 content and perhaps only one-tenth of its volatiles content. After all, CO_2 is by far the most abundant volatile roasting product. The CO_2 content of the roasted bean varies from 1 to 1.5 per cent. The aromatic coffee essence is only about 0.05 per cent. The CO_2 sublimes at -108 F (-78 C); dimethyl sulfide, the most odorous coffee volatile, boils at 100 F (38 C); and the volatile acetaldehyde boils at 68 F (20 C). During essence collection, if the moisture of the air is not excluded or if the coffee beans are wetted with water, the amount of associated moisture collected can be one-hundred-fold greater than the coffee essence. For example, there is only a fraction of 1 per cent coffee aroma essence in the CO_2 gas. With moisture present, the coffee essence is dissolved in the much larger amount of condensed water.

Coffee Essence Stability

If air enters the coffee aroma system, the naturally fruity, pleasant, sweet, and fresh coffee aroma constituents will develop a tobacco-like stale coffee odor and a strong, brew-like taste. The condensate will develop objectionable odors and become sulfurous (like H_2S). These condensates (if not too diluted with water ice crystals or frozen CO_2 crystals in liquid nitrogen traps) are usually light to dark yellow. The lighter essence colors that are clear, deep yellow to yellow-green are purer and fresher. The yellow color confirms the presence of sulfur compounds; the green color is related to acetyl-carbonyl and diacetyl. The pungency and fruitiness of the aroma is caused by acetaldehyde; fruitiness also comes from other aldehydes. The coffee essences will deteriorate in minutes if they are not kept below 32 F (0 C) keeping the associated water frozen. If coffee essence and little water are collected, the essential oil may separate out as a floating phase over the ice. This separation can sometimes be completed by centrifuging. Coffee essences and their contacting aqueous solutions may be evaluated in flavor, aroma, and potency by dilution in instant coffee. Water condensates saturated with CO_2 are acid at 4.0 pH. The collection of grinder gas coffee aroma essence is informative but is not in the main source of coffee aroma.

Carbon Dioxide.—With 0.5 to 1.5 weight per cent of CO_2 in bulk roast coffee beans, the volume of CO_2 gas at NTP[5] is about 2 to 3 times the

---

[5] Normal temperature and pressure.

bulk volume of the roast coffee. For example, 100 cu ft roast coffee at 1.1 per cent CO_2 has about 200 cu ft of CO_2. This situation has been described by other workers as a roast coffee bean having 100 psig or about six atmospheres of CO_2 pressure. This would be true if the CO_2 gas were in the voids in the beans; but the roast bean is openly porous as can easily be seen under the microscope. Therefore, the CO_2 gas must be ad- or absorbed on the bean surfaces or within the coffee oil or both. The charcoal adsorption capacity of CO_2 is about 50 volumes CO_2 gas per volume of charcoal. Depending on the degree of roast, more or less charring occurs and not necessarily on the outside of the bean. With a 16 per cent roast weight loss, 11 per cent may result from "free water" liberation, 2 per cent from bound water and 1.5 per cent from CO_2 from carbohydrates ($C_6H_{10}O_5$). There is a small part of carbon that forms during pyrolysis of organic substances. If there is 0.3 per cent of carbonaceous matter in the bean, 100 gm (300 ml) of bean could adsorb about 50 ml CO_2 gas. This partly explains the CO_2 adsorption. Carbon dioxide is soluble in vegetable oils, amines, and carbohydrates, all of which are present in the roast bean. Cellulose adsorbs gases. The roast coffee readily combines with water, hydrocarbons, aldehydes, etc. This is evidenced by the solvent desiccation effect on the first effluent leaving a column of dry roast coffee when extract water is admitted.

Coffee Volatiles Adsorption

Further, almost every patent dealing with the removal of aroma and flavor volatiles from roast coffee uses (1) higher coffee temperatures, and (2) lower atmospheric pressures around the coffee. Adsorption isotherms for charcoal, silica gel, and other adsorbents show reduced capacity of retention with increasing temperatures and decreasing pressure. Charcoal is an excellent adsorber for acetone, holding half its weight in acetone when saturated. Charcoal is also a good adsorber for aldehydes, esters, acetic acid, and its homologues, also methyl, and ethyl alcohol. Furthermore, commercial adsorbers like charcoal and silica gel are reactivated by steam to release their adsorbed volatiles. These adsorption phenomena are amply discussed by Mantell (1951); Lewis, Squires, and Broughton (1943); Perry (1962); McBain (1931); and physical-chemical texts and research papers. Adsorption liberates heat; the more chemical in nature are the affinities, the more physical adsorption becomes a chemical reaction. The affinity roast coffee has for water is greater than its affinity for other substances, like aldehydes, CO_2 ketones, and sulfides. Therefore, added water may displace them.

Charcoal is a very good adsorbent of the coffee essences; it immobilizes the adsorbed aroma, and they neither stale nor escape.

The addition of water to roast coffee (directly or from the atmosphere) releases volatile aromatics and CO_2, because of the selective preference of the fiber structure for water. The wetting of the roast bean with water destroys the adsorptive power of the dry cell surfaces for aldehydes and other coffee essence constituents.

DVA Method

Another way to collect grinder gas coffee aroma is to use vacuum and heating of roast coffee. This draws off the coffee volatiles as described by Lemonnier (1954), who uses a medium roast with about two or more per cent of moisture. The patent gives neither acidity evolved, per cent organic substances, nor the aromatic potency of the distillates. Lemonnier emphasizes the rapid rate of coffee essence deterioration. He does not explain, however, how he can spread this coffee

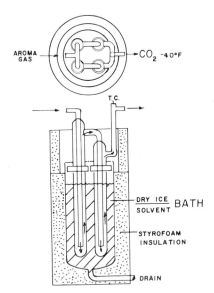

FIG. 259.   DRY ICE COOLED COFFEE ESSENCE RECEIVER

essence on the instant coffee powder without its becoming oxidized. The product specified in the patent based on collecting the essence-water condensate at yields of 1 lb per 200 lb batch of R & G coffee is largely water. If 200 ppm true coffee essence were in the Lemonnier traps it would be 20 gm essence and 454 gm water. Figure 259 shows one type of cold trap for coffee essence.

Aroma laden coffee gases, whether from grinders or percolator vents, after being cooled to about 35 F (2 C), can be made to liberate the volatile coffee essence by passage through dry ice traps at −108 F (−78 C) so that the effluent CO_2 gas is below −40 F (−40 C). The sketch shown (Fig. 259) illustrates one such system in which a 1-in. pipe forms a labyrinth for gas passage inside a 2- or 3-in. tube. Quick-coupling connectors help in disassembling the lower thimble where the essence and water ice crystals are formed. A Freon-dry ice bath effectively keeps the tubes at bath temperature; a thermocouple indicates exit gas temperature. All surfaces must be of stainless steel with a sanitary smooth finish to facilitate cleaning the equipment thoroughly between runs. For handling about 1,000 cu ft of percolator vent gases (after an ice water condenser) in 10 min, about 15 linear ft of flow path are required so that coffee aroma is not detected at the CO_2 exhaust point. About 6 to 8 in. of styrofoam insulation are required about the bath shell for proper insulation. Under the removal circumstances described, it is doubtful if more than 5 gm of true coffee essence are collected in 500 gm of water. This is about 1 per cent coffee essence solution (no free essence phase) which would be highly unstable in the water phase at room temperature. To overcome the disadvantages of a batch essence collection, the system should be continuous. Continuous movement of R & G coffee through a heated screw and trough jacket followed by a cooling screw and jacket will suffice. A heat transfer coefficient of about 2 Btu per hr per sq per ft per deg F can be expected. Lemonnier's patent describes conditions of the distillation for acetic acid and its homologues with small amounts of phenol-type compounds.

Factors in Liberating Volatiles

The variables controlling the amount and rate of coffee volatiles liberated are blend, roast, water content, grind, temperature of grounds, and system pressure. If the water, acetic acid, etc., were free, they would readily distill over in minutes. The fact that the volatiles distill over only partially in hours means that the water, acids, and essences are held on the coffee grounds by physical, and perhaps chemical, forces. The use of a vacuum necessitates a liquid air coolant for condensing and is a disadvantage of the vacuum system. Heat transfer coefficients also are poorer under vacuum and require larger heat exchangers. The use of liquid nitrogen for such an essence recovery system is too expensive. The Lemonnier method for recovery of "dry" vacuum aroma is relatively inefficient (because of the method and low essence yields from R & G coffee) as compared to steaming R & G coffee.

Completeness of Volatiles Recovery.—The coffee volatiles liberated in any kind of coffee aroma recovery process must be carried over to the instant coffee without substantial loss or change so as to retain a well-rounded coffee flavor and aroma.

Wetting ground coffee liberates most of the coffee volatiles promptly. When coffee temperatures rise to 300 F (149 C), oil flotation and darkening of the grounds will result. Under such circumstances sublimation of caffeine and some oils occurs. Caffeine sublimes at 351 F (177 C), at atmospheric pressure, and at considerably lower temperatures under vacuum, as verified by Klein (1962).

As water is driven off from the R & G coffee and its moisture decreases, the rate of liberation of flavor acids and aromatic volatiles diminishes. Water is the key to freeing coffee volatiles. The concentration of acetic acid distilled over from the roast coffee based on starting concentrations of 0.30 per cent of acetic acid in the coffee and 4.0 per cent moisture is about 7 per cent of acetic acid. Table 69 shows acetic acid vapor-

TABLE 69

ACETIC ACID VAPOR—LIQUID EQUILIBRIA DATA

BP		Per Cent Acetic Acid	
F	C	Liquid	Vapor
. . .	. . .	1	0.6
. . .	. . .	2	1.2
. . .	. . .	3	1.7
. . .	. . .	4	2.3
. . .	. . .	6	3.6
. . .	. . .	8	4.8
212.4	100.2	10	6.2
212.7	100.4	20	13
213.1	100.6	30	19
213.8	101.0	40	26
214.9	101.6	50	34
216.0	102.2	60	44
217.9	103.3	70	54
221.0	105.0	80	68
227.7	108.7	90	82

liquid equilibrium data. Mild coffees give more volatile aromas and acids than Brazil or Robusta Coffees. Acid yields under this type of collection system are only about three-fourths of the 0.30 per cent acetic acid in the roast coffee. These aqueous acid distillates with coffee aroma essence are unstable. They form gray, cloudy colloids and turn to reddish-black precipitates in hours at room temperature with an accompanying flavor deterioration.

DVA Water Removal.—Water, time, temperature, and oxygen (air) contribute to such chemical changes. Hence, it is of interest to see the effect of water removal. Solvent extraction concentrates the organic essence portion of the dry vacuum distillate. Ethyl ether or other solvents immiscible with water can be used to transfer about three-fourths of the acidity and coffee flavor to the solvent phase. This can be done by countercurrent extraction followed by solvent stripping. The resulting solvent concentrate may have 25 per cent water; the original DVA distillate has 95 per cent water. Storing at 20 F (-7 C) this "lesser volatile portion" (as differentiated from essence portion), which is about half acetic acid (equivalent), shows it is relatively stable for many months. A polymerized resin settles out of solutions held at higher temperatures. The dry vacuum condensate has some of the coffee essence (or more volatile portions). If an effective preliminary ice water cooled heat exchanger is used to condense out the bulk of the water before allowing the aromatic gases to pass on to the liquid nitrogen traps, coffee essence with little water is frozen out as ice, as reported by Lemonnier. It is not uncommon to obtain sweet, pleasant sulfurous odors from the dry ice collected in liquid nitrogen traps, and to have these odors change almost instantly to foul cabbage-like odors. R & G coffee after DVA processing still has some coffee flavor and aroma.

Cupping DVA.—All DVA distillates enhance the flavor of a cup of instant coffee at a proportioned add-back level. Figure 260 shows a micro-syringe for such work. For example, one drop of distillate per cup of instant coffee containing 2 gm of powder corresponds to a collection of 1 liter of DVA distillate per 250 lb roast coffee. At 80 cups of instant coffee per pound of roast coffee, this distillate will fortify 20,000 cups of instant coffee. The instant coffee flavor is largely removed. Such fortified instant coffee powders have richer, smoother, and fuller coffee aroma and flavor. It is difficult to add an aqueous DVA back into dry instant coffee powder; hence, the ether-extracted and ether-stripped DVA is used for this purpose.

DVA Distillates.—These carry a strong smoked-ham odor and pungency that are attributed to phenol-type coffee compounds. This is verified by adding 1 per cent ferric chloride to the distillate which forms a black solution. Other tests for phenol are also positive: (1) the addition of hydrochloric acid to a furfural-containing solution forms a resinous precipitate; (2) aniline turns red in presence of acetic acid and furfural. The red resin that forms in DVA is not extractable with ethyl ether indicating a polymer. Diacetyl, bp 189 F (87 C), can be isolated by fractional distillation from the DVA ether extract.

Resins in the DVA Ether Extract.—When resins form, water solubility decreases and the solution darkens to a deep reddish color. Vacuum evaporation of the DVA ether extract containing resin will separate out a pale yellow distillate. The resin residue remains behind. This distillate has a strong, pungent acetic acid odor and is soluble in water. DVA ether extract is soluble in 95 per cent ethanol, acetone, and glacial acetic acid which would make an attractive stable solution of coffee flavor. These solvents tie up the water, making for greater stability of coffee volatiles. Pure acetic acid will give a smooth flavor to instant coffee.

DVA Properties.—The DVA ether extract represents about 0.2 per cent of the R & G coffee. The more coffee essence in the DVA ether extract, the less stable it is in storage.

Other tests on DVA ether extract show a white needle crystal deposit from yellowed chloroform extract. The needles are soluble in caustic

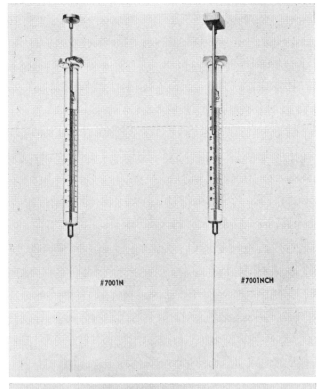

HAMILTON MICROLITER SYRINGE #7001N

0.1 ul capacity ◆ Subdivision of graduation .01 ul ◆ Plunger 0.006" tungsten wire, bottoms
at needle point ◆ No hold up or dead volume ◆ Direct reading ◆ Patent pending

#7001N — Syringe with 7 cm length needle

#7001NCH — Syringe with Chaney Adaptor and needle

Courtesy Hamilton Company Inc.

FIG. 260.   MICRO-SYRINGE

soda and bicarbonate and might indicate a polyhydroxy benzene. Hydrochloric, sulfuric, and phosphoric acids all cause resin formation in the DVA distillate. The resin is soluble in caustic soda and contains about 0.1 to 0.3 per cent sulfur, possibly occluded; the resin could also be a furan (C_4H_4O) polymer. About three-fourths of the dry DVA is acetic acid equivalent to about five per cent propionic acid; it also contains furfural and its derivatives. Dry DVA is very pungent. Redistillation of DVA ether extract down to 1 mm Hg in about six fractions at 302 F (150 C) eliminates water fractions, leaves others that freeze at 0 F (-18 C) and float out droplets of a pale yellow-green coffee essence.

Steam Distillation of Roast Coffee

Steam distillation is used as a general term for such coffee aroma displacing methods as: (1) wetting roast coffee particles with moist gas; (2) steaming roast coffee at varying pressures; and (3) adding hot water to roast coffee. The effects are all the same, and coffee volatiles released can be condensed through a series of cold traps. Moist nitrogen gas was used by Rhoades (1958) in his gas chromatography analyses with coffee essence collection in liquid nitrogen cold traps.

The same volatilizing process can be carried out continuously commercially. For example, the wetting of R & G coffee in the percolator with extract at 220 F (104 C) causes some steam to lead the extract flow. The steam wets the R & G coffee and drives off coffee aroma and flavor volatiles before the particles are covered by extract. In the case where steam is used to preheat the R & G coffee in the percolator column, the production of coffee aroma and flavor volatiles occurs faster and in greater quantity. The coffee essence collection scheme is substantially as already described in patents by Lemonnier (1954), Heyman (1947), and others. The vented gases pass through an ice water condenser and leave at about 35 F (2 C) to remove as much moisture as possible. This richly flavored condensate is restored to the drawn off extract.

Vapor Composition.—Each pound of moisture-saturated air at 35 F (2 C) carries 0.004 lb of water. Assuming about the same for liberated CO_2 gas, every 1000 lb roast coffee gives 90 to 160 cu ft of CO_2. This is 10 to 18 lb CO_2, 0.06 lb water and 0.4 lb coffee essence theoretically.

In practice, this ratio of essence to water is never realized; it is more nearly 10 to 20 times as much water as essence in the dry ice or liquid nitrogen-cooled condenser. The reasons for this are: (1) the effluent gases entering the dry ice or liquid nitrogen-cooled condensers are at much higher temperatures than 35 F (2 C); (2) the displacement of coffee aroma essence is not complete; and (3) there is water vapor dilution from air. However, when efficient volatiles collections are made, the coffee essence to water ratio can be reduced to about one. Batch essence recoveries are less practical than continuous recoveries. Percolator vent gases, whether produced by steam or the rise of hot extract are the best source of coffee essence for collection.

Properties of Volatile Condensates.—The first ice-water-cooled condenser trappings are usually water, clear when fresh, to slightly colloidal gray when old. The dry ice or liquid nitrogen-cooled traps, if they do not have too much water carryover, collect yellow ice with potently aromatic coffee essence and perhaps droplets of water and an insoluble dark yellow liquid. The odors emanating during the handling of these traps range from fruity, to cabbage-like, to tobacco-like. The tobacco odor is associated with conditions that have allowed the coffee aroma to become oxidized. Coffee essence recoveries of the yellow-to-green oil that floats on water are about 50 ppm of the roast coffee, with possibly another 50 to 100 ppm dissolved in the aqueous phase. The yellow-green coffee essence will mostly evaporate in a few minutes at room temperature and will turn dark reddish with a barbecue-tobacco-like odor. Once exposure to air occurs, cooling does not seem to stop deterioration of the essence. Nitrogen gas protection is helpful at above freezing temperatures, but best coffee essence stability is obtained at temperatures below 20 F (-7 C). This may be the melting point of the eutectic of coffee essence with water. At this temperature coffee essence is usually a beautiful pale green.

Aqueous distillates from R & G coffee have about 2 per cent acetic acid and 2.8 pH. This is because it takes about 10 lb steam condensate to heat 100 lb R & G coffee to 212 F (100 C). This is 0.3 lb acetic acid in 10 lb of water, or about 3 per cent acetic acid. Table 69 shows the liquid-vapor phase concentrations for acetic acid; distillation separations of water and acetic acid are not efficient.

Titration of aqueous coffee distillates is practically identical to 3 per cent acetic acid when pH is plotted vs milliliter 0.1 N NaOH. Removal of the distillate acid with anion resin gives an amine (possibly tri-methyl amine) odor in the alkaline effluent. It has a definite coffee flavor when added to instant coffee. The alkali equivalent is about 10 ppm of the R & G coffee.

Polymers.—The percolator vent gas condensates form resinous red colloids changing to black that later settle out. These are polymers of phenols and aldehydes or furan formed in the acetic acid. There is an assortment of aldehydes and phenols in the aqueous coffee distillates. Polymerization rates are faster at higher acid concentrations and higher temperatures. Phenols are unstable and redden on exposure to air and light. Depending on the mode of percolator venting, distillates may have only about 0.25 per cent acetic acid (pH 4.0). The flavor factor in the aqueous coffee distillates is primarily phenols and acetic acid, respectively smokey and pungent. Where large fractions of water are frozen out as ice in the coffee essence cold traps, the essence concentrates to a slush. The richer coffee essence portion which melts at about 20 F (−7 C) can be centrifuged away.

Steaming R & G Coffee.—Steam distillation of R & G coffee at 15 to 20 psig is carried on only until the coffee has been heated to the steam temperature corresponding to the pressure used. If the distillation is carried beyond this point, the flavor and aroma of the distillate are lowered in quality as are the non-volatile solubles flavor portion left in the coffee. Prolonged steam distillation of R & G coffee causes a bitter flavor that is associated with a greater acidity; the pH of distillates falls from about 4.0 nearly down to 3.0. The evolution of R & G coffee aroma should occur in less than 5 min at 212 F (100 C) at atmospheric pressure, much as it occurs when household coffee is prepared.

Oxidation.—Oxidation of an aqueous percolator vented distillate, which is relatively free of aroma essence aldehydes, causes little to no flavor change, even with formation of black precipitate. But oxidation of the coffee essence results in an unpleasant aroma and flavor in the coffee cup. The volatile aqueous and essence (aroma and flavor) constituents differ, but both give improved flavor to instant coffee. The former gives more flavor and smoothness, and the latter gives more aroma. Percolator vent distillates that discolor from yellow-to-red-to-black are accompanied by a loss in fresh coffee odor. They develop a tobacco odor and unpleasant cup taste on addition to instant coffee. During these precipitation changes, pH does not change which indicates that acetic acid is not directly involved. Prolonged steaming of R & G coffee gives the distillate an odor similar to a warmed-over pot of coffee. The brew pH from that R & G coffee may fall from 5.0 to 4.7.

Acid and Essence Volatiles.—By not allowing the percolator vent distillate gases to reach 212 F (100 C), only about one-twentieth of the total volatile acids (0.35 per cent in the R & G coffee) is distilled. By holding the vent gas temperatures several minutes at 212 F (100 C), about three-quarters of the volatile acids in the R & G coffee can be distilled. Thus the coffee essence volatiles come off mostly below 212 F (100 C), and the volatile acids and probably the phenols come over above 212 F (100 C) with prolonged steaming. The harsh taste of coffee extracts from R & G coffee that has been steamed for several minutes at 212 F (100 C), can be smoothed by adding back to the extract the removed aqueous and essence coffee distillates. Neutralizing the acid distillate with NaOH, distilling off water to concentrate the acid salt, and finally reacidifying with HCl or cation resin, concentrates the coffee acid portion before it is added back to the extract prior to spray drying. Such evaporative concentration of the extract solubles before add-back of acid and essence reduces volatilization losses during spray drying.

FLAVOR FORTIFIED COFFEE EXTRACT

Restoration of the aqueous and essence distillate trappings to the coffee extract before spray drying is essential to obtaining the best balanced coffee flavor and aroma from the powder. Since the coffee essence constituents readily deteriorate, however, the resulting powder with essence residue must be packed with inert gas immediately after spray drying to preserve its enhanced coffee aroma and flavor. Promptness in protective packaging is essential as once oxidation starts, it seems to be an auto-catalytic chain process, and it will continue after vacuum and inert gas packaging.

Distillation of Coffee Extracts

The procedures of the Milleville (1948 and 1950) patents, which have been useful in fruit juice flavor concentration, flash distill 10 per cent of the feed juice under vacuum. This is followed by column distillation with reflux. This method suggests concentrating the volatile coffee essences in coffee extract in the lighter boiling product. Acetic acid, which has a higher boiling point, would not be in the distillate residue. A major difference between commercial coffee extracts and fruit juices is that percolator extracts have components formed by hydrolysis. These are objectionable in aroma and flavor, and their recovery is undesirable. Flash and still distillation of coffee volatile components, using coffee extracts without hydrolysis solubles, may have some disadvantages. Coffee essence constituents are much more reactive than fruit juice. To protect the coffee essence aldehydes, the distillation should be under vacuum which corresponds to room temperature boiling points, and preferably lower. Furthermore, the coffee essence constituents in water solution and with the least amount of air will still oxidize and polymerize to form precipitates. The use of vacuum requires liquid nitrogen-cooled recovery traps, and the distillation system must be free of air. This is not easy to achieve.

Azeotropes.—The separation of the coffee essence constituents by distillation is complicated because of azeotropes. For example, methyl furan and water boil at 137 F (58 C), and 78 per cent methyl furan and 22 per cent methanol boils at 125 F (52 C). There are also ternary azeotropes such as methyl furan-acetone-water, bp 132 F (56 C). It would take considerable testing to determine all the azeotrops that may form from the coffee essence constituents. They may only represent about 100 ppm (0.01 per cent in the distillate) even with a high reflux ratio. In order to recover significant amounts of distilled coffee essence, the evaporative system has to be fed continuously. Altogether the number of problems and techniques required to be overcome are sufficient to discourage this distillation approach.

Oxidation.—Any entrance of air to the distilling system will oxidize the essence and water mixture. Then the still system must be thoroughly cleaned with caustic soda to free it from its foul, sickening, nasal-irritating, disagreeable, pyridine-like odors. Since furan polymerizes, it will eventually foul the packed distillation column. Some distillation odor notes are similar to fufural or dried fruits (apricots and/or prunes). Rubbery odors are not uncommon when working with coffee volatiles.

The most volatile fractions carry over into the vacuum system cold traps. Sufficient concentration of coffee essence is accomplished to condense yellow distillate with perhaps green to orange colorations, and a strong coffee aroma. The flash extract distillate residence time in the still must be very short to separate essence as well as to minimize time for deterioration of the essence in water solution.

The essence in water is still quite dilute when taken from the top of the fractionating column, and it is very unstable in this condition. Hence, the objective of the essence separation is difficult to achieve. Since the flash distillation of the coffee extract releases only a small fraction of its essence, the overall coffee essence yields are small. These are also not representative of the original coffee aroma and flavor.

Partial Extract Evaporation.—Removing some water from coffee extract does have some commercially applicable features. For example, by taking the second half of the percolator extract drawoff, which is at a lower concentration of solubles than the first half, the extract can be concentrated by a vacuum evaporator from about 20 to 50 per cent solubles. This technique removes most of the hydrolysis volatiles. The more concentrated coffee extract can then be combined with the richer natural-flavored first half of the extract drawoff for spray drying. Using this procedure, there is less loss of natural coffee volatiles in spray drying. A further improvement in the flavor of instant coffee powder may be obtained by rendering the flavor acids of part of the coffee distillate non-volatile by neutralizing them with NaOH, removing most of the water by distillation, and then acidifying the concentrated residue by cation resin treatment. The released concentrated acids along with condensed volatiles from the distillation and/or other sources may then be added back to the regular coffee extract before spray drying.

Caramel Taste.—If one tastes coffee extract (diluted to standard testing strength) during progressive stages of vacuum evaporation, it can be observed that the removal of the volatiles that come off first actually improves the extract flavor. For example, it is often found that the foul off-flavors of low-grade coffee as well as the hydrolysis volatiles are removed. Then a caramel or burnt taste develops increasingly with the progressive removal of water. If distillate is returned at this point, the caramel-burnt taste is greatly reduced or even eliminated.

Vacuum Evaporators.—Figure 261 illustrates a type of laboratory vacuum still that can be used for such preliminary investigations. Figure 262 illustrates a commercial-sized vacuum rotary wiped wall film evaporator.

Courtesy Buchler Instruments, Inc.

FIG. 261.   LABORATORY VACUUM ROTARY FLASK FILM EVAPORATOR

Coffee Aroma Essence and Distillates.—The removal of volatile, natural off-flavors, and undesirable hydrolysate flavors which come off in the first stages of vacuum distillation could be carried out commercially to eliminate the caramel-burnt flavors if a practical way could be found to avoid damaging the desirable acidic and other flavor components.   Then coffee essence could be added to the concentrated extract which could subsequently be spray dried with a high degree of coffee aroma and flavor retention.   Figure 263 shows a schematic diagram of a film evaporator.

Ethyl ether extract of aqueous distillate, after stripping off the ether under vacuum, contains about 15 per cent water; it consists of an oily and an aqueous layer.   The two layers contain about 40 or more volatile organic chemicals, mostly aldehydes, carbonyls, sulfides, esters, alcohols, and unsaturated hydrocarbons such as isoprene.   The aqueous layer contains acetic acid and its homologues, phenols, furans, furfurals, and others.

The layers cannot be quickly and sharply separated. The oily layer precipitates a furan polymer while the aqueous phase precipitates a furfural-phenol-aldehyde polymer. Such resinification removes coffee volatiles. When dimethyl sulfide oxidizes to sulfoxide, bp 374 F (190 C), this means the loss of one of the most important coffee aroma and flavor volatiles. This reaction is related to what is commonly known as staling. The instability requires careful processing techniques to recover the volatiles without change. Distillation of aqueous media does not appear feasible.

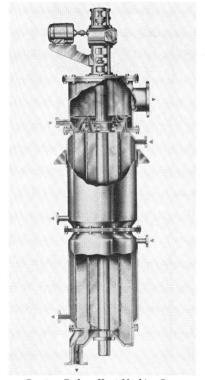

Courtesy Rodney Hunt Machine Company

Fig. 262.   Industrial Vacuum Rotary Wiped Film Evaporator

Process Rules.—The coffee essence volatiles are low boiling compounds, and if a wholesome coffee aroma and flavor is to be retained, *all* natural coffee volatiles must be recovered. They must be recovered without chemical change. In order to do this, the volatiles must be released naturally (brewing or steam distillation of R & G coffee) and be frozen imme-

diately. Freezing removes water and lowers temperatures, thereby lower-
ing rates of chemical reactions. The coffee volatiles must receive minimum exposure to oxygen, air, oxidizing conditions, and daylight. There
must be no iron, copper, or other metallic or foreign contamination. For
stability, the coffee essence should be removed from the bulk ice and be
maintained below 20 F (-7 C). Coffee aroma volatiles are best recovered from continuous process systems which also allow: (1) larger
amounts of roast coffee to be stripped, and (2) shorter process periods.

The coffee aroma and flavor volatiles recovered must be promptly fixed
so that they do not deteriorate and are not lost before reaching the
consumer.

LOCKED-IN FLAVORS

The sealing of volatile flavors in a solid gum structure is usually
referred to as "locking-in" the flavor. However, the sealing of flavors as
used here also includes gelatin encapsulation and fixation in solid carbohydrate sugars.

History.—The technique of spray dry sealing of volatile flavor essences
is relatively new. It was commercially applied shortly after 1950. It did

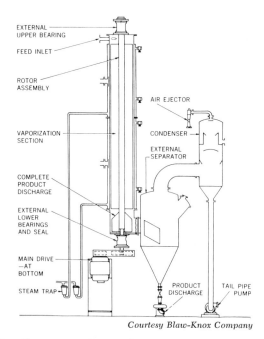

Courtesy Blaw-Knox Company

Fig. 263. Industrial Vacuum Rotary Wiped Film Evaporator

not gain full importance until about 1955. Earlier work dealt with emulsifying fruit flavors in gelatin as typified by an Olsen and Seltzer (1945) patent assigned to General Foods Corporation. It discloses how gelatin flavors were prepared for gelatin desserts like JELL-O. A Griffin (1951) patent injected flavor oils into sorbitol, a molten carbohydrate, which on cooling to room temperature, solidified into a brittle film. Griffin used spray chilling of droplets. Other inventors used gums instead of sorbitol and spray drying instead of spray chilling. Broderick[6] (1954) describes this development as do other references in the bibliography at the end of this chapter. Figure 264 (A and B) shows an homogenizer.

Phases.—The key factor in these flavor fixations is the immiscibility of the oil and aqueous gum solution. The aqueous gum solution is the continuous phase, and the droplets are the discontinuous phase. If the flavor constituents are soluble in the aqueous-gum phase, they would be evaporated in spray drying. By adjusting the concentration of the aqueous gum solution and its ratio to the essence or oil so that there is considerably more than enough flavor essence to saturate the aqueous phase, an immiscible essence phase is obtained. In spray drying, the oily droplets are left coated with the dry gum. In the case of vegetable oils, which are practically immiscible with water, a comparable loss of oil flavors from the water evaporating gum phase is not a problem.

Drying.—Spray drying preserves most of the volatile essences. The essence is in cells within the dry gum lattice. As yet, however, no coffee processor has invested in a process to collect enough coffee essence for commercial purposes. The gum-fixed coffee aroma and flavor can be used as a powdered flavor for candies, beverages, cakes, icings, etc., but no such dry natural coffee aroma and flavor essence has yet appeared on the market.

Stability of Locked-in Coffee Flavor.—Coffee essence is a very unstable mixture of extremely volatile organic compounds. Yet it is retained relatively faithfully within this gum cell structure for years in air at room temperature. Liquid coffee essence, otherwise, can only be kept stable at temperatures below 0 F (-18 C) for any length of time. The removal of air, water, and acids are, no doubt, key factors in stabilizing the coffee essence. The impermeability of the gum cell wall prevents volatility losses.

Gum Emulsion.—The modes of emulsification and spray drying are not critical. For example, one part of coffee essence can be emulsified in a gum arabic solution consisting of four parts gum and eight parts water. A homogenizer can reduce the essence particles to micron size. Figure 264

---

[6] Listed under "Spray Dried Powdered Flavors."

shows a homogenizer and a detail of the valve. The emulsion can then be spray dried in air at 300 F (149 C) inlet and 200 F (93 C) outlet to remove the water to about a 3 per cent moisture residual. The same technique can be used with coffee oil. A dye (du Pont oil blue in acetone) can be added to the emulsion to examine the size of homogenized droplets under a microscope. The dried powder will not release the volatile essence until the protective gum is dissolved away in water. The fixed coffee essence powder can be added to instant coffee powder at a

Courtesy Manton-Gaulin Mfg. Company, Inc.

FIG. 264A. HOMOGENIZER

fraction of the original amount of essence found in nature. For example, 10 ppm of the coffee essence (50 ppm powder) is sufficient to give an appreciable aroma, flavor, and smoother cup of instant coffee. No antioxidants are required.

Hard Candies.—These have rather faithful citrus and some fruit flavors. The methods used for candy suggest possibilities for coffee flavor fixation. The referenced articles from *Candy Industry* (*Technology*) *and Confectioners Journal* show that hard candies are prepared by adding color, flavor, and powder acid (i.e., citric) to molten sugar at about 300 F (149 C). After kneading, the batch is cut to ribbons, and shapes of hard candy are formed. An alternative and more recent technique is to spray the flavor on powdered sugar and then sinter the powder into a solid mass, Leighton (1956). These methods are suitable for adding coffee flavor as an oil or essence onto a sugar powder with sintering. But the solid sugar, with little surface to weight ratio, is not suitable for instant coffee use.

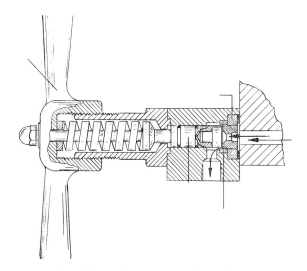

FIG. 264B. HOMOGENIZER VALVE DETAIL

U.S. Department of Agriculture Method.—The U.S. Department of Agriculture system patented by Turkot (1959), and Eskew *et al.* (1960) offers a continuous way to inject volatile fruit flavor essences into molten sugar, followed by cooling within seconds. Figure 265 shows a flowsheet of the method used. This method has not yet been proved a satisfactory product with coffee essence, although it should be satisfactory with coffee oil. Coffee oil, or coffee oil fortified with essence and emulsified with invert sugar, is quite stable. It gives off natural coffee aroma and imparts a natural coffee flavor after months of storage at room temperature in air. Candies flavored with such a creamy mixture have a fine natural coffee flavor that cannot be duplicated in any other way. Coffee flavor as

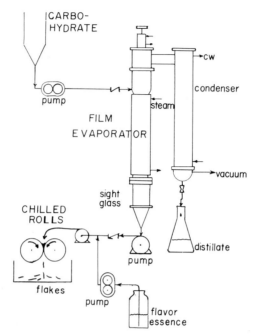

FIG. 265.   FLOWSHEET U.S.D.A. FLAVOR ESSENCE INJECTION
INTO MOLTEN SUGAR

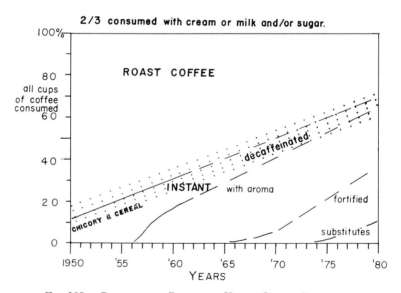

FIG. 266.   CURRENT AND PROJECTED USE OF COFFEE BEVERAGES

such is not a commercially available substance. Hence, coffee candies are often artificially flavored. This coffee flavor stability in a sugar-oil emulsion probably stems from the fact that no free water is available for deteriorative reactions.

Capsules.—Since about 1957 the National Cash Register Company of Dayton, Ohio, has commercially prepared encapsulated chemical liquids. When the gelatin capsules are ruptured, the chemicals react with other chemicals from ruptured capsules to form a color. This substantially represents their capsule-coated papers that make impressed copies without use of carbon paper. The upper side of the lower paper is coated with one encapsulated reagent, and the under side of the upper paper is coated with the other encapsulated reagent. Typing or writing ruptures the capsules.

Many other substances have been encapsulated according to the patents by Green (1957). The spray dried locked-in flavor technique is the means used to attain such encapsulations. The Southwest Research Institute (1959) at San Antonio, Tex., has encapsulated gasoline and other volatile substances by preparing discrete droplets in aqueous gum solution, and then drying to a gum film about the droplets. These systems can successfully encapsulate coffee essence, since the techniques are only variations of a gum seal about the many tiny volatile essence cells.

Summary

With the numerous methods of adding-back or retaining natural coffee flavor, a broad and acceptable coffee flavor appeal can be presented to the consumer. Figure 266 shows the inroads that instant coffees have made in the roast coffee market. It is expected that flavor-fortified and flavor-modified coffee beverages will continue their growth.

BIBLIOGRAPHY

Freeze concentration

ADAMS, J. M., and LEWIS, W. 1934. Growing large single ice crystals. Rev. Sci. Instr. 5, 400–402.
ANON. 1959. ECO extract pump. Chem. Eng. News 37, No. 21, 81.
ANON. 1961. Freeze-concentration. Food Eng. 33. No. 11, 98.
ANON. 1962. Freeze-concentration systems. Food Eng. 34, No. 2, 43.
ANON. 1962. Freeze desalting. Chem. Eng. 69, No. 16. 60, 62.
ANON. 1949. Orange juice vacuum evaporation. Food Inds. 21, 906–910, 930–933.
ANON. 1960. Saline Water Conversion. Advances in Chemistry Ser. No. 27, Am. Chem. Soc., Washington, D.C.
ANON. 1954. Sperti juice. Chem. Eng. News 32. 3132.
ANON. 1948. Squeezing ice. Chem. and Ind. 62, 759.
BADGER, W. L., and McCABE, W. L. 1936. Elements of Chemical Engineering. McGraw-Hill Book Co., New York.
BESSER, E. D., and PIRET, E. L. Controlled temperature dielectric drying. Chem. Eng. Prog. 51, No. 9, 405–410.

BILHAM, P. L. 138. Freeze concentration of fruit juices. J. Soc. Chem. Ind. 57, No. 6, 589–593.
GEMMILL, A. V. 1950. Centrifuging. Foods Inds. 22, No. 12, 63–74.
HEID, J. L., and BEISEL, C. C. 1948. Vacuum evaporation orange juice. Food Inds. 20, No. 4, 78–79.
HEISS, R., and SCHACHINGER, L. 1951. Fundamentals of freeze-concentration of liquids. Food Technol. 5, No. 6, 211–218.
LAWLER, F. K. 1951. Commonwealth Engineering Company orange juice process. Food Eng. 23, No. 10, 68–79, 210–212.
MORRIS, T. N. 1937. Concentration of fruit juices by freezing. Chem. Eng. News 15, No. 27, 615–618.
MOTTERN, H. H. 1937. Concentrating apple juice. Fruit Prod. J. Am. Vinegar Ind. 17, No. 3, 68–70.
OLIVE, T. R. 1948. Freeze concentration becomes practical. Food Inds. 20, 1432–1433; also Chem. Eng. 55, No. 10, 118–119.
REAVELL, J. A. 1937. Concentration of fruit juices and fruit drying. Chem. and Ind. 1, 618–621.
RECTOR, T. M. 1950. Research background of frozen concentrated orange juice. Chem. Eng. News 28, No. 4, 242–245.
SCHWARZ, H. W., and PENN, F. E. 1948. Production of orange juice concentrate and powder. Ind. Eng. Chem. 40, 938–944.
TING, H. H., and McCABE, W. L. 1934. Crystals. Ind. Eng. Chem. 26, 1201–1207.
WEBER, M. G. 1931. Concentrating fruit juices by freezing. Food Inds. 3, No. 5, 187.

Analytical chemistry

CARTRIGHT, L. C., and SNELL, C. T. 1947. Gases from roasted coffee. Spice Mill 70, No. 2, Part I (Feb. 16), 26; No. 3, Part II (March 16), 24.
GREENBAUM, F. R. 1955. Report of chemical process for testing coffee aroma and flavor. Tea and Coffee Trade J. 109, No. 2, 40, 42.
HUGHES, E. B., and SMITH, R. F. 1949. Volatile constituents of roasted coffee. J. Soc. Chem. Ind. 68, 322–327.
IBRAHIM, F. B. 1959. Gas chromatography of coffee aroma volatiles. Master's Thesis, Chemistry Dept., Univ. of Houston, Houston, Tex.
JACOBS, M. B. 1949. Coffee flavor components. Am. Perfumer Essent. Oil Rev. 53, No. 3, 231–232.
JOHNSTON, W. R., and FREY, C. N. 1938. Volatile constituents of roasted coffee. J. Am. Chem. Soc. 60, 1624–1627.
KNAPMAN, G. E. H. 1958, 1959, 1960, 1961. Gas Chromatography Abstracts. Butterworth Scientific Publications, Washington, D.C. (also London).
MERRITT, C., SULLIVAN, J. H., and ROBERTSON, J. H., 1957. Volatile components of coffee aroma. Analytical Report No. 12. U.S. Army QM Corps., Natick, Mass.
MONCRIEFF, R. W. 1950. The aroma of coffee. Food 19, Part I, 124–126; Part II, 176–179, London.
NATARAJAN, C. P., MANI, G. S., and BHATIA, D. S. 1954. Volatile value of Indian coffee and substitutes. Bull. Central Food Technol. Research Inst. 3, 307–309, Mysore, India.
REICHSTEIN, T., and STAUDINGER, H. 1950. Coffee aroma. Angew. Chem. 62A, 292; also 1955, Perfumery Essent. Oil Record 46, 86–88; also 1955, Coffee and Tea Inds. 78, 91.
RHOADES, J. 1958. Analyses of coffee volatiles by gas chromatography. Food Research 23, No. 3, 254–261. Also Coffee Brewing Institute (C.B.I.) Publication No. 34. See listing of other C.B.I. publications in Chapter 19 Bibliography.
RHOADES, J. 1960. Analysis of the volatile constituents of coffee. Agri. and Food Chem. 8, 136. Also Coffee Brewing Institute (C.B.I.) Publication No. 52. See listing of other C.B.I. Publications in Chapter 19 Bibliography.

RITTER, R. B. 1960. Aroma, key to increased soluble sales. Tea and Coffee Trade J. *119*, No. 3, 24, 28, 87, 94, 95.

SETHNESS, R. E. 1924. Coffee's aromatic principals. Tea and Coffee Trade J. *46*, No. 4, 570–572.

ZLATKIS, A., and SIVETZ, M. 1960. Analyses of coffee volatiles by gas chromatography. Food Research *25*, 395–398.

Staling of coffee flavor and aroma

BENGIS, R. O. 1935. Coffee staling unpreventable. Food Inds. 7, 490.

ELDER, L. W. 1940. Staling vs. rancidity in roasted coffee. Antioxygens produced by roasting. Ind. Eng. Chem. *32*, 798–801.

ELDER, L. W. 1937. Staling vs. rancidity in roasted coffee. Oxygen absorption by the fat fraction. Ind. Eng. Chem. *29*, 267–269.

JOHNSTON, W. R. 1938. Oxidizability of roasted coffee. Ind. Eng. Chem. *30*, 1284–1286; 1939, Spice Mill *62*, No. 1, 56–57, 61–62.

PRESCOTT, S. C., EMERSON, R. L., and PEAKES, JR., L. V. 1937. The staling of coffee, I. Food Research 2, 1–20; The staling of coffee, II. Food Research 2, 165–173.

PRESCOTT, S. C., EMERSON, R. L., WOODWARD, R. B., and HEGGIE, R. 1937. Contribution No. 94, Dept. of Biology and Public Health, Boston.

PRESCOTT, S. C. *et al.* 1924. Report on coffee research. Tea and Coffee Trade J. *46*, No. 1, 39–47; and Spice Mill *47*, No. 1, 21–30.

PUNNETT, P. W., and EDDY, W. H. 1930. What flavor measurement reveals about keeping coffee fresh. Food Inds. 2, 401–404.

PUNNETT, P. W. 1938. Effect of humidity on coffee flavor. Tea and Coffee Trade J. *74*, No. 4, 17.

PUNNETT, P. W. 1958. Staling. Tea and Coffee J. *114*, No. 5, 20, 58.

PUNNETT, P. W. 1960. What causes staling of roasted coffee? Tea and Coffee Trade J. *118*, No. 6, 20, 43–44.

SCHUMAN, A. C., and ELDER, L. W. 1943. Staling vs. rancidity in roasted coffee. Relative effects of moisture, aroma oxidation, and aroma evaporation on staling. Ind. Eng. Chem. *35*, 778–781.

Spray dried powdered flavors

ANON. 1956. Advances in spray drying improve flavor quality. Food Eng. *28*, No. 2, 76–78, 155.

ANON. 1956. Locked-in gum emulsion flavors. Am. Perfumer Aromat. *67*, No. 1, 63.

ANON. 1956. Powdered flavors. Am. Perfumed Aromat. *67*, No. 4, 254–256.

ANON. 1955. Spray dried flavors. Chem. Eng. News *33*, 5094.

ANON. 1957. Spray drier flavors. Candy Ind. and Confectioner's J. *109*, Aug. 30, 31.

BRODERICK, J. J. 1954. Superior powdered flavors. Food Eng. *26*, No. 11. 83.

METCALFE, L. S. 1956. Spray drying of flavors. Am. Perfumer Aromat. *67*, No. 4, 64.

SWAINE, R. L. 1957. Ideal flavor matches shelf life. Candy Ind. and Confectioner's J. *109*, Aug. 20, 13–15.

WELLNER, G. 1953. New coating process traps full flavor. Food Eng. *25*, No. 8, 94, 136, 138.

Flavor in carbohydrates

ANON. 1956. Hardy candy formulations. Candy. Ind. and Confectioner's J. *107*, Nov. 27, 18–19.

LAWLER, K. 1962. Foam mat drying goes to work. Food Eng. *34*, No. 2, 68–69.

LEIGHTON, A. E. 1957. Charms (hard candy). Candy Ind. and Confectioner's J. *108*, Jan. 8, 5–10.

LEIGHTON, A. E. 1956. Life-savers. Candy Ind. and Confectioner's J. *107*, Nov. 27, 19–32.

STRASHUN, S. I., and TALBURT, W. F. 1953. Puffed powder from juice. Food Eng. *25*, No. 3, 59–60.

Flavor in capsules

ANON. 1960. NCR micro-encapsulation. Chem. and Eng. News *38*, Oct. 3, 64.

ANON. 1959. SwRI capsules. Chem. and Eng. News *37*, July 13, 42.

CHALLANGE, F. 1959. Aspects of Organic Chemistry of Sulfur. Butterworth Scientific Publications, Washington, D.C. (also London).

DARGAS, A. 1959. Capsule factory. Scherer, Air. Eng. Nov., 36–39.

DUNLOP, A. F. 1953. Furans. Reinhold Publishing Corp., New York.

KLINGSBERG, E. 1960. Pyridine and its Derivatives. Four Parts. Interscience Division, John Wiley and Sons, New York.

MARTIN, R. W. 1956. Chemistry of Phenolic Resins. John Wiley and Sons, New York.

MEGSON, N. J. L. 1960. Phenolic Resin Chemistry. Academic Press, New York.

QUINN, E. L., and JONES, C. L. 1935. Carbon Dioxide. Am. Chem. Soc. Monograph No. 72, Reinhold Publishing Corp., New York.

REID, E. E. 1960. Organic Chemistry Bivalent Sulfur. Chemical Publishing Co., New York.

Flavors in fruits, vegetables, tobacco, dairy products, and perfumes

ANON. 1960. du Pont builds big chromatograph. Chem. Eng. News *38*, No. 7, 58.

ANON. 1958. Filter balances cigarette smoke. Chem. Eng. News *36*, No. 33, 38.

ANON. 1959. Gas chromatograph profiles of beer. Chem. Eng. News *37*, No. 35, 45–46.

BENTLEY, H. R., and BERRY, E. G. N. 1959. Tobacco Manufacturing Committee, 6–10 Bruton St., London.

DATEO, G. P. *et al.* 1957. Volatile sulfur components of cooked cabbage. Food Research *22*, 440–447.

FARBER, L. 1957. Pungency of onion and garlic by volatile reducing substances. Food Technol. *11*, 621–624.

FARBER, L. 1958. Volatile reducing substances and coffee. Food Research *23*, No. 1, 72–78.

JACKSON, H. W. 1958. Flavor research on cheese. Perfumery Essent. Oil Record *48*, 256–258.

KEPNER, R. E., and WEBB, A. D. 1956. Volatile aroma constituents of grape. Am. J. Enology 7, No. 1, 8–18; 1957; *also* Food Research *22*, 384–395.

KIRCHNER, J. G. 1949. Chemistry of Fruit and Vegetable Flavors. Advances in Food Research. Vol. II, 277–283, Academic Press, New York.

MERORY, J. 1960. Food Flavorings. Avi Publishing Co., Westport, Conn.

MITCHELL, J. H., and LEINEN, N. J. 1957. Chemistry of Natural Food Flavors. U.S. Army QM Corps, Washington, D.C.

MURCH, A. F. 1957. Concentrating advances bring superior flavors. Food Eng. *29*, No. 12, 90–92.

NOLAND, J. S., and SHRINER, R. L. 1958. Odorous Constituents of Yellow Corn. U.S. Department of Agriculture, Report from Univ. of Iowa, Iowa City, Iowa.

PANOYOTOV, I., and IVANOV, D. 1958. Aldehydes in rose oil. Perfumery Essent. Oil Record *48*, Part I, 231–234; Part II, 290–296.

SJOSTROM, L. B., and CAIRNCROSS, S. E. 1958. Physico-chemical research on flavor. J. Anal. Chem. *30*, No. 2, 17–23A.

Wood and wood distillation

ANON. 1906–1955. Wood Distillation Bibliography (fifty years), Oregon Forest Products Laboratory, Corvallis, Ore.

Hawley, L. F. 1923. Wood Distillation. Am. Chem. Soc. Monograph, 36–83, Reinhold Publishing Corp., New York.

Husaini, S. A., and Cooper, G. E. 1957. Fractionation of wood smoke. Food Technol. 11, 499–502.

Ott, E., and Spurlin, H. M. 1954. Cellulose. Vol. I. Interscience Division, John Wiley and Sons, New York.

Flavor chemistry

Anon. 1956. The use of chemical additives in food processing. Food Protection Committee, Publication 398, National Research Council, Washington, D.C.

Conant, J. B. 1939. Chemistry of Organic Compounds. The Macmillan Co., New York.

Feiser, L., and Feiser, M. 1961. Advanced Organic Chemistry. Reinhold Publishing Corp., New York.

Guenther, E. 1948. The Essential Oils. Six Vols. D. Van Nostrand Co., Princeton, N.J.

Hartman, R. J. 1939. Colloid Chemistry. Houghton Mifflin Co., Boston.

Jirgensons, B., and Fox, A. 1958. Colloid Chemistry. Academic Press, New York.

Jirgensons, B., and Straumanis, M. E. 1962. Colloid Chemistry. The Macmillan Co., New York.

Klein, P. 1962. Sublimation of caffein under vacuum can packing. Institute of Food Technologists meeting, June, Miami, Fla.

Lewis, W. K., Squires, L., and Broughton, G. 1943. Colloidal and Amorphous Materials. The Macmillan Co., New York.

Mantell, C. L. 1951. Adsorption. 2nd Edition. McGraw-Hill Book Co., New York.

McBain, J. W., 1931. Sorption of Gases and Vapors by Solids. G. Routledge Sons, London.

Merory, J. 1960. Food Flavorings. Avi Publishing Co., Westport, Conn.

Moncrieff, R. W. 1946. The Chemical Senses. John Wiley and Sons, New York.

Morrison, G. H., and Freiser, H. 1957. Solvent Extraction in Analytical Chemistry. John Wiley and Sons, New York.

Perry, J. H. (Editor). 1962. Chemical Engineering Handbook, McGraw-Hill Book Co., New York.

Sivetz, M. 1949. Acids in beverage flavor. Food Inds. 21, No. 10. 74–75

Sivetz, M. 1959. Improved soluble coffee. Food Eng. 31, No. 5, 92–93.

Sivetz, M. 1949. Pure carbon dioxide. Food Inds. 21, No. 6, 62–63.

Small, J. 1946. pH and Plants. D. Van Nostrand Co., Princeton, N.J.

Aromatized instant coffee

Bredt, C. 1934. Where does the gas in roasted coffee come from? Food Inds. 11, No. 8, 348–349.

Brown, C. A., and Zerban, F. W. 1955. Sugar Analysis. John Wiley and Sons, New York.

Calmon, C., and Kressman, T. R. E. 1957. Ion Exchangers in Organic and Biochemistry. Interscience Division, John Wiley and Sons, New York.

Cheronis, N. D., and Entrikin, J. B. 1957. Semi-micro Qualitative Organic Analyses: The Systematic Identification of Organic Compounds. Interscience Division, John Wiley and Sons, New York.

Dreisbach, R. R. 1952. Pressure-Volume-Temperature Relationships of Organic Compounds. Handbook Publishers Inc., Sandusky, Ohio.

Fox, S. W., and Foster, J. F. 1957. Introduction to Protein Chemistry. John Wiley and Sons, New York.

Fritz, J. S., and Hammond, G. S. 1957. Quantitative Organic Analysis. John Wiley and Sons, New York.

HASSLER, J. W. 1941. Active Carbon, the Modern Purifier. West Virginia Pulp and Paper Co., New York.

HEWITT, E. J. et al. 1957. Identification of volatile sulfur components of cooked cabbage and the nature of precursors in the fresh vegetable. Food Research 22, 440–447.

JACOB, M. B. 1951. The Chemistry and Technology of Food and Food Products, Vol. II (Coffee). Interscience Division, John Wiley and Sons, New York.

KIRCHNER, J. C. 1950–1951. What makes flavor in fruit: Yearbook, U.S. Department of Agriculture, Washington, D.C.

KUNIN, R. 1958. Ion Exchange Resins. John Wiley and Sons, New York.

LEIGHTON, A. E. 1952. Textbook on Candy Making. Manufacturing Confectioners Publishing Co., Oak Park, Ill.

MERRITT, M. C., and PROCTOR, B. E. 1959. Effect of temperature during the roasting cycle on selected components of different types of whole bean coffee. Food Research 24, 672–680. Also Coffee Brewing Institute (C.B.I.) publication No. 46. See listing of other C.B.I. publications in Chapter 19 Bibliography.

MINER, C. S. 1934. Acidity of Roasted Coffee. National Federation of Coffee Growers of Colombia, 120 Wall Street, New York.

SAMUELSON, O. 1953. Ion Exchangers in Analytical Chemistry. John Wiley and Sons, New York.

SHRINER, R. L., FUSON, R. C., and CURTIN. D. Y. 1956. The Systematic Identification of Organic Compounds. John Wiley and Sons, New York.

SIGGIA, S., and STOLTEN, H. J. 1954. An Introduction to Modern Organic Analysis. Interscience Division, John Wiley and Sons, New York.

PATENTS ON COFFEE AROMA

The following chronological lists of patent numbers on the various phases of coffee aroma technology are cited in full detail among others in Appendix I. They are listed there in two sections: U.S. patents, and foreign patents, each chronologically. A list of inventors arranged alphabetically is also given in the same appendix.

A. COFFEE OIL—STEAM DISTILLATION—CONDENSATION AT LOW TEMPERATURES—
AROMA PRESERVATION—SOLVENT TRANSFER—GRINDER GAS—EXTRACTION

4,922/1847	997,431/11	Br 383,170/31
115,302/1871	1,214,875/17	1,836,931/31
116,298,9/1871	1.237,931/17	Br 408,613/34
119,959/1871	1,251,359/17	2,017,892/35
177,592/1876	1,292,458/19	2,022,467/35
246,274/1881	1,324,662/19	2,043,443/36
270.787/1883	1,365.443/21	2,054,689/36
339,114/1886	1,367,715,6/21	2,062,109/36
344,597/1886	1,367,724,5,6/21	2,098,961/37
439,318/1890	1,393,045/21	2,149,876/39
474,531/1892	1,398,115/21	2,155,971/39
617,434/1899	Br 246,454/25	2,156.212/39
701,750/02	Br 260,960/25	2,159,027/39
726,279/03	1,605,115/26	Can 389,192/40
754,943/04	Fr 694,602/30	2,204,896/40
Can 394,579/41	Sw 269,390/50	2,738,276/56
Can 399,060/41	Fr 963,554/50	2,750,998/56
2,28,138,9/42	2,494,928/50	2,758,927/56

2,286,334/42	2,539,157/51	Dutch 59,834/57
2,288,284/42	Sw 272,240/50	2,853,387/58
2,306,061/42	2,522,014/50	2,875,063/59
2,314,988/43	Sw 272,990/51	Can 572,026/59
2,335,206/43	Sw 277,290/51	Can 576,810/59
2,345,378/44	2,542,119/51	2,903,359/59
2,350,903/44	2,557,294/51	2,918,372/59
2,389,732/45	2,562,206/51	2,929,716/60
Br 575,118/46	2,563,233/51	2,931,727,8/60
2,405,487/46	2,564,332/51	2,947,634/60
2,420,615/47	2,569,217/51	Br 844,514/60
2,432,759/47	2,614,043/52	Can 603,954/60
Br 614,139/48	2,665,198/54	2,976,158/61
2,457,315/48	2,680,687/54	2,981,629/61
Sw 263,267/49	2,720,936/55	3,021,218/62
2,481,470/49	2,771,364/56	Can. 654,696/62
2,513,813/50	Can 535,118/57	Can. 656,891/63

B. FIXED, LOCKED-IN, OR ENCAPSULATED FLAVORS, USE OF CARBOHYDRATES

324,050/1885	2,367,269/45	Br 654,950/51
1,324,538/19	2,369,847/45	2,566,410/51
1,504,459/24	Br 582,918/46	2,788,276/57
1,641,446/27	2,422,145/47	2,800,457,8/57
1,866,414,5/32	2,419,031/47	2,809,895/57
2,036,345/36	2,428,636/47	2,816,039/57
2,088,622/37	2,432,698/47	2,816,840/57
2,258,567/41	Sw 250,804/48	2,826,504/58
2,305,620,1,2/42	2,457.036/48	2,864,707/58
Sw 217,126/42	Sw 264,898/50	2,899,313/59
2,340,235/44	Sw 272.240/50	2,904,440/59
2,360,342/44	2,555,463-8/51	2,906,630/59
		2,929,716/60

C. FREEZE CONCENTRATION OF COFFEE EXTRACT AND OTHER FOOD PRODUCTS

723,152/03	2,090,985/37	2,436,218/48
955,659/10	2,091,493/37	2,448,802/48
981,860/11	Br 485,540/38	2,453,109/48
1,002,137/11	2,119,182/38	2,480,954/49
1,058.279/13	Ger 669,185/38	2,482,507/49
1,137,265/15	2,159,248/39	2,503,395/50
1,359,911/20	2,241,726/41	2,504,735/50
1,402.004/22	2,248,634/41	2,513,991/50
1,465,020/23	2.301,901/42	2,550,615/51
1,507,410/24	2,319,994/43	2,552,524/51
1.546,669/25	2,324,526/43	2,552,525/51
1,576,136,7/26	2,337,317/43	2,666,707/54
Br 278.799/26	2,340,721/44	2,734,355/56
1,636.890/27	2,343,169/44	2,735,779/56
1,641,429/27	2,379,427/45	2.751,687/56
1,738,275/29	2,395,498/46	2,765,235/56
1,933,960/33	2.408,260/46	2,800,001/57
1,979,124/34	2,416,945/47	2,801,920/57
1,996,988/35	2,419,909/47	2,888,353/59
1.999.712/35	2,424,663/47	2,903,371/59
Br 429,474/35	2,431,496/47	2,977,234/61
		3,023,111/62

CHAPTER 15

Physiological and Psychological Effects of Coffee

MARKET VALUE

At the consumer level, marketing of roast coffee is influenced in varying degrees by such factors as price, advertising, packaging, availability, and taste. This holds true for almost any food product. For the processor, however, green coffee is purchased in the open market within the framework of supply and demand where the factors of advertising and packaging carry little weight. Here the roaster must weigh the intrinsic quality of the raw material against price and delivery date. Prices generally reflect this relationship and are a good relative index of quality. Good quality high grown Colombian mild coffees, for example, brought more than 45¢ per lb in 1962. At that time, other types of good quality mild coffees brought more than 40¢ per lb; lesser quality mild coffees brought 36¢ per lb; Brazilian coffees brought about 30¢ per lb; and Robusta coffees brought about 18¢ per lb.

Since the grower is primarily interested in the volume of his production, the buyer and importer must carefully examine all samples for quality and uniformity as deviations affect his final product.

Thus the experienced roaster, fully aware of regional taste preferences, geographical water variations, prevailing standards of pricing, and competition will adjust his blend and his price to provide a profitable business. In some European markets, where price competition is nominal because of the existence of cartels, the roaster has more latitude in dealing with what may be termed "a captive market." For this reason, the roaster is not likely to disclose information concerning the prices he pays for raw materials or the composition of his blends. In more competitive markets, price is governed more by competition than by the intrinsic quality of the product. There is no doubt that the roaster who understands the nuances of public acceptance and preference as well as variations in geographical and economic areas can use his "know-how" in purchasing and processing to great business advantage.

There are several reasons for this. Although efforts of the Coffee Brewing Institute (C.B.I.) and lower coffee prices since 1957 have resulted in improved brewing methods and cup quality in the United States, coffee in most American restaurants remains barely acceptable in quality. This is largely because coffee suppliers provide restaurants with the quality they are willing to pay for and this is usually marginal in flavor.

Even good quality restaurant coffee may be poorly brewed. At other times, the indifference or ignorance of the restaurateur or his customers may be responsible. Furthermore, as restaurant coffee is often held for hours after brewing, there is little merit in using good quality coffees. Suitable remedies, however, are slowly being evolved in this area. Many restaurants extract coffee in urns to save labor. But many urns produce an inferior brew. Furthermore, about two out of three people use cream or milk and almost as many use sugar. These additions dilute and mitigate bad coffee flavor and serve to reduce the intrinsic difference between good and mediocre coffees and brews. For these reasons, the restaurateur and his coffee supplier are often justified in selling blends and brews that are barely acceptable.

In areas where there are alkaline, brackish, organically or chemically contaminated waters (and this includes municipal chlorination), coffee quality may be considerably altered. What one becomes accustomed to is considered good. The use of genuinely good coffees is wasted unless poor water conditions are remedied. Although remedial action may be simple and economical, it is often neglected.

In the home, the choice of coffees may be more discriminating. But as long as there are the masking influences of water, cream, sugar, and varying methods of preparation, the housewife with economy in mind tends to purchase the lowest priced product. Thus in both roast and soluble coffees, the public is the basic stimulus to the existence and growth of businesses that provide mediocre products. Only a few firms offer genuinely high quality coffees and only a relatively small percentage of customers will seek these brands and prepare them in a manner that yields the best flavor. In Europe, where coffee is a relatively more expensive commodity, consumers of the latter type are encouraged.

Despite the influences that intervene between the purchase of coffee and the final brew, there remain basic enjoyments in a cup of coffee that need to be examined.

BASIC OR PRIMITIVE FACTORS IN AROMA AND TASTE

Recognition and association of aromas is a primitive and essential part of all animal and human life. Recognition usually implies association, and thus is a very personal thing. Association may further imply continual use and habits which can be translated into conditioning, custom, perhaps even ritual and tradition. The latter associations may stimulate emotions such as pleasure, disgust, anticipation, and hate. In other words, aromas may produce important emotional effects on oneself or on others. Pleasant aromas are piney, flowery, and spicy, and may be associated with eating and sex. Unpleasant aromas are rotten, putrid, and musty, and others associated with illness and death. Unfamiliar odors may be threatening until some association is established. The distilled aromas from an oak or bay log campfire, or from a charcoal preparation usually involve pleasant associations. Cooking odors may be easily recognizable and pleasant. The aromas from roasting, grinding, or brewing coffee are usually pleasant experiences, even to children. Coffee aroma, particularly for adults, provides an anticipation of a friendly meal or "coffee break."

To the experienced coffee taster, coffee aroma can mean much more. It may reveal that the coffee is over- or under-roasted. It may indicate a robusta botanical variety or a high grown mild coffee with its exquisite characteristic aroma. The intensity of the aroma, as well as its quality, may disclose whether it is a high or low grown coffee. Other odors may signal contamination caused by mold or improper fermentation. Or, the aroma may reveal conclusively that the roasted coffee is stale.

SPECIES AND PLACE OF ORIGIN

An expert taster can evaluate a green coffee if he knows its geographical point of origin. Canephora varieties, of which robusta is most commonly used, have the least taste appeal, and bring the lowest price on the world market. Arabica varieties comprise three types: Brazilian and low or high grown mild coffees. Brazilian coffees are grown without shade on large plantations and are mostly dried in the cherry. These have a neutral coffee flavor but lack the desirable and pleasant aroma and flavor characteristics of high altitude shade-grown arabica coffees. On the other hand, mild coffees will vary in quality among themselves depending on geographical origin which, in turn, is directly related to soil, sun, temperature, disease, shade, rainfall, and other natural, as well as agricultural growth factors. The country, state, and plantation of origin are usually indicative of the history and properties of the green coffee. See Cheney (1947) and Ukers (1935). The buyer examines such physical properties of the green coffee as odor and appearance, as indices of quality in cupping after roasting. Discoloration may be a sign of age, flavor loss, or fermented flavor. Non-uniform green coffee beans result in non-uniform roasted coffee. Black beans or "nipped" beans and "quakers" can give the cup a dirty taste. Foreign matter among the beans is a sign of careless cleaning, and is therefore a warning to be alert to other indications of sub-standard quality.

CUPPING—EVALUATING COFFEE FLAVOR

Preparation and Examination of Coffee and Brew

Cupping refers to the critical evaluation of the flavor and odor of coffee as a guide to purchasing or processing blends. Cupping is also used on coffee sampled in-process to evaluate the choice of green coffee and of process conditions. Green coffee beans are roasted to a point short of full flavor development to reveal any off-flavor notes. A few hundred grams of green beans are roasted in a laboratory sample roaster in order to evaluate roasting qualities. The green coffee samples usually represent a maximum of about 250 bags. In all cases cupping is carried out under carefully standardized conditions of sampling, roasting, grinding, and brewing.

Representative Samples.—The green coffee sample should be representative of the lot, but may be non-representative as a result of a non-uniform lot, poor sampling, or, on rare occasions, deliberate misrepresen-

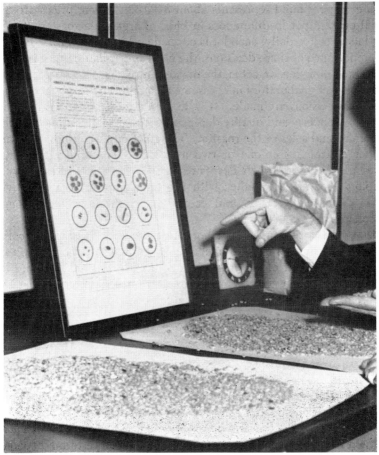

Courtesy National Coffee Association—U.S.A.

Fig. 267. Green Coffee Beans Being Examined

tation. The buyer's decision often is based on the reputation and warranty of the seller. The transaction is confirmed by sampling the coffee bags (by means of a trier) upon their receipt and comparing this sample with the sales sample. Bag lots of coffee bought on description are sufficiently well understood by the buyer. Here again, the bags of coffee are sampled and checked for grade. Figure 267 shows examination of green coffee beans. Where difference of opinion exists as to coffee grade, there may be an adjustment in price or return of the coffee. To settle disputes, a taste board of arbitration may be called in but this is not a usual procedure. The coffee seller's reputation must therefore be good in order to gain quick and continual acceptance of coffee offers to the trade.

Buying and Selling.—Since 250 bags is about 40,000 lb green coffee, each cent per pound represents about $400.00. Often, prices are quoted based on $^1/_4$¢ per lb differences in bids. Large-scale roasters buy many bag lots of coffee daily; each lot is cupped and bargained for. Because of the importance of these decisions, the chief buyer and cupper is usually a well paid employee, or, often, the owner himself.

The cupping laboratory may assume an aura of mystery where top management decisions are made. It is, in fact, a most important room where weighty monetary and quality decisions are made which directly influence the profits and sales of the roaster. The chief cupper usually has another cupper in training or one or two assistants. The ability to categorize coffee properties and their flavors expertly is the result of many years of cupping experience together with the development of a sensitivity to coffee aromas and tastes, and careful judgment in coffee buying and processing.

Brew Preparation.—After laboratory roasting, the green coffee is usually coarsely ground and smelled just before evaluation of cup flavor. Ten grams of roast coffee are weighed and placed in a 5 fl oz (150 ml) glass. Several such samples and reference samples are prepared. Each is identified with a tray sample of the green coffee beans below the tray of roast coffee beans. Freshly-boiled (pure) water is poured into the R & G coffee until it froths and fills the head of the cup. After about 5 min, when some of the floating coffee grounds have been wetted and many particles have sunk, the floating grounds' cover is "broken" with a taste spoon. This releases gases and allows the grounds to become more fully wetted for complete extraction. During this "break" time, the aroma from the cup is evaluated as is the aroma from the settled wet grounds. Each aroma is distinctive and often revealing. Most of the coffee grounds are then removed from the solution surface with a perforated spoon, and each sample is cupped. The samples must not be so hot as to insensitize the tongue or mouth, nor so cool that the full coffee flavor is altered. The cupping may be done with a personalized spoon of heavy silver plate or sterling silver to effect faster cooling.

Cupping.—A strong inhalation of air sucks in the brew from the spoon, making a loud, gurgling sound. This method of intake effectively cools the coffee brew as its aroma rises into the nostrils. The spoonful of coffee is then spit out into a cuspidor, and additional samples are similarly evaluated. Figure 268 shows the cupping table, cuspidor, grinder, etc., and Fig. 269 shows the act of sucking or spraying the coffee into the

Courtesy Coffee & Tea Industries magazine

FIG. 268. CUPPING TABLE

mouth. It is good practice not to cup too many samples at a time since one's taste sensitivity is progressively reduced. Sometimes cupping of many samples is necessary when coffee bag lots are small and taste help is short. Rinsing one's mouth with tepid water is often desirable to wash out carry-over of cup flavors (especially when distinctive), and to freshen the mouth. Eating a saltine-type cracker also helps to remove coffee aftertaste between cup samplings. Cupping is done preferably from a swivel stool (adjustable height) at a rotary table with an easily cleaned stone or plastic surface. The room should be clean, quiet, orderly, free from coffee odors, and with a comfortable room temperature. Smoking tobacco should be prohibited. The room should be free of phones and personnel

Courtesy Instituto Brasileiro do Cafe

Fig. 269.   Cupping Table

traffic. The fewer persons cupping, the better; as the cups of coffee cool rapidly and a non-uniform taste impression may result from the presence of too many tasters.

Soluble Coffee Powders

Two grams of instant coffee are weighed and placed into 5-oz porcelain cups (white). See Table 75, p. 94. When all the cups of instant coffee have been prepared and identified, pure boiling water is poured over the powder until the solution is about $^1/_4$ in. from the lip. The aroma from the cups may be smelled during or just after pouring for any revealing notes. Thereafter, the cups of beverage are allowed to cool. A thin-walled Wedgewood type porcelain cup allows rapid heat loss and early cupping. The rate of powder solubility, residual foam, floating oil or specks, and beverage turbidity, as well as any sediment at the bottom of the cup are noted. Dirty or foamy rings left during the cooling and cupping period are undesirable. Normally every Tote-Bin (800 lb) of instant coffee should be representatively sampled and cupped before release for packing. Soluble coffee is cupped to assure quality to the consumer, whereas green coffees are cupped to assure a good buy. It is desirable to keep close control of R & G coffee quality by frequent laboratory cup tests carried out quickly by means of a vacuum filter.

Extracts.—These cups are prepared by measuring out the proper extract volume, depending on concentration, to give 2 gm of soluble coffee per 5 fl oz of beverage.

Plant Percolator

Extracts are representative of the soluble coffee flavor achieved, but are usually several times stronger in flavor and aroma than the corresponding powder produced from such extract. Percolator extracts taste more acid than the powder in the cup. For tasting control, solubles concentration is cited as unit weight per unit volume. It is often desirable to use more coffee solubles per cup of beverage than the standard concentration of two grams per cup so as to effect a stronger and different flavor sensation.

Factors in Evaluation

The color of the roast coffee beans and brew is often an influential and significant factor in evaluation of aroma and flavor. If the taste evaluator is ill, physically or mentally, it is usually safer not to use his judgment in vital matters until he feels normal.

Laboratory Supplies and Facilities

Although these items should be standard, they are often inadequate. As their lack often reflects shortcomings in coffee evaluation, the more important laboratory aspects are cited below.

Heat Load.—The cupping room is often a beehive of preparation of hot water, hot cups, and hot plates. Unless adequate ventilation is provided, the room becomes uncomfortable for work. Tasters become less sensitive, and employees may become sick. Temperature and humidity control throughout the year is highly desirable.

Roaster.—The laboratory roaster is another source of considerable heat. The roaster may cause much coffee aroma and smoke in a confined area and should be in a room separated from the cupping operation. The room in which the coffee is roasted needs to be provided with an air supply so that a positive once-through air flow can be maintained to sweep away the smoke and combustion gases. Otherwise, oily products of coffee roasting deposited within the wall and cabinet surfaces of the room may cause a cleaning and staling problem. Figure 270 shows a battery of coffee sample roasters. A sample is being withdrawn in order to observe the color of the roast. This may be compared with a standard sample.

Courtesy Pan American Coffee Bureau
Fig. 270. Battery of Coffee Sample Roasters

Laboratory Location.—A common fault in the location of cupping rooms is that plant roaster air is drawn in. This background coffee aroma in the cupping room (1) reduces the freshness of the air, and (2) reduces the cupper's sensitivity to aroma and flavor. To enable the color of the roast coffee to be examined visually, the room should have, if possible, natural northern light which is diffuse. It should be built with acoustical tile and be so far from the plant machinery that vibrations and noises are not noticeable. An adjoining storage room should be provided for green coffee samples as the odor of green coffee in a cupping room is also undesirable.

Laboratory Equipment.—A dishwashing machine is needed to remove oil from cups and glasses, as well as to protect the employees from carry-

over of colds. It is convenient to have a large hot water supply using a
6-gal thermostatically-controlled hot water urn. This maintains water at
190 F (88 C) which, upon transfer to kettle, gives boiling water quickly.
Storage space should be available for 5-gal bottles of spring or distilled
water where good tap water is not available. A wall location, apart from
the cupping room, is needed for a coffee bean blending tube. This is
mostly used for mixing green coffee bean trier samples to obtain representative composite mixtures. Also a splitter counter area is needed for
splitting bean and instant coffee samples. At times, when bean sizes are
non-uniform, it is desirable to measure the variation with a set of standard
perforated screens. Figure 271 shows the full scale hole sizes in such

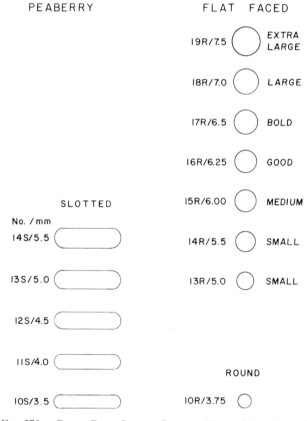

FIG. 271. GREEN BEAN SCREEN GRADING HOLES (FULL SCALE)

grading screens. Adequate stocks of coffee bean trays of plastic, metal, or
paper composition, are also needed. A laboratory grinder with adjustable
fineness control is essential for daily routine grinding. A spare set of

grinder plates is desirable as plates under continual use wear out in less than a year. Flooring should be smooth plastic or ceramic tile since most roast coffee spillages are sticky, corrosive, and oily. Daily sweeping, if not washing, may be necessary. One or two desks are needed for tasting personnel to maintain records on coffee evaluations, storage data, correspondence, and purchase contracts. Drainage racks for washed jars and glassware are also desirable. Cabinet space for storage of competitive coffee samples as well as experimental process samples is needed. Towels, filters, brewing equipment, etc., are also required.

EVALUATING COFFEE FLAVOR

Odor and Taste Terms

The most important thing in tasting coffee is to be able to recognize accepted trade classifications, and desirable aromas and flavors, as well as uncommon and undesirable flavors. These taste responses are complex in themselves when analyzing a given coffee sample, but subjective reactions and environmental circumstances can make taste and aroma analysis even more difficult. Only by repeated tasting and evaluation with different groups of tasters can satisfactory taste and aroma reactions be confirmed and communicated.

Taste is a complex subjective sensation imparted to the palate and nostrils through the mouth. It can be a pleasant, indifferent, or unpleasant experience. Taste has overtones of heat, coolness, irritation, and numbness. The ability to analyze or associate the taste impression largely results from years of working experience. In this time, there have been revealed many differences in coffee taste. The taste sensations are due to colloidal texture, oil droplets, acidity, and particularly to the amount and composition of the volatile coffee flavor substances. The basic coffee flavor arises from non-volatile solubles; but much of the appealing coffee flavor comes from the few parts per million of very volatile aromatic chemical constituents. These are discussed in detail later in this chapter in the section on Associating Flavors with Identified Chemical Constituents (see pp. 103–104). The addition of these substances to brew, extracts and powders can simulate tones of natural coffee flavors.

Natural coffee flavor to the experienced taster is a special phenomenon, and any abnormal odor or taste sensation cannot come within the accepted flavor framework. Flavor varies with concentration, temperature, cleanliness of utensils, the taster's immediate conditioning (e.g., tasting coffee after eating sweet cake or sour plum). The taster's subjective opinions can influence the objectivity of the coffee flavor examination. The following list presents odor and taste terms as used in the coffee trade.   Ukers (1935) and Howard (1959) offer glossaries of sensory terms.

TASTE AND ODOR TERMS

The following list is a compilation of terms commonly used to describe the taste characteristics of coffee

Acidy	A desirable flavor, as it occurs in high grown coffees, that is sharp and pleasing, but not biting. Definitely associated with flavorful acid content.
Acrid	A burnt flavor that is sharp, bitter, and perhaps irritating.
After taste	A taste that remains in the mouth longer than usual after eating or drinking.
Aged	Aged coffee implies a carefully regulated storage to bring out a heavy body. This must not be confused with "old" crop.
Aroma	Volatile pleasant smelling substances with the characteristic odor of coffee. These come from coffee usually when boiling water comes into contact with freshly ground coffee.
Astringent	A flavor that causes puckering and a bitter impression (shrinkage or contraction of tissue).
Bitter	An unpleasant taste which is sharp and disagreeable, such as that of quassia or quinine. Some people get an acid taste impression while others a bitter taste from the same coffee. Iron contamination causes bitterness.
Bland	A taste which is smooth and flavorless, such as that of butter.
Body	A taste sensation or mouth feeling of more viscosity, usually associated with heavy coffee flavor but in no way reflecting any increase in true physical viscosity of the cupping fluid.
Burnt	A smell and taste like that of burnt carbohydrate, protein, or oil, e.g., charcoal.
Brackish	A distasteful, bitter, salty characteristic.
Caramelized	A sweet, almost burnt flavor, like caramelized sugar. A desirable taste note if complemented with coffee flavor. Loss of coffee flavored volatiles enhances the caramelized flavor.
Dirty	An undesirable "fuzzy" taste that dominates the coffee flavor background.
Earthiness	An undesirable taste or odor resembling the odor of freshly uncovered earth; usually due to molds.
Fermented	A chemical change caused by yeast or enzymes in the green coffee. Such fermented flavors are similar to those obtained when sugar ferments to alcohol or vinegar. A pronounced flavor of fermentation is undesirable.
Grassy	A flavor found most often in early pickings of new crop coffees and caused by immature beans, suggestive of an intense, fresh greenness, such as new mown hay or lush grass.
Green	A taste caused by under-roasting, thus failing to develop full coffee flavor. Somewhat pasty. A sourish flavor imparted by "green" beans, i.e., those that have never matured. It should be distinguished from grassiness.
Harsh	A taste which is unpleasantly sharp, rough, or irritating.
Hay	Odor and taste like dried grass. Hay flavor is common in dried foods.
Instant	Characterized by furfurals and hydrolyzed cellular solubles and volatiles not normally found in brewed coffees.
Musty	A taste akin to earthiness. Similar to a closed closet; moldy.
Natural	A "natural" coffee denotes an unwashed coffee, i.e., one prepared by drying the whole berry (dry process) rather than by fermenting the outer pulp (wet process). Usually blander, a "natural" does not have the development of flavor and acidity characteristic of washed wet process coffees of the same growth, and often not the clarity and uniformity of cup, but may have as much or more body. "Natural" most often refers to dry process unwashed mild coffees. Most Brazilian coffees and Robustas are "naturals."

New crop	A fresh light coffee flavor and aroma which enhances the normal characteristics of a coffee blend, particularly flavor and acidity. Not to be confused with wildness or greenness which are frequently present in new crop coffees.
Old crop	A flavor and aroma in which the normal characteristics of a mature, greenish coffee are weakened or toned down, particularly acidity and flavor, but which can also reflect a deterioration of these qualities into a woody or papery flavor with little or no body.
Pungent	A pricking, stinging, or piercing sensation; not necessarily unpleasant; e.g., pepper or snuff.
Quakery	A "peanuty" flavor caused by undeveloped, dead beans which show up very light in the roast.
Rioy	An unpleasant flavor, which produces a penetrating character that cannot be hidden by blending. It is somewhat medicinal (iodine) with possibly woody or fermented overtones.
Robusta	Robustas have a bland flavor and little aroma compared with mild coffee, having little acidity or "true" aromatic coffee flavor. At best, they can be neutral, but with a straw-like flavor, but the majority contain varying degrees of a rubbery flavor and a urine-like aroma. The high caffein content (twice that of Arabicas) no doubt contributes to the distinctive flavor characteristics and probably is the cause of their being more bitter than other coffees. Robustas are the lowest priced of all coffees, followed by Brazilian coffees and then higher grown mild coffees.
Rubbery	An odor similar to braked car tires on pavement. Usually undesirable but very characteristic. Instant coffee held at above 120 F (49 C) for days develops such an odor with sickening overtones.
Sour	A somewhat, unpleasant flavor having a sharp, acid taste.
Stale	A sweet but unpleasant flavor and aroma of roasted coffee which reflect the oxidization of many of the pleasant volatiles and the loss of others. A change in the flavor and acid constituents causing a partial bland tone.
Sweet	A pleasant flavor like sugar.
Wildness	The presence of one or more extreme flavor characteristics, usually akin to sourishness or fermentation, found in poorly prepared coffees, mostly "naturals."
Winey	Reminiscent of wine flavor and body, usually in high grown coffees.
Woody	A taste caused by deterioration of the coffee; akin to wood.

REASONS FOR CONTINUAL TASTING, BUYING, CONTROL, AND COMPETITION

The importance of tasting when purchasing green coffee beans has already been discussed. The significance of tasting at various points thereafter (blending green coffees, roasting blends or roasting separate types of green coffees, blending after roasting, after packaging of ground coffee, after various stages of storage, after extraction, and after spray drying) will be discussed later in this chapter (see pp. 92–96).

The three other main reasons for taste testing are: (1) to identify and evaluate individual taste elements of the composite product; (2) to compare the differences between standard test samples and commercial products; and (3) to measure consumer preference. Tasting to identify flavor properties, applying this experience to process control, then relating this information to consumer acceptance, are very broad areas. Yet without this expert ability to choose green coffee and to guide the preparation of the final regular and instant coffee product, only limited success in aroma and flavor development and marketing can be obtained. Measuring consumer taste acceptability and preference is a recent marketing tool, difficult to use because of the many variable factors that guide public preference. These include individual subjective taste reactions as well as the consumer's reactions to price, advertising, convenience, and conditioning. A consumer may become habituated to a poor coffee and be repelled by one that is commonly accepted as a better one.

SUBJECTIVE REACTIONS OF TASTER

The experienced taster endeavors to buy coffee, to assess its value, and to obtain uniformity of coffee flavor from his plant, at a profit. The consumer also has a subjective reaction of pride in his purchase and means of preparation. Every person does not receive the same taste impression from a single coffee sample. People differ in metabolism, race, sex, age, conditioning, and upbringing (Gates 1946) and heredity factors play an important part in variances of taste impression. Some persons are more sensitive to certain odors and tastes than others. Some illnesses may affect nasal or other vital taste organs. There are also inherited differences in threshold sensitivity to sweets, acids, salts, etc. Taste blind spots have been found in certain percentages of the population. For example, 70 per cent of persons tested found phenylthiocarbamide bitter; the rest found no taste. Another type example is hydrochloric acid. At various half dilutions it exhibits sweet, salt, bitter, and astringent tastes. No two persons are likely to have exactly the same taste threshold values for a specific substance, and indeed the same person does not have the same sensitivity at all times. Sensory analyses of foods have been reported by Amerine et al. (1962), Dawson (1951), Peryam et al. (1957), Moncrieff (1958), Wenzel (1948 and 1955), and Williams (1947).

Psychological factors that enter into odor and taste impressions are: the individual's personal attitudes, prejudices, standards, customs, experiences, health, fatigue, immediately previous stimulant (e.g., plums taste sour after candy but sweet after grapefruit), the degree of need for the food served, the person's predisposition to the labeling, the place of test (noisy, clean, uncomfortable, dark), familiarity with the food (people as a rule do not like new foods), and the normal appearance of the food. With greater taste experience, the taster can distinguish disagreeable off-flavors. One must be relaxed and predisposed and not forced to taste too many samples. Tasting without reference samples is difficult as is considering more than one taste property at a time.

The consumer seldom consciously considers these factors when obtaining a taste impression. Such obvious factors as price, advertising, custom, convenience, or taste conditioning can be controlling factors in the consumer's choice of coffee even if he has a relatively "normal" taste impression.

There is the case of Norwegian seamen who prefer to drink strong Liberica coffee on their fishing trips to the milder, normal coffee blends and lighter roasts used on land. The impact of the stronger "gamey" coffee is preferred in their isolated condition.

REGIONAL PREFERENCES OF COFFEE CONSUMERS

United States

There are three general areas in the United States using different coffee types. The East Coast uses coffees that are less aromatic (they are high in Brazilian coffees) and have a dark roast as is common in cities and densely populated areas. On the West Coast milder coffees have been used. This may be a result of shorter water trade routes from Central America. Roasts are lighter here than on the East Coast. In the South, from Florida to Texas, a good portion of mild coffees are used in the blends, but the South uses a darker roast than either the East or West coasts. Northern and Central United States roasts are light. Also, in the South, some chicory is used. In the United States, 45 to 60 cups of brew per pound of roast coffee give a thin cup flavor against about 30 cups of brew per pound of roast coffee in Latin America. The difference in strength of cup flavor is striking when one is traveling from one area to the other. In the United States, vacuum, drip, and percolator are the most common methods of coffee brew preparation. In Latin America, the addition of ground roast coffee to just-boiled water with steeping is more common. The home percolator brew method basically drives off most of the volatile coffee flavors. With continual heating of brew in the presence of air and spent coffee grounds, a uniformly heavy but not a natural coffee flavored cup is prepared. Thus the popularity of percolation over the years has been sustained more by tradition than by interest in retaining natural volatile coffee flavor.

European Countries

Present or past colonial affiliations contribute to the use of major percentages of Robustas in France, the United Kingdom, Portugal, Belgium, Italy, and Holland. The roasts are dark, and the cups of coffee taste accordingly.

In the Scandinavian countries about 75 per cent of Brazilian coffees are used at a light roast. The coffee thus is not very aromatic, but is clean and neutral-tasting. Per capita income and coffee consumption are the highest in the Scandinavian countries because of tradition and, no doubt, the relatively higher standard of living. On the other hand, soluble coffees are least used in these countries of high coffee consumption.

West Germany has had the highest import duty on coffee of all European nations. This is 5 DM per kg, or about $0.60 per lb. Thus coffee is a relatively more expensive commodity to the German housewife when coffee retail prices and income are considered. She takes her coffee purchase seriously and uses it carefully. Since duties more than double the cost of the green coffee, West Germany imports hardly any low grade coffees. For this reason, aromatic and flavorful brews are found in West Germany, especially in the north where the blends have a high fraction of mild coffees. Southern Germany and Switzerland have heavier, yet good tasting coffee, but chicory is commonly used. A French or dark roast in France is appropriate to the Robustas used there. Italy has a wide assortment of imported coffees. Many are of poor quality, and most coffees are brewed through espresso machines. A very dark roast is used. The demitasse cup of espresso coffee is about four times as strong in cup solubles as American type coffee. Yet due to the nature of preparation, a relatively good coffee flavored beverage is prepared. This cup cannot be fairly compared with the 5 fl oz cup used elsewhere because it is usually only about $1^1/_2$ fl oz (45 ml) and is consumed with much sugar to give a syrupy drink (after or between meals). A good flavored cup is obtained here from mediocre coffees because the solubles extraction is not exhaustive and does not allow the extraction of bitter objectionable tasting parts of the coffee. This is dramatically illustrated by dispensing more water into the espresso cup, say 3 instead of $1^1/_2$ fl oz. The resulting cup is really unpalatable. The Italian restaurateur may tell you that it is "cafe Americano" but it is not. Turkish coffee deserves mention because it is finely ground, almost pulverized, and is steeped and consumed in its entirety except for the coarse dregs. This cup is oily, heavy-bodied, and strong tasting.

Regional uses of coffee include special variations of blend, roast, and preparation. In Europe, the consumer who can afford it has a wider assortment of whole roast coffee beans to choose from than his American counterpart. The opportunity for staling in bulk roast bean sales is greater and is accepted as a part of natural coffee flavor much as it is by most lay tasters throughout the world. The influences of soluble coffee consumption patterns are also reflected regionally. For example, soluble coffees were accepted first and still lead in use in the eastern part of the United States and are currently more than 40 per cent of all purchases. The West Coast of the United States has the least usage of solubles, which now account for 25 per cent of all coffee purchases. Europe, in general, has only a few per cent of soluble coffee consumption. The United Kingdom is an exception; there, two-thirds of all coffee sales are soluble coffees but it has the least per capita coffee use in Europe. Decaffeinated coffees account for about 10 per cent of the coffee sales and are used more in the United States, Germany, and Switzerland. Kaffee-H.A.G., the firm that decaffeinates green coffee, does business throughout the world.

Regional taste preferences are also shaped by the waters available to the public. For example, in the Midwest part of the United States, many surface waters and subsurface waters particularly, are alkaline and brackish. This water neutralizes coffee acidity. Thus, roasters in the area prepare a light roast, short of full flavor development, so as to attain the highest acidity. This offsets the acid neutralizing effect of alkaline water. A better tasting coffee can also be obtained by using more roast coffee per unit of water. The dirty background taste created by water impurities discourages the coffee roaster from using the best coffees. The situation encourages the use of harsh, acidy, and "gamey" flavored coffees that would not be so acceptable in pure drinking water. Chlorinated waters with organic matter make a particularly bad cup of coffee. Many coastal waters in Europe are brackish, and this is an obstacle to preparing the best flavored coffee beverages. After examining the effects of origin, content, and composition of coffee acidity on coffee flavor, the neutralizing effect of alkaline waters is discussed in Chapter 19, pages 219, 224, and 241.

COFFEE FLAVOR ACIDITY

Origin, Content, and Composition

Acidity in most foods and beverages is a key factor to its flavor properties and appeal. Table 70 shows the pH values of common foods and chemicals. In coffee flavor, acidity is important both in apparent or free acidity, pH, which is perceptible to the taste, and total titratable acidity.

TABLE 70

PH VALUES OF COMMON FOODS AND CHEMICALS

Foods			
		Cow's milk	6.6
Limes	1.9	Shrimp	7.0
Lemon juice	2.3	Pure water	7.0
Ginger ale-apples	3.0		
Orange juice	3.3	Chemicals	
Sauerkraut	3.5	0.1 N HCl	1.0
Tomatoes	4.2	0.1 N acetic acid	2.0
Carbonated water	4.5	0.1 N boric acid	5.1
Carrots & coffee	5.1	0.1 N NaHCO₃	8.4
Molasses	5.2	Milk of magnesia	10.5
Cabbage	5.3	0.1 N NH₄OH	11.1

Most freshly brewed coffees have a pH of 5.0 to 5.1; pH is quite uniform as a result of the buffering action of the soluble and colloid components. Mild coffees grown at high altitude have more natural acidity; Brazilian coffees have noticeably less acidity; and Robustas have the least acidity. Robusta brews are pH 5.5 in pure water; in alkaline waters a pH of 6.0 is not uncommon. At these pH values, the coffee tastes bland and flat.

Holding freshly brewed coffee in an urn for hours forms acids reducing brew pH from 5.1 to below 5.0, which may cause curdling of milk or cream. Acidities of instant coffees, resulting from acids formed in the hydrolysis of celluloses, often reduce beverage pH to 4.8 or 4.9; at pH 4.7 curdling of milk is highly probable. Furthermore, some distinction between volatile and non-volatile acids is desirable. As a rule, organic acids are relatively stable compared to aldehydes which can be oxidized to acids. Chlorogenic acid can be hydrolyzed to caffeic acid and quinic acid, thus increasing the acid content of the coffee brew. Such acid changes are also accompanied by coffee flavor changes.

Miner (1934) has exact data on the percentage of green bean weight loss during roasting vs the acid content of the resulting brew. Acidities are the highest before a light, palatable roast is attained; then the acidity falls off to as little as one-fifth as roasting weight loss on a dry basis attains 8 per cent. The acidities are reported as ml N/20 acid per 30 ml brew prepared by mixing 160 ml water with 12.5 g roast coffee (36 cups per lb). Thirty milliliters of brew represents $30 \div 160 \times 12.5 = 2.344$ gm roast coffee. Lake Michigan water (about 125 ppm alkalinity) was used to prepare the brews. The end point acid neutralization was not reported. However, the brew acidity Miner found in the light roast coffee (5 ml N/20 NaOH) is reasonable at pH 7.0 end point (5 ml $\times$ N/20 is 0.25 meq/30 ml brew). An allowance of 0.075 meq/30 ml brew is made for the water alkalinity, and the total brew acidity is $0.25 + 0.075$ or 0.325 meq/30 ml brew (2.344 gm coffee), or the acidity is about 0.14 meq/gm roast coffee.

Mabrouk and Deatherage (1956) give the percentages of coffee acids in roast coffee. Their conversion to meq acid/gram roast coffee is 0.345, which is not in good agreement with the above even considering that their work was based on five rinses of the grounds and Miner's was not. (Another reason for the difference might be that Miner's reported coffee acids were only partly neutralized, and were not freely titratable.)

Clements and Deatherage (1957) give the major volatile acid constituents. These are about 0.066 meq/gm roast coffee. In other words, the volatile acid equivalent is one-fifth of the total non-volatile acid equivalent. Table 71, Acid Content of Roast Coffee, lists each of the major identified acids in coffee. Each acid has a different effective acid strength depending on the buffering properties of the solution and acid dissociation. Hence, each acid in coffee is not equally neutralized when alkaline water reacts with such an acid mixture. Also, each acid has characteristic aroma and/or flavor properties which contribute individually to the overall impression of acidity and coffee flavor.

TABLE 71

ACID CONTENT OF ROAST COFFEE[1] (EXHAUSTIVE EXTRACTION[2])

	Wt Fraction	Mol Wt	Mg/Gm, R & G	Meq[3]/Gm, R & G
Non-Volatile Acids				
Chlorogenic	0.046	354	46	0.1290
Caffeic	0.003	180	3	0.0170
Quinic	0.003	192	3	0.0170
Citric	0.005	210	5	0.0240
Malic	0.005	134	5	0.0400
Tartaric	0.004	150	4	0.0270
Oxalic	0.002	126	2	0.0180
Pyruvic	0.0006	88	0.6	0.0070
Sub Total				0.2790
Volatile Acids				
Acetic	0.0036	60	3.6	0.060
Propionic	0.0002	74	0.2	0.003
Butyric	0.0001	88	0.1	0.001
Valeric	0.0002	102	0.2	0.002
Sub Total				0.066
Total				0.345

[1] At 10 gm (light roast) R & G coffee per cup, there are 3.5 meq acidity per cup.
[2] Calculated from data presented by Clements and Deatherage (1957).
[3] Milligram equivalent.

All the coffee acids are not freely titratable; the acid salts produce a buffering action.

Soluble Coffee Acids

A number of acids form in percolator carbohydrate hydrolysis, and some other acids form in the hydrolysis of chlorogenic acid.

With a yield of 0.38 solubles from roast coffee (assuming all the non-volatile acids are in the soluble coffee powder and the volatiles are mostly lost in spray drying) there results 0.279 (from Table 71) divided by 0.38 or 0.73 meq acidity per gram of soluble components. Titrations to pH 7.0 on numerous commercial soluble coffees show that each gram in 100 ml of water takes 0.60 ml of 0.1 N NaOH solution, hence, each gram of solids contains 0.60 meq of non-volatile acids. While this appears to be less than the *potential* acidity of 0.73 meq per gram from exhaustive atmospheric extraction shown above, the discrepancy is explained by two factors. (1) In practice, much less than exhaustive extraction at atmospheric pressure is obtained. (2) Titrating with NaOH to pH 7.0 does not neutralize all the acidity actually present. The facts are presented more accurately in Chapter 19, page 244, under the heading Hydrolysis and Natural Acids.

The large neutralization effect of mildly alkaline waters on the acidity of these soluble components should be noted. A 100 ppm alkaline water has 0.20 meq neutralizing ability per 100 ml beverage (1.5 gm solubles). Thus 0.20/0.57 is 35 per cent neutralization of the beverage acidity raising the pH from about 4.8 to 5.1. A water twice as alkaline neutralizes 70 per cent of the coffee acidity raising the pH to 5.9, which results in a very flat tasting cup of coffee.

The neutralizing effect of alkaline water when preparing brewed coffee is not so marked because of the mass of coffee grounds present. Still, the relative pH of the final cup will be raised several tenths of a pH unit. A definite flattening of taste will be experienced in the brew. Less acid brews also are darker since its soluble components act as their own color indicator. A 300 ppm alkaline water will just about completely neutralize soluble coffee acidity to pH 7.0 and leave a distasteful product. The neutralizing effect of cream and milk are such that adding 20 ml of cream to a cup of "black" coffee at pH 5.2 raises the pH to 5.4 to 5.6.

Acetic Acid.—At 0.30 per cent of roast coffee (0.05 of 0.35 meq/gm roast coffee) except for chlorogenic acid, acetic acid is the highest individual acid and coffee flavor contributor. The amount of acetic and homologous acids in percolator coffee extract is about 1 per cent of the soluble components. After spray drying, almost no acetic acid is left in the powder. When acetic acid (pure or from a coffee source) is added back to a cup of instant coffee, it contributes zest and smoothness to the coffee flavor. The acetic acid cannot be taken from any source, since minute impurities incompatible with coffee flavor can cause an off-flavor.

Steam distilled roasted ground coffee acquires about 10 per cent moisture. Thus the acetic acid in the grounds-free water has a concentration of about 4 to 6 per cent, and somewhat less in the distillate or about 4 per cent. When coffee extracts are concentrated, the 0.30 per cent acetic acid in solution gives about 0.25 per cent acetic acid in the distillate. If half the coffee extract water is evaporated, almost half the acetic acid is evaporated also. In the case of recovery of volatile acids from roast coffee with 5 per cent moisture, under a vacuum grounds heating system (dry vacuum aroma), the acid content of the distillate rises to 8 per cent acetic acid equivalent, as coffee moisture is removed. Distilled coffee vapors occur as percolator vent condensate and markedly enhance the flavor of a cup of instant coffee when replaced at an acid level equivalent to the original. Percolator vent condensate has a pH of 3.7 and contains 0.30 per cent acetic acid equivalent. The harsh acid bite in the taste of some low grown mild coffees is associated with a high acetic acid equivalent at light roasts.

Fatty Acids.—During roasting, the glyceride fats and oils are partly broken down to release fatty acids. The acid content is small but their presence affects taste texture because of the reduced surface tension.

Acidity and Roast.—Miner (1934) shows that titratable acidities of roast coffee can be reduced to as little as one-fifth from the just palatable roast to the almost burnt roast. This range is somewhat broad. Titratable acidities within the palatable roast range on average blend coffees in the United States can only be reduced to one-half or possibly one-third from light to dark roasts. The lightest roast, which gives palatable coffee, corresponds to a 12 per cent weight loss based on green bean weight. About 10 per cent of this is due to loss of water. A very dark or slightly burnt roast would show around 18 per cent weight loss. Again, about 10 per cent of this is due to water loss. Hence the losses due to chemical changes which affect flavor and acidity would be about 2 per cent for the light, acid roast and 8 per cent for the dark, less acid roast. Considering this loss in acidity in Robusta coffees, which are not very acid, the blandness of the resulting cup at pH's above 6.0 is an important reason for their lack of taste appeal. In the preparation of roast coffee for soluble coffee processing, the roast loss is higher and the roast color is darker than with a coffee roasted for brewing purposes. Hence, the roast coffee for soluble processing has less original acidity than the one for brewing.

Acidities in Soluble Coffees.—So far it has been shown that soluble coffee powder has almost as much acidity as brewed coffee, but that the powder has lost almost all of its volatile acids. The loss of these volatile acids is important because of the loss of acid *taste* (pH), but more importantly because of acid *flavor* loss (characteristic volatiles). Although the volatile acids are only about one-fifth of the total acids in the extract, their relative loss under varying drying conditions is measurable and noticeable in the taste. For example, a given roast coffee brewed to give 1.5 gm solubles per 100 ml solution may have a titratable acidity (to pH 7.0) of 0.9 meq (0.6 meq/gm solubles). The percolator extract of the same coffee at 36 per cent solubles yield will have a higher acid content of about 1.0 meq/1.5 gm solubles. This 33 per cent concentration extract will result in a powder having 0.9 meq acidity/1.5 gm solubles (from a large spray dryer producing a range of particles of about 200 to 300 mu).

However, spray drying the same extract from lower solubles concentrations, or producing a range of particle sizes markedly smaller, will result in a powder having as low as 0.6 meq/1.5 gm solubles. Freeze drying the extract gives powder acidities of about 0.9 meq/1.5 gm solubles. This approximates the spray drying of larger particles with reduced *surface to weight* ratio. Extract cup pH's will be 4.9 and as high as 5.5 with larger acid losses.

The above information may be summarized as follows:

	Meq acidity per gm solubles
Brew coffee	0.60
33 per cent extract	0.67
Coarse powder	0.60
Fine powder	0.40
Freeze-dried powder	0.60

Fine spray-dried powder may lose as much as one-third of its acidity; coarse spray-dried and freeze-dried powder loses little.

Refluxing coffee brew and extracts at 212 F (100 C) for several hours will increase original acidities about 25 per cent. This acidity and associated flavors are repulsive. Oxidation of aldehydes, ketones, and alcohols form acids. In the absence of oxygen under the same conditions, undesirable taste changes occur and acids may not form.

An alkali titration pH of instant and brewed coffees is shown in Fig. 311 in Chapter 19.

Taste Differences Resulting from Roast, Blend, Extract, and Grind

Taste differences in the soluble coffee product are a result of the type of green coffee used and processing factors. If the "cook" or superintendent of the processing does not taste his product, he cannot do justice to his preparation. This is true in a home kitchen or in a large food processing plant. If the basic material is poor, one cannot expect a good end product. On the other hand, a good basic material does not assure a good final product. In fact, there are some soluble coffee plants that process so poorly that even the finest Colombian coffees result in drab, flavorless, barely acceptable instant coffee. There are other soluble coffee processing plants that use a mediocre blend of green coffee beans and yet produce an acceptable quality of soluble coffee. Good processing means the best recovery of available natural coffee flavors with a minimum of "instant flavors," i.e., those that are not natural to brewed coffee and which result from hydrolysis and losses of volatiles.

Roasting Influences on Flavor.—Although it is common practice to roast blends of green coffee, some bean mixtures do not roast uniformly. Even if bean sizes are the same, Brazilian coffees will roast before Robustas and high grown mild coffees. In other words, the Brazilian coffees will be over-roasted, while the mild coffees are brought to full flavor development. If bean sizes vary, small beans roast first and may almost burn while the larger average size beans are brought to proper flavor development. The roaster strives for the development of the fullest coffee flavor. If a green coffee blend has coffee beans of similar size but of differing moisture or age, the beans with the greater moisture and the newer crop will roast more slowly. Broken beans, malformed beans, quakers and hollow beans tend to burn when roasted with normal coffee beans. Elephant or marigojipe large sized beans roast slowly. Being unable to roast each part of a green coffee blend to the point of fullest flavor development means that the fullest flavor value is not being attained from that blend. It is advantageous, and in some cases necessary, to roast the different varieties of the green coffee blend separately to allow the fullest development of flavor and then to blend the separately roasted portions.

Roasting for Full Flavor Development.—Tumbling coffee beans are heated with 500 F (260 C) turbulent air to secure rapid heat transfer from the air into the bean. The bean first loses its free moisture while its temperature remains at about 212 to 220 F (100 to 104 C). Then when all the free moisture (about 10 per cent) has been evaporated, the bean temperature rises slowly while bound moisture (about 1 or 2 per cent) is evaporated slowly. So far, only minor chemical changes have occurred in the bean, and practically no coffee flavor has yet been developed. At about 400 F (204 C) bean temperature, the absorption of the heat by the coffee bean is augmented by the liberation of heat as pyrolysis reactions occur within the bean. Pyrolysis is chemical change with degradation and synthesis occurring simultaneously at elevated temperatures. Pyrolysis is not burning since it occurs within the bean cells in the absence of air.

Pyrolysis products are caramelized sugars and carbohydrates, acetic and homologous acids, aldehydes and ketones, furfural, esters, fatty acids, amines, carbon dioxide gas, sulfides, etc. This is the phenomenon of coffee flavor development. The pyrolysis occurs in tens of seconds and must be abruptly stopped at the desired point, usually related to bean color. During the pyrolysis period, bean color changes from pale brown to almost black in less than a minute. The chemical composition of the coffee bean is also changing rapidly. Light colored roasts taste grassy, acidy and pasty, to nutty. Darker roasts pass from full flavor to burnt progressively, liberating most of the desirable aroma volatiles. Ultimately, the roast bean can be turned to carbon, much as is done in the preparation of charcoal. The overall roasting time, from the entrance of the green coffee until discharge, is 5 to 10 min in a continuous roaster, and up to 20 min on a batch roaster. Long roast times give an undesirable "baked" taste. Darkly roasted beans have visible oil running out of their ruptured cells to the bean surfaces. Blue smoke or oily aerosol smoke is liberated from the beans during pyrolysis. The pyrolytic reactions are stopped by cooling the beans with air or water. A reason for a light roast, below full flavor development, is to attain high cup acidity. A reason for a dark roast, beyond full flavor development, is to drive off objectionable flavors. A broader flavor impression can be made by using three portions of one grade of coffee and roasting to three stages of flavor development. This is practiced by at least one roaster of Brazilian coffees. The three degrees of roast are more appealing in taste than any one of the single degrees. The three-degree roast blend can achieve wider limits of acidity and dark roast tones than the single roast.

Permitting a higher weight loss and darker roast on the Brazil part of a blend while bringing the high grown mild coffees to optimum flavor development usually secures most value from the green coffee. When this distribution of flavor development occurs naturally in a blend, separate roasting of bean types is not justified. Uniformity of bean roast can usually be indicated before tasting by examining the uniformity of bean colors and of ground coffee color. Burnt and light colored beans show that they did not roast uniformly. Roasting cannot markedly diminish Rioy flavors; in some coffees with slight off-flavor, a dark roast may improve it. Table 72 lists some taste effects in soluble coffee caused by roasting.

BLENDING COFFEES FOR FLAVOR, PRICE, AND UNIFORMITY

The three major coffee types are Brazilian, mild coffees, and Robustas. Botanically, the first two are Arabicas and the last is a Canephora. The Brazilian coffees are relatively non-aromatic and neutral-flavored in the cup while the high grown mild coffees are very fragrant and acidy, often with heavy body in the cup; low grown mild coffees are thinner in aroma and body in the cup. The neutral-flavored Brazilian coffees, priced lower than mild coffees, make them a good base flavor for blending. For example, 50 per cent Brazilian coffees, 25 per cent high grown mild coffees, and 25 per cent low grown mild coffees make a relatively acceptable commercial blend of roast coffee. Choosing blends for soluble coffees is a different matter. Processed soluble coffee not only tastes different from brewed coffee, but each soluble coffee plant process brings through parts of the natural coffee flavor in varying degrees and with some modifications and losses. The constant goal in the manufacture of soluble coffee is to minimize the losses and changes.

Coffee Blends.—Blending is basically required when endeavoring to maintain uniformity in flavor in a natural product, where the original source of beans is not always uniform, as a result of variations in supply,

TABLE 72

SOLUBLE COFFEE TASTE EFFECTS CAUSED IN ROASTING

Taste	Cause
Thin-bodied, burnt, oily, carbon-like	These taste characteristics are caused by dark roasts where the roasting process has been carried beyond full flavor development and/or optimum volatiles content until most volatiles of a desirable nature are driven out, leaving a mostly low-acid residue of solubles. The ruptured cell structure of the bean tends to release many oily colloids. Dark roasts are usually applied to low grade coffees to drive out some undesirable aromas and flavors.
Bland, pasty, nutty, green, baked	These taste characteristics are caused by light roasts which have brought the bean roast short of the best flavor and aroma development. Similar taste characteristics are derived by *too slow a roast*, where there is drying but not the type of chemical destructive distillation (pyrolysis) that is necessary to fully develop the flavors inherent in a good quality green coffee.
Unbalanced flavors, both burnt and green	These tastes are developed from "non-uniformly" roasted beans which may mean roasting a mixture of beans with different physical properties, such as large and small beans, old and new crop, dry and moist beans, dense and less dense beans, etc.
Full-bodied, acidy, aromatic	By blending after roasting, it is possible to roast each coffee to the fullest flavor development from an assortment of green beans varying in type, density, moisture, age, size, perfection, etc. Roasting of blended green beans is done to simplify the roasting step, but many green coffee blends are not suitable for such preparation. Separate roasting of single kinds of coffee takes more labor but brings out the fullest flavor of each type, and the resultant taste differences can be appreciated.
Heavy flavor, pyridine-like, stale	A heavy, undesirable flavor can be carried into instant coffee by excessive water quench of the roasted coffee. Residual absorbed water on the bean releases the protective carbon dioxide gas and allows sufficient oxygen to enter the bean or grounds so that considerable staling and chemical change occurs before the roast and ground coffee enters the extraction process.

price, quality, and time or place of delivery. Teas, wines (grapes), whiskies, perfumes, spices, synthetic and natural flavors are examples of other products which require blending.

Coffees of different growth areas, botanical origin and/or taste are blended to form a wholesome, appealing product. When a coffee blend satisfies consumer taste, consumers are retained, but only by maintaining this taste consistently. The coffee blender must endeavor to retain this taste profitably and competitively in spite of changes in the nature of his green coffee supply. On the other hand, the blend may have to be altered occasionally to suit changes in public tastes.

Blends are influenced by the degree of roast preferred in certain areas and countries whether regular roast and ground or soluble coffee is to be sold. Roasters supply low priced and high priced blends as well as blends for home and restaurant use.

Blends, therefore, are dynamic, and their composition changes because of market and agricultural factors. Blending requirements of large coffee roasters with national distribution differ from those of the small regional roaster. Where a widely distributed brand name roast coffee represents a large percentage of coffee from one country, a uniform blend is limited to coffee varieties (or equivalent coffees) available only in large quantities. A large coffee roaster cannot, as a rule, buy small quantities of coffee grown in limited quantities. There would not be enough of this limited type to make a uniform blend all year round. Some small roasters buy premium mild coffees that are in limited supply, and priced not much higher than the better mild coffees. Similarly, a low-priced coffee can be evolved. Some countries allow their colonial products to be imported duty free. In those countries the use of certain coffees will be economically advantageous if not compulsory, e.g., France preferentially imports Robusta coffees from its African colonies; Holland does the same from Java; and England takes much of the Uganda Robusta coffees of Africa. Some other countries have import-export quota restrictions and/or duties, as well as barter agreements so that free trade is restricted.

Dynamics of Blends.—About 1923, Brazilian coffees (Santos 7's up to 4's) were the major United States import. This was followed by an upgrade shift toward Santos 4's and less use of Brazilian coffees through the 1930's. During and after World War II, less Santos and more mild coffees from Central America were used, especially on the United States east coast, as a result of ship sinkings in the Atlantic Ocean by German submarines. More milds have always been used on the United States west coast because of proximity of the mild coffee growing countries of Central America.

United States roast coffee blends changed from the extremes of 80 per cent Santos with 20 per cent mild coffees before 1940 to less Santos and more mild coffees after World War II. Although major blends for solubles have been about half Santos and half mild coffees, in the latter 1950's economies in blend patterns were made in which more Portuguese West African Robustas were substituted for Brazilian and mild coffees.

There are about 1,000 coffee roasting firms in the United States, and each considers his blend the "best." According to Uribe (1955) and industry practices, the most widely processed coffees in the United States are a blend of about half mild and half Santos coffees (also see annual U.S. Department of Commerce import figures). Uribe clearly presents the factors which influence the composition and the reason for changes of different roaster's coffee blends.

By blending several coffee types at varying roast levels, formulations at many price levels can be prepared that will appeal to a wide range of tastes. Coffee flavors vary according to their growth conditions and their preparation for market. Some coffees have strength; some have rich flavor or "body"; others have acidity, aroma, and so on.

Identifying Blends.—There is no secrecy about coffee blends to the experienced taster, roaster, and buyer. Knowing the taste of many single coffee varieties, anyone skilled in the art can usually duplicate a competitor's blend and roast within the range of public taste. Whole green or roast beans can sometimes be separated and identified from mixtures by their characteristic shapes and varying roast shades.

Blends of competing roast and ground or soluble coffees can be determined within 20 per cent by taste, analytical methods, and "trade talk."

A competitor's blend is in itself important, but what is more important is the roaster's ability to maintain a profit while also maintaining coffee quality and uniformity with a changing green coffee supply year after year. One must know his competitors and their products and there must be continual taste analysis of competitive coffees.

Single varieties of coffee are consumed in the countries of origin and even in some coffee importing countries where tastes or governmental policies are so formed. Single varieties of coffee in some cases do not have wholesome taste properties, and they limit roasters to a single, possibly vulnerable source of supply. Therefore, it is advantageous to have coffee blends of several varieties. Blends also give the formulator a wider latitude in the coffee flavors he can develop.

Although there are three major coffee taste types (mild, Brazilian, and Robustas), each growth area and type of coffee yield green beans of varying taste properties from time to time, depending on soil, weather conditions, curing methods, and other factors.

Taste Experience.—The references listed, Uribe (1955), Papashvily (1962), National Coffee Association and trade journal articles, give good coffee blends. One can buy straight varieties, cup-test them, and blend them to expand one's own experience.

Cost of Blends.—Low cost green coffee blends are continually sought, consistent with uniformity and quality standards set for the end product. A proper use and understanding of green coffee taste properties, sources of coffee varieties, flavor development in roasting, blend substitution, consumer taste tolerances, and competitor product quality help keep a balance between costs and product quality at all times.

Mild coffees are usually more expensive than Brazilian coffees; the latter are usually more expensive than Robustas. Since neutral Brazilian coffees are the lowest priced acceptable coffees in large supply, the majority of roasters use Brazils to control the cost of their blends. For instant coffees, Robustas are the lowest priced coffees, and their content in the blend strongly influences product cost and taste.

Taste Tolerances.—The average coffee consumer cannot detect gross blend changes of less than 25 per cent on the major fraction of a roast coffee blend (depending on roast and type of blend substitution). Expert tasters often can detect 10 to 15 per cent blend changes, and sometimes less as in the case of the substitution of mild for Brazilian coffees or neutral Robustas or vice versa. When substituting one mild coffee for another or one Brazilian coffee for another (excluding those with noticeable off-flavors), nearly 100 per cent substitution can often be made without detectable taste change in the cup of brewed coffee. This is in spite of the fact that one straight type of mild coffee may have a noticeably different flavor from the substitute. This great taste insensitivity to blend changes among consumers allows the coffee blender and buyer some economic and processing freedom within the framework of a relatively uniform product and price. Roasters must maintain uniform blend flavors even though some coffees are available only part of the year and coffee quality varies from place to place, from the beginning of one crop to the end of the same crop, and from year to year.

Tasting is specialized work, even an art. It is influenced by consumer tastes, flavors of the competitor's coffee, and the blender's business abilities and whims. Notwithstanding this scope of variation, outstanding coffee taste qualities can be classified and attributed to particular varieties, sources, and grades year after year.

Before 1950, the U. S. Armed Forces (Koehler, 1950) used ratios of Brazilian to Colombian coffees of 50/50 and 60/40; from 1950 to the present, the ratio has been 70/30 and is considered a better blend than the product used by the average United States citizen.

Blends for Soluble Coffee.—A processor must know how the performance of his process compares to others in the field. He must be able to assess the yield of natural coffee flavor and aroma that is being obtained in the final powder. The distinct flavor contributions from each type of green coffee and roast must be recognized. Thus, blends for soluble coffee are chosen to achieve a certain body, acidity, aroma, and flavor in the soluble coffee cup as distinguished from the blends chosen for the cup brewed directly from roast coffee. Some examples of soluble coffee flavor effects caused by blend and roast are given in Table 73 and in Fig. 272.

The importance of blending in soluble coffee production and the different nature of the problems involved compared with those of R & G coffee production are illustrated by the case history of an experienced and expert coffee roaster who started to manufacture soluble coffee without experience in that field. At first, he did not believe that the characteristics

TABLE 73

SOLUBLE COFFEE TASTE EFFECTS CAUSED BY BLEND

Taste	Blend Composition
Flat taste	(a) Robustas are not acid, thus give a bland cup when used at high percentages. (b) Local alkaline consumer water neutralizes moderate acidity blend chosen. (c) Local consumer uses warm water (with dissolved air), not rolling boil.
Lacks aroma	(a) Low in aromatic mild coffees. (b) High in Brazilian coffees. (c) High in Robustas.
Thin body	(a) High in Brazilian coffees. (b) High in low grown mild coffees.
Good body, winey	(a) High in high grown mild coffees. (b) High in heavy flavored neutral Robustas. (c) Blend has naturals (Haarer 1962).
Off-flavor	(a) Rioy flavored coffees used. (b) Robustas with gamey type flavor used, e.g., Uganda. (c) Fermented coffees used. (d) Other types of foul-flavored coffee used.

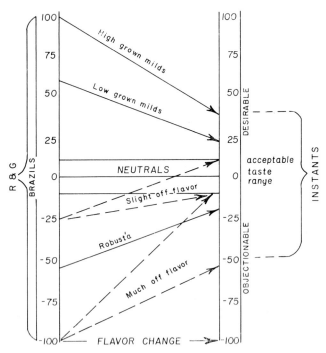

Fig. 272.   Flavor Level Change from Roast <br> to Instant Coffee

of different coffees affected the final product. Then he found that some natural coffees produced a winey, desirable instant coffee. In his enthusiasm, he bought 10,000 bags of foul, heavy-bodied natural coffee which required four months to absorb into normal production; thus he learned that natural coffees and others may differ greatly in their taste effects on instant coffee.

Figure 272 shows some of the major flavor factors that result from using different types of coffee in preparing instant coffees. Reasonably good soluble coffee plant processing is assumed; obviously, the best Colombian mild coffees can be made unpalatable by poor plant processing. The important point is that the broad spectrum of flavor enjoyed with naturally roasted coffees is much narrower for instant coffee, yet many instant coffees do not taste as bad as the brewed coffee from which they were originally prepared.

Taste Effects Due to Grind.—Grinding has several obvious effects on coffee flavor. Often roast and soluble coffee processors use a high water quench to end the roast by quick cooling. But with enough water, a residual moisture of up to 7 per cent is left. For roast coffees, 3 per cent moisture is usually the maximum "free-loading" weight if major flavor loss is not to occur. Moisture additions soften the bean so that fewer fine particles occur on grinding. This causes the volatile aromas and CO_2 gas to evaporate. Aroma loss and chemical alteration lead to a heavy, undesirable cup flavor. A notable stale flavor can develop in a few hours after grinding, if prompt vacuum pack protection is not provided. In the case of the 7 per cent particle moistures, the natural CO_2 gas protection is lost. In the commercial grinding range, the bean surface is increased five- to ten-fold, and a more permeable surface is exposed than exists at the whole bean surface. The marked loss of pleasant coffee aroma and CO_2 gas is very noticeable at the grinder.

Brew from finely ground coffee has a different taste from that made from more coarsely ground coffee because fine grounds give up more surface soluble substances and colloids. The oiliness, turbidity, and taste texture of a cup of brew from finely ground coffee are easily noticeable. A finer grind releases more coffee solubles faster; therefore, when comparing the same weight of roast coffee per unit weight of water, the finer grind makes a stronger tasting cup. In domestic use, the faster staling of finer grinds is also more noticeable even if a water quench has not been used on the roasted beans. In soluble coffee manufacture, finer grinds also release more fatty acids, oil, and proteins into the extract, and these contribute to good retention of the volatile aromatics in the extract and powder. Fine grinds produce better percolator filtering of the extract.

Taste in Process Control.—The object in processing any food is to bring out the best flavor possible with the raw materials used. The key factors then, are the *taste effects* achieved and their *causes*, as identified, understood, and continually controlled. *Taste control is the key to overall process and product control.* In processing soluble coffee, this is essential because there are so many variables. Surprising as it seems, few soluble coffee or food processing plants have such formalized overall taste control as a vital part of their process. Major pride is taken in quality control tests, but from an operating viewpoint this is test data after the product is finished. By this time, tons of "out-of-standard" product may have been produced. It subsequently must be released "as is," or be worked back into the normal product at low concentrations. In any case, there is a loss in product quality and labor, and other costs are incurred. Quality control tests on the final product are, of course, useful, but they must be considered within the framework of quality of process, equipment (instruments), and plant personnel (knowledge, training, experience, and dependability). Thus the soluble coffee plant superintendent must carry out the processing and exercise authority at a focal point for gathering and receiving all process data using his eyes, nose, tongue, and other senses. Effective process control is then achieved by checking this data with processing personnel and control instruments and making necessary equipment adjustments. The effective process plant superintendent thus helps control product taste, process conditions and operators. The unit process operator cannot do this due to his limited responsibility, activity, and training. Without overall supervision (with sharply delineated work area responsibility and authority), the overall effect for flavor process control is correspondingly impaired. With central supervisory authority and surveillance, continual probing, and feedback, an effective control of human relations, equipment, mechanics, and cookery (food processing) with repeated tasting can insure proper process and product adjustments. With continual taste monitoring, the adjustments are usually small and infrequent so that processing conditions are relatively stable, yet allow for the correction of deviations.

Taste Factors Contributed in Processing Soluble Coffee.—There are differences in the gross composition of coffee solubles obtained in the cup when brewing roast coffee or when dissolving soluble coffee that have a direct bearing on the resulting flavor. Table 74 shows the solubles recovered in brewed and instant coffees, and Table 75 shows standard cup strengths for brewed and instant coffees. Thus for brewed coffee, only about 16 to 20 per cent of the R & G Coffee ($^2/_3$ to $^3/_4$ solubles) out of a possible 25 per cent (1.0) solubles is drained off into the cup. With instant coffees, the full 25 per cent solubles is leached out with hot water,

TABLE 74

SOLUBLES IN BREWED AND INSTANT COFFEES

	Brewed, gm	Instant, gm
Coffee Solubles Portion		
R & G coffee used per 5 oz (150 ml) cup	10.0	10.0
Exhaustive Extraction		
1. *Atmospheric solubles*[1] available with boiling water per 10 g R & G coffee.	2.5	2.5
2. *Hydrolyzed solubles*[2] available per 10 g R & G coffee.	0.0	0.8
Actual Extraction		
1a. Atmospheric solubles[1] dissolved from grounds.	2.0 (80%)[3]	2.5 (100%)[3]
b. Atmospheric solubles[1] recovered.	1.6 (64%)[3]	2.5 (100%)[3]
2. Hydrolyzed solubles[2] dissolved and recovered.	0.0 (0%)[3]	0.8 (32%)[3]
3a. Total recovered solubles from R & G coffee.	1.6 (64%)[3]	3.3 (132%)[3]
b. Total solubles yield, per cent on R & G coffee.	16	25 + 8 = 33

[1] Atmospheric solubles are the soluble material extracted from R & G coffee at atmospheric pressure.
[2] Hydrolyzed solubles are the soluble product resulting from adding water chemically to the starchy components of spent or partially spent coffee grounds by means of water at higher temperatures and pressures than boiling water at atmospheric pressure.
[3] Per cent based on 2.5 gm atmospheric solubles available with 212 F (100 C) water.

but 8 to 12 per cent more are dissolved by hydrolysis. This exhaustive extraction leaches out substances that would not normally be dissolved. This contributes some bitter flavors such as are experienced when the same coffee grounds are extracted with boiling water several times. This is the combined taste contribution from successive extractions. In addition, solubles of instant coffees have 30 to 40 per cent of substances that have been largely dissolved from carbohydrates at elevated temperatures. Most of these substances are simple sugars which are rather tasteless in the pure form. But some hydrolyzed proteins carry flavor. The side chemical reactions in hydrolysis produce foul-smelling and foul-tasting by-products that are not completely removed in the passage of the hydrolyzed solubles through the length of the percolator coffee bed. Once one has smelled and tasted these objectionable products of hydrolysis, they are easy to recognize in any soluble coffee product. Where percolation procedures heat treat coffee solubles and where hydrolysis yields are at about 15 per cent of roast coffee with a total solubles yield of 40 per cent of roast coffee, these objectionable hydrolysis flavors are more prominent in the cup flavor and aroma. Furthermore, the exhaustive extraction of coffee solubles with normally boiling water at 212 F (100 C) is altered in the pressure extractors to use waters up to 350 F (177 C). This causes hydrolysis of naturally available atmospheric solubles; this would not occur in brewing at home. Percolator extract at high solubles concentration gives different solubles equilibrium in extraction. This eliminates colloidal oils and proteinaceous matter which are more abundant in brewed coffees. Soluble coffees are clear and have no turbidity. Colloids causing turbidity carry a great deal of coffee flavor and contribute a smooth taste as colloids do in most foods. Lack of colloids in soluble coffee gives instant coffee a harshness and a loss in buffering capacity as well as loss in flavor level. The net result is that the percolator coffee extract, because of its method of preparation, is aromatic and has much more acid than a comparable brew. In fact, when the extract assumes a biting to harsh impression, it is likely that the yield taken is too high.

It has been found from experience that average, normal, palatable-taste strength for instant coffee is 2.2 gm of powder per 150 ml cup and the same for brewed coffee is 1.6 gm of solubles per cup; hence the standard procedure in taste testing is to compare them at these strengths. Table 74 shows that 16 per cent of the R & G coffee is extracted in brewed coffee or 72.6 gm/lb, and 38 per cent in instant coffee or 172.4 gm/lb. The 72.6 ÷ 1.6 = 45 cups/lb and 172.4 ÷ 2.2 = 80 cups/lb. Table 75 shows the source of the extracted solubles in each case.

TABLE 75

STANDARD SOLUBLES CUP STRENGTH FOR BREWED AND INSTANT COFFEES

| 5 fl oz or 150 ml cups/lb R & G → | 45 Brewed | | 80 Instant | |
Solubles cup strength →	gm	%	gm	%
(a) Atmospheric extract	1.6	1.1	1.6	1.1
(b) Hydrolysates	0.0	0.0	0.6	0.4
Total	1.6	1.1	2.2	1.5

If the amount of coffee solubles in the percolators is at too high a temperature for too long a time, a destruction of coffee flavors occurs which leaves a residual flavor that tastes like caramel. Many commercial instant coffees are characterized by the hydrolysis and caramel flavor, and little or no natural coffee flavor or aroma.

Basic differences in chemical composition of instant coffee which influence cup taste

(1) Instant coffees have about half the caffeine of a brewed cup.
(2) Instant coffees have almost no oil nor colloids.
(3) Instant coffees have more carbohydrates and acidity.
(4) Instant coffees have many fewer aromatics which are mostly volatiles and therefore less natural coffee aroma and flavor.
(5) Instant coffees are usually taken to a darker roast than brewed coffees.
(6) Instant coffee flavor is less sensitive to blend changes.

(7) There is a wide application of some percentage of Robustas to instant coffee blends.

(8) Instant coffee acidity is more completely neutralized by alkaline waters, therefore because of the absence of buffering substances, taste is flattened.

(9) Instant coffees have lost almost all their acetic acid, and have different sources of acidity from those of brewed coffees.

(10) Instant coffees (without oil or aroma) do not stale appreciably, but have a flavor which may have been caused by heat.

(11) A good deal of aromatic flavor is lost during percolation and this is evident in the extract by a markedly low flavor level relative to that potentially available. Such detection of low yield of flavor can only be gained from taste experience.

Table 76 shows taste effects and their causes in percolation; Table 77 shows taste effects and their causes in spray drying.

TABLE 76

SOLUBLE COFFEE FLAVOR EFFECTS CAUSED IN PERCOLATION

Flavor	Cause
Acid, astringent, dry, straw aroma	A high hydrolysis yield of solubles is accompanied by acids. These odors and flavors are easily identified. These aromas and flavors are objectionable and foreign to brewed coffee flavor. The cup pH may be low—around 4.80, depending on blend.
Caramelized, harsh	Although a caramel flavor is a distinctive one and a part of both regular and instant coffee flavor, it is only when this flavor is dominant that it is objectionable. This may occur in the percolator, with excessive time—temperature conditions destroying volatiles that constitute the flavor of coffee. Heating or evaporation of the extract also destroys or removes volatile flavors.
Weak cup, flat	A loss of coffee volatiles can contribute to a weak-flavored cup. A high hydrolysis yield dilutes the coffee flavor. Contamination by iron, copper, or aluminum can also destroy coffee flavor rapidly. Exposure of extract to air (oxygen) causes flavor loss. Too large a solubles inventory[1] within the percolator system also gives a flat cup due to the increased residence time of coffee flavor constituents.
Heavy, pyridine, heat treated, sickening	Holding of aromatic coffees in the percolator system under long cycle times and with forward intercolumn heating of extract produces a characteristic flavor that is easy to identify. A similar odor and flavor can be developed by holding instant coffee powder for prolonged periods at elevated temperatures in an air stream or by allowing moistened coffee grounds to become oxidized.

[1] Inventory is the total solubles content of the percolation system. It varies with operating variables and with operating conditions which may influence the time and temperature of exposure. Desirable conditions: fine grinds and fast water flow reduce residence time of the coffee and give the highest instant powder quality.

The chemical properties of what is extracted and dissolved to constitute soluble coffee differ markedly from brewed coffee, and therefore a corresponding flavor difference is to be recognized. Aside from the flavor difference due to differing chemical composition, there is also a flavor difference resulting from different modes of extraction; e.g., time, temperature, concentrations of soluble components, modes of heat application, oxygen exposure, storage conditions, metal contamination, and proportions of reworked coffee. Table 76 summarizes this.

The major losses in coffee flavor occur when coffee extract is atomized and dries into hollow spheres. The instantaneous evaporation of water takes with it over 90 per cent of the volatile coffee flavor constituents. Until 1952, most instant coffees were as fine as talcum powder. Carbohydrates were added and they had poor solubility. "Instant Coffee" was not so named until large particles (about 300 mu) were produced. The net result was, however, better coffee flavor retention with a particle that had less surface per unit of weight. The small milk drier became obsolete. So far, no one has endeavored to develop the preparation of larger, thicker walled beads commercially. Although some of the following flavor factors are derived in the other plant process steps, they are summarized in Table 77 since it is during spray drying that these factors come into play.

TABLE 77

SOLUBLE COFFEE FLAVOR EFFECTS CAUSED IN SPRAY DRYING COFFEE EXTRACT

Flavor	Cause
Flavorless	An extraordinarily high percentage of the extract flavor content is lost when extracts are dried from low concentrations. This loss is particularly obvious at extract concentrations below 25 per cent and the retention of flavor is most obvious at above 35 per cent. Also warm extracts or heated extracts lose more of their flavor in spray drying than the same colder extract. A powder with small average particle sizes also lacks flavor as does a powder with excessively low moistures, e.g., 1 per cent instead of 3.5 per cent which is normal.
Burnt and caramelized	An uncommon flavor occurrence, but it can occur with high inlet and outlet air temperatures. Wall buildup of powders where charring occurs with the intermittent fall off of charred fragments into normal production powder.
Heat treated, sickening	Powder is exposed to hot air for hours or days.
Dusty texture	Due to fine powder no matter how prepared. Air adsorption on particle surfaces and intrinsic character of fines. This is a taste foreign to brewed coffee.
Sulfurous oily heavy	Incomplete combustion in direct oil-fired driers allows air contaminants to be adsorbed on the powder. Complete combustion of sulfur still results in adsorption and low sulfur content fuels should be used.

FLAVORS CAUSED BY DETERIORATION, CONTAMINATION, AND STALING OF COFFEE

From the time the coffee is picked from the tree until it is used to prepare a beverage, there are numerous points at which deterioration and off-flavor may occur. The following examples are illustrative and not exhaustive of these situations.

Changes During Harvesting

Some of the major and more frequent sources of contamination occur during the processing of the cherry until the green coffee is dry. In many coffee growing and curing areas, individual growers may only harvest, ferment, and dry a few bags or a few dozen bags of coffee. These small, variegated lots are sold to a mill that grades, cleans, and blends the beans. Thus the mill processor cannot always be sure of the cup quality of the final classified bagged coffees, but goes largely by his years of experience with physical examination of the beans as well as his knowledge of the reputation of the supplier of beans.

The ripe cherries should be picked when they are blood red if washed coffee is to be produced. Often immature cherries are picked which sometimes can be removed in flotation during washing. If they are not removed, then they do not roast well and are easily picked out of the roast as light colored beans with no coffee flavor and with off-flavor. In order to pick only mature cherries, continual picking is needed but actually only a few pickings are made. The Coffee Harvest Timetable (Table 78) shows that the harvest periods last from 2 to 6 months.

Processing Green Coffee

The bulk of the coffee ripens in a period of four weeks in many areas (see Chapter 3). Sometimes itinerant help is used in this case to aid in the harvest. Lesser pickings are made in the month previous to or after the peak harvest. The point is that most of the coffee cherry must be freed of mucilage by fermentation, washing, and then drying in a very short time. Most coffee processors seldom have sufficient fermentation tank capacity, personnel, drying facilities, or water to do the jobs required on schedule. There is a real dilemma should it rain when sunshine is needed for drying the coffee beans on the patio. It is at this time of work at fever pitch that off-flavors may develop in the moist green coffee. For example, if fermentation does not occur rapidly enough, fresh picked cherries must be held up longer than desirable until their fermentation is possible. This may result in a "wild ferment" in the piles of broken cherries. Furthermore, coffee that has been washed free of fermentable mucilage cannot always be dried fast enough. In order to rotate the inventory of green coffee beans that are not yet dry, partially dry coffee is stored in bins with wood sides on concrete floors while the wetter coffees are dried on the patio or in drying machines. When rotation is not fast enough, the piles of stored coffees may become moldy and develop musty odors and flavors. For this reason, piles of incompletely dried coffees must be turned over to allow fuller bean exposure to air movement. Then, the beans must be dried as soon as possible to 12 per cent moisture by machine. To process the coffee rapidly, higher temperatures and drier air may be used which may damage the flavor of the coffee. The result is that the flavor level and properties of the coffee

TABLE 78

COFFEE HARVEST TIMETABLE[1]

Country		Harvest	Arrival at Ports
Brazil		May–September	July
	Main Crop		
Colombia	Medellin	October–January	All the year
	Armenia	March–May	
	Manizales	October–January	
	Bogota	April–July	
	Girardot & Neiva	April–June	
	Honda & Libano	March–June	
	Bucaramanga	October–December	
	Cucuta	March–May	
	Small Crop		
Colombia	Medellin	September–December	All the year
	Armenia	September–December	
	Manizales	April–June	
	Bogota	November–January	
	Girardot & Neiva	October–January	
	Honda & Libano	November–January	
	Bucaramanga	April–June	
	Cucuta	October–December	
Venezuela		November–March	December
Ecuador		June–August	June (Washed coffees) July (others)
Haiti		November–March	November
Salvador		November–March	December
Guatemala		October–May	November–December
Nicaragua		November–February	December
Mexico Tapachula		January–March	November–December
Others		October–December	
Costa Rica		October–March	November
Dominican Republic		October–March	November
Ivory Coast		October–January	November–December
French Equatorial Africa and Cameroons		November–February	December–January
Madagascar		June–October	October–November
British East Africa Robusta		September–October	October–November
Arabica		October–December	November–December
Angola		June–November	August
Ethiopia		October to March	October
Arabia		September–March	October
Indonesia		Three harvests per year	All the year

[1] Compiled from chart issued by Jacques Louis Delamare.   Le Havre, France, and other sources.

suffer.   Fermented and moldy flavors usually do not develop in every coffee bean.   They develop in enough beans to cause a flavor taint in the batch.   This is one reason why coffee lots of 50 to 250 bags or less are kept separate.   One coffee lot may be tainted because of conditions described above, and another lot may not.

   Parchment Damage.—The coffee bean below the fruity mucilage layer has a parchment layer.   If that is not broken, the taint cannot penetrate the bean.   But in practice sufficient numbers of these parchment shells are damaged or penetrated during pulp removal that such taint does enter some beans. Subsequently, these beans must be removed by hand-picking or electronic sorting after the bean density and bean size grading. It is instructive to take an unsorted green coffee sample, remove the dis-colored and damaged beans from one-half of the sample and then roast all three fractions for tasting. The removal of only 5 per cent of damaged beans may raise the quality of the 95 per cent portion of the coffee to exportable grade when the original sample might be unexportable.

Partly Dry Coffee Beans.—Drying coffee beans with the radiant energy of sunshine while turning the beans over with a wooden rake prevents mustiness from mold. Tarpaulin covers for the partly dried beans at night prevent localized moisture from condensing. Even after the beans are dried to 12 per cent moisture, graded and bagged, there are still con-ditions that may cause off-flavor to develop in the coffee bean. Coffee beans that are not exported after drying may absorb considerable mois-ture in the rainy season. This may cause mold to grow and even fermenta-tion to develop in the green coffee beans which are now without their protective parchment.

Bean Storage.—Another major source of coffee flavor loss is the holding of bagged green coffee which is ready for export in a warm, damp climate like the shipping ports of coffee-growing countries. In a matter of weeks under such storage conditions, the flavor of these coffees will have notice-ably deteriorated. In months these coffees, once greenish blue and waxy, become pale, straw-colored, and dull in appearance and give a flavorless cup of coffee. During the current world surplus of coffee, Brazil has had tens of millions of bags of coffee stored in the hot, humid port of Santos for years. These coffees have become bleached in appearance and papery in flavor—in other words, relatively worthless in flavor content.

Aged Coffees.—These come most commonly from Venezuela. They are good quality coffees that are held for several years in the cooler, high altitude climates. Although these coffees may once have had some winey or gamey flavor, they are definitely heavy-flavored in the cup after years of aging. Such coffees are not commercially important in world trade. They appeal only to certain gourmets who can afford to pay the premium price for such heavy-flavored coffee types and who have acquired a taste for them.

New crops of coffee are often grassy and thin-bodied. They may reflect the grower's anxiety to get his coffee to market early for some price advantage. Thinness and grassiness are not desirable flavor prop-erties.

Naturally Dried Coffees.—In Brazilian, Robusta, and some mild coffee growing areas where water is scarce, or the harvester does not remove the pulp, the cherries are dried as picked. Such dried coffees are called "naturals." Although washed coffees, as a rule, have better flavor than "naturals," there are some "naturals" that have a winey and heavy body in the cup with hardly any off-flavor.

Altitude.—High grown coffees (5,000 ft above sea level) grow more slowly. This seems to be associated with their greater and better flavor. For example, the body in the cup of high grown Colombian coffees is rich, winey, and buttery with a characteristically appealing aroma. Mild coffees from 2,000 ft altitudes, which grow more quickly, are usually thin-bodied to harsh in flavor and give only fair aroma.

Pests.—Although green coffee is not a food for rats and insects, it can suffer infestation from a few types of boring weevils. Infestation is rare and usually caused by gross negligence in cleaning and storing the green coffee beans; when it occurs, fumigation is necessary especially before coffee enters a consumer country in order to avoid confiscation.

Foreign Matter.—Contaminants normally found among green coffee beans are corn kernels, kidney beans, fruit pits, twigs, nails, pebbles, sand, and even stones. Buttons, strings, and personal items like coins are common since the laborers literally live in the coffee. Iron contaminants are particularly bad. Dissolved iron is a catalyst in the oxidation of roast coffee flavors. Copper behaves similarly.

Storage of Green Coffee.—Mold growth may start in bags of coffee on the ground. Bagged coffee should be placed on wooden pallets so that earth moisture cannot reach it and natural air ventilation can maintain uniformity of temperatures and humidity. Sealing green coffee in moisture-tight bags like polyethylene results in non-uniform moisture distribution and causes mold growth.

Odor Absorption.—Storage of odor-carrying products near green coffee may cause coffee to absorb enough of the foreign odor to contaminate it. For example, paint, turpentine, solvents, asphalt, manure, and spices may do this. Precautions must be taken both on shipboard and shore not to store green coffee bags near such commodities.

Storage Humidity.—There was a time before 1940 when green coffee shipments from Latin America frequently were damaged. This was due to moisture condensation on the beans when the ships passed from the warm Gulf Stream into cold ocean waters. The result was moldy growth and off-flavored lots. Today, most ships have enough moisture control and air circulation through their holds so that this does not happen. Local moisture may condense even in stationary bins due to changes in day to night temperatures. This necessitates dehumidification of the air and its continual circulation throughout the coffee beans in the bin to assure uniform storage conditions. In prolonged bulk storage it is desirable to rotate and move the coffee beans at intervals.

An example of contamination occurs where green coffee is stored in bags in an open shed during the rainy season in the coffee growing countries or in high, damp locations. The equilibrium moisture in the green coffee beans rises sufficiently under such circumstances to cause the beans to swell and rupture the bag, spilling themselves all about the floors and other bags, initiating conditions for mold growth and fermentation reactions. Moist coffees stored in the absence of adequate air circulation can become putrid and rank, and thus offensive in taste and smell. Beans that are dried below 10 per cent moisture often undergo loss in flavor. Poor sanitation conditions in the coffee processing and storage areas may cause contamination through foods, tobacco, rats, birds, and insects.

Bag and Markings.—Green coffee beans are usually bagged for export in clean, new jute fiber bags. Jute is a fibrous plant of India. Sometimes yucca fiber bags are used, from Mexico, but they are not as fine a fiber or pliable. A known case of coffee contamination occurred when the persons bagging the green coffee stenciled the bags with their owner's mark after the coffee was in the bag. The stencil solvent soaked into the adjacent coffee beans and contaminated the whole lot. Bags should be stenciled before they are filled.

The foregoing flavor factors have been primarily directed toward *green* coffee Now the flavor influences on *brew extract* and *instant coffee powder* will be reviewed.

Heat Treatment.—Tobacco odors and tastes are often encountered in coffee volatiles that have been oxidized. These also occur in pots of brew that have been reheated, percolated, and refluxed. This appears to be related to the pyridine content, and is often a sickening odor. Stale coffee typifies this type of odor. The odor of reheated brew has a strong resemblance to that of extinguished cigars. The volatiles of tobacco smoke are quite similar to the volatiles of coffee aroma. Nicotinic acid occurs in coffee. Pyridine has the same basic nitrogen ring chemical structure as nicotine.

Coffee Extract Flavor Loss.—If iron, copper, or copper alloys are used in the extract piping systems, these metals catalyze flavor oxidation, and produce change and loss. Coffee extract contaminated by metal is flat in taste. A not uncommon practice is to use aluminum beakers and vessels for holding extract; the acidity of the extract dissolves the aluminum in time, and this too contributes to flavor loss. Spray drying extracts from concentrations below 25 per cent yields a relatively flat, flavorless cup; whereas drying extracts above 35 per cent show a striking retention of flavor. When large volumes of coffee extract stand for many hours, fine suspended tars carry down coffee flavor; centrifuging the extracts causes even more flavor loss. Freeze concentration of coffee extracts not only gives a higher extract concentration, but noticeable amounts of hydrolysis flavors also are coagulated out with the ice. Coffee extracts held at about 60 F (16 C) for over 24 hr often become sour or acid in flavor due to fermentation. This sourness may not be serious enough to require rejection. It may be possible to rework such powder at a suitable level, with normal production powder to dilute the off-flavor.

At 40 F (4 C), extracts may be kept 24 hr with hardly a noticeable flavor change. But at 80 F (27 C) the extract will lose a great deal of flavor in a few hours. More dilute extracts will undergo faster deterioration. Also, the exposure of the extract to air causes faster flavor loss and change. By continually tasting extracts undergoing such flavor alteration, the degree and kind of flavor change may be noted. Usually a type of heaviness in body and flatness in flavor results. The key factors that contribute to these flavor losses are (1) low concentrations of soluble components, (2) warm temperatures, (3) too many hours holding time, (4) air exposure, (5) a high level of bacterial contamination, and (6) metal contamination.

Oxygen Free Extract.—Even in the absence of oxygen, coffee flavors change. Thus, the coffee extract in a pressurized can with nitrogen gas must be held below 40 F (4 C) and have a low free water content to offer reasonably stable coffee flavor. For decades in England, an evaporated coffee extract with chicory has been sold, but with the introduction of instant coffee the sale of this liquid extract has fallen off. Stripping the oxidizable volatiles from coffee extract removes some of its taste appeal but gives the extract more stability otherwise. The retention of natural coffee aroma and flavor in nitrogen pressurized cans at room temperature is not satisfactory. Frozen coffee extracts keep indefinitely. When maintained at 40 F (4 C) (after thawing) extracts keep reasonably fresh for about two weeks. Continual exposure of extract to oxygen even at this temperature causes the natural coffee flavor to become stale in a manner associated with extracts. Similar flavor changes sometimes occur during freeze concentration with air exposure.

Instant Coffee Powder.—The flavor of this product is relatively stable, at 3 per cent moisture content. One reason is that there were hardly any volatiles in the powder until about 1957 when the so-called "aromatized" instant coffees with coffee oil and volatiles were introduced commercially in the United States. The unaromatized instant coffee powder will keep for years if dry. It will keep better in the absence of oxygen. When instant coffee powder absorbs moisture to raise moisture above 4 per cent, coffee flavor deterioration occurs with a heavy, sickening taste note. A similar off-flavor develops when the powder is exposed to air at temperatures over 125 F (52 C) whether fusion occurs or not. Powder dried to more than 5 per cent moisture will deteriorate under normal storage and handling. Powder dried to low moistures (1 to 2 per cent) loses more flavor in the drying process. Particles with a large surface/weight ratio (fines) have less flavor than coarse particles regardless of how the result is achieved. Powder handled in rooms with relative humidities higher than 40 per cent absorbs moisture and rapidly becomes sticky.

The powder as collected from the spray drier, within the hour of collection, has superior aroma and flavor retention for a few days. When powder from the spray drier is vacuum or inert gas packed, it has a small but noticeable flavor advantage over air packed powders. The present method of packaging powders causes considerable breakage of particles. This increases the surface area with an associated loss in desirable coffee flavor. As instant coffees retain more aroma and natural volatiles, they become more susceptible to staling and flavor deteriorations characteristic of an instant coffee flavor change rather than a roast coffee type of staling. Although coffee is not normally exposed to sunlight, there is every reason to believe that the radiant energy of sunlight will also cause oxidation in the jar. Thus the use of jars that absorb ultraviolet light has some merit. In review, Table 79 lists flavor factors in coffee evaluation, and Table 80 lists illustrative types of taste tests.

ASSOCIATING FLAVORS WITH IDENTIFIED CHEMICAL CONSTITUENTS

Until now the coffee aromas and flavors discussed have been associated with individual taste experience. Other familiar flavors and odors are encountered in our everyday lives. But to the chemist and flavor compounder, the ultimate sources of flavor and aroma are the constituent chemical substances. It happens that analytical techniques applied during the last decade have opened entirely new vistas in separating natural aromatic volatiles. This allows a nasal association of a natural aroma with a chemical entity. In simple compounding of a few volatile chemicals, these aromas can be blended to give acceptable impressions of natural fruits, flowers, cheeses, and other foods. In fact, flavor compounders have been preparing additives, fortifiers, and some synthetic flavors for over 50 years. Progressive knowledge and better analytical instruments and experience have been developed to this end. This work is, in fact, a revelation of human impressions, reactions, and sensations concerning pure chemical compounds. It becomes, in some respects, a work of art to blend these individual chemicals into a pleasing impression, as for example perfumes or for a recognizable fruit flavor such as cherry for candy or bever-

TABLE 79

FLAVOR FACTORS IN COFFEE EVALUATION

Green Coffee

Botanical—Arabicas versus Robustas
Mild coffees versus Brazilian coffees (both Arabicas)
High versus low grown mild coffee
Different geographical origins (includes cultivation and green
    processing)
Physical properties (including foreign matter)
Flavor properties (and causes)
Blending facto. s
Storage
Deterioration and/or contamination

Roast Coffee

Mode of roasting (optimum development)
Degree of roast
Blending before or after roasting
Storage
Deterioration and/or contamination

Coffee Solubles (extract)

Percolation mode (grind)
Solubles yield
Extract solubles concentration
Storage (time, temperature, and setting)
Deterioration and/or contamination
Spray drying mode
Blending extracts

Coffee Solubles (powder)

Physical properties
Flavor properties
Blending of powders
Storage and shipping
Packaging mode
Deterioration and/or contamination

Other Factors

Status versus competitor product quality
Subjective versus consumer acceptance
Modes of beverage preparation
Influence of water
Technique of tasting
Recognition of flavor contribution from discrete chemical con-
    stituents. For example, acetic acid, caffein, normal butyral-
    dehyde

age use. Flavor firms have shunned coffee as a complex and very unstable mixture. Consequently, no really good coffee flavor has been developed although the study continues.

VARIATIONS IN COFFEE VOLATILES COMPOSITION

The quantitative analytical figures reported by Zlatkis and Sivetz (1960) for coffee essence entities and composition were based on condensation of vented gases from a soluble coffee percolation system which was in commercial production. These aromas, although typical of coffee, cannot represent all types of coffee.   Each coffee, depending on botanical variety, natural origin, processing history and especially roasting will have a variable volatiles composition.

Hughes and Smith (1949) show this roast variation for pyridine (up to 200 ppm); furfural (up to 80 ppm); and acetaldehyde (from 40 to 80 ppm).   The percentage of each component varied with roast loss.   In the

TABLE 80

TASTE TESTS TO ILLUSTRATE COFFEE FLAVORS AND AROMAS

Regular Coffee Brew

1. Cup Strength: 30 vs 40 vs 50 cups per pound roast coffee—Silex.
2. Heat Treatment: fresh brew vs brew heated vs brew boiled.
3. Roast Flavor Development: light vs optimum vs dark roast—same coffee brew.
4. Altitude of Milds: a 5000 ft vs 2000 ft coffee to demonstrate flavor value.
5. Comparison Major Type Coffee: Milds, Brazils, and Robustas.
6. Compare Freshness of Crop: old crop vs new crop from same area.
7. Grind: fine vs coarse
8. Freshness of Roast Coffee: (a) Ground coffee—hours to days old vs fresh.
       (b) Whole bean—days to weeks old vs fresh.
9. Contamination: (a) Air bubbling through brewed coffee vs fresh.
       (b) Iron (FeCl₃) at 1 mg/cup—5 ppm.
       (c) Copper (CuCl₂) at 1 mg/cup—5 ppm.
10. Off-flavor: (a) Rioy, (b) fermented, (c) musty, (d) dirty, (e) harsh.
11. Aging (as differentiated from just held coffees in warm climates):   Venezuelan aged vs newer or current crops.
12. Uniformity of Roast:
       (a) 20 min vs 5 min roast.
       (b) Blend of new and old crops.
       (c) Blend of low and high moistures.
       (d) Blend of small and large beans.
       (e) Beans before and after picking out "blacks," mottled, quakers, etc.
13. Comparison of Commercial Coffees Available Locally and World-wide.

Cups of Instant Coffee

1. Cup Strength: 1.7 vs 2.0 vs 2.3 gm per 5 fl oz cup.
2. Water: (a) boiling vs warm, (b) distilled vs chlorinated vs brackish vs alkaline vs with organic matter, (c) distilled vs local tap.
3. Original Roast Coffee vs percolator extract vs spray dried powder.
4. Powder: (a) Before and after packaging.
       (b) Coarse vs fine; crushed coarse vs fine.
       (c) Dried from cold vs warm extract.
       (d) Dried at high vs low bulk density, e.g., carbonated extract.
       (e) Prepared from redissolved fines.
       (f) With high and low residual moisture.
       (g) Fresh vs powder held at 125 F for hours to days.
       (h) Normal production vs with charred powder from drier walls.

region of 14 to 19 per cent roast weight loss, furfural concentrations fell to 20 ppm and total aldehyde concentrations rose to 90 ppm.   Rhoades (1960) shows similar acetaldehyde concentration increases with darker roasts.   Diacetyl, CH_3COCH_3CO, and acetyl propionyl, $CH_3COC_2H_5CO$, both are at about 15 ppm concentration in roast coffee within the range of palatable roast losses.   The acetyl propionyl ratio to diacetyl rises to about

TABLE 81A[1]

ODOR THRESHOLD OF CERTAIN ROAST COFFEE CONSTITUENTS

Compound	Odor Similarity	Concentration, Parts per Billion, mg per 1,000 l of Air
n-Butyric acid	Perspiration	9
Pyridine	Burnt	1
Hydrogen sulfide	Rotten eggs	0.2
n-Butyl sulfide	Foul, sulfurous	0.1
Coumarin	New-mown hay	0.02
Ethylmercaptan	Rotten cabbage	0.0007

TABLE 81B[2]

Compound	Boiling Points C	F	Concentration, Parts per Million, mg per l of Air
Ethylacetate	77	171	0.7
Ethylmercaptan	37	99	0.05
Pyridine	115	239	0.03
Valeric acid	186	367	0.03
Butyric acid	162	324	0.01
Propylmercaptan	67	153	0.006

TABLE 81C[3]

FLAVOR THRESHOLDS OF ORGANIC ACIDS

Acid	Concentration Normality × 0.001	Parts per Million, mg per l of Water	× 0.001 gm H ions per l
Formic	1.8	83	0.6
Acetic	2.8	168	0.3
Butyric	3.5	308	0.3
Valeric	3.7	378	0.2
Oxalic	2.0	252	1.2
Tartaric	3.2	480	0.7

[1] Wenzel (1955).
[2] Allison and Katz (1919).
[3] Taylor et al. (1930).

1.7 in dark roasts according to Rhodes (1960). Merritt, C. et al. (1957) and Hughes and Smith (1949) report chemical variations in coffee due to degree of roast as does Rhoades (1960) for coffee volatiles.

Aldehydes

Acetaldehyde is very volatile, bp 70 F (21 C), and is found in most fruits; it distinguishes itself as a pungent, fruity aroma. Merck's Index (1960) cites acetaldehyde as being irritating to mucous membranes. At the levels acetaldehyde occurs in coffee aroma, it is only faintly irritating to mucuous membranes. Acetaldehyde fruitiness is only encountered

TABLE 82

COFFEE AROMA ANALYSIS[1] (Per cent)

	Roasted[2] Coffee Aroma	Roasted[3] Coffee Aroma	Roasted[4] Coffee Aroma	Brewed[4] Coffee Aroma
Aldehydes				
Acetaldehyde	17.9	19.9	25.6	22.8
Propionaldehyde	8.0	4.5	3.2	2.6
Butyraldehyde		0.7	0.3	0.1
Isobutyraldehyde		3.0	6.8	6.2
2-Methylbutyraldehyde		6.8		
Valeraldehyde		7.3		
Isovaleraldehyde	18.2	5.0	1.5	1.0
Acrolein	0.6			
Dimethyl acrolein	T[5]			
Methyl ethyl acrolein	1.4			
Ketones				
Acetone	0.5	18.7	21.0	25.6
Methyl ethyl ketone	14.2	2.3	8.2	6.4
Methyl vinyl ketone	0.5			
Diacetyl	10.3	7.5	6.4	8.4
2,3-Pentanedione			6.7	8.8
2,4-Pentanedione	0.2			
Heterocycle Compounds				
Furan	2.5	3.2	1.2	0.6
2-Methyl furan	5.1	4.7	3.0	1.0
2,5-Dimethyl furan	0.3			
Propyl furan	T			
Butyl furan	T			
Pyrrole	0.5			
N-Methyl pyrrole	T			
Dimethyl pyrrole	T			
Sulfur Compounds				
Hydrogen sulfide			1.5	0.8
Carbon disulfide	0.3	0.2		
Dimethyl sulfide	0.6	1.0	1.2	0.8
Methyl ethyl sulfide	0.3			
Dimethyl disulfide	3.1			
Methyl ethyl disulfide	T			
Methyl mercaptan		0.1	1.2	0.7
Thiophene		0.1		
Esters				
Methyl formate	4.9	4.0	3.4	2.9
Methyl acetate	5.7	1.7		
Ethyl formate		0.3		
Nitriles				
Acrylonitrile	0.5			
Allylcyanide	1.1			
Alcohols				
Methanol	0.9	0.2	8.2	10.9
Ethanol	0.3		0.3	0.4
Hydrocarbons				
Isoprene		3.0	0.3	0.03
C_4-C_7 Paraffins		2.0		
Oxides				
Carbon dioxide		3.8		
Total	97.9	100.0	100.0	100.03

[1] Ritter (1960).
[2] Merritt, C. *et al*. (1957).
[3] Zlatkis and Sivetz (1960).
[4] Rhoades (1958 and 1960).
[5] T. Trace, tentatively identified.

TABLE 83

CONCENTRATION CHANGES IN AROMA CONSTITUENTS FOR ROASTED, BREWED, AND INSTANT COFFEE[1]

Compound	Roasted Coffee, ppm	Brewed Fresh Coffee ppm	% Re- tained	Brewed 6-Day-Old Coffee ppm	% Re- tained	Instant Coffee ppm	% Re- tained
Acetaldehyde	2.43	1.74	72	1.39	57	0.71	29
Propionaldehyde	0.30	0.20	67	0.15	50	0.038	13
Butyraldehyde	0.03	0.006	20	0	0	0	0
Isobutyraldehyde	0.64	0.47	72	0.42	65	0.14	22
Isovaleraldehyde	0.14	0.073	52	0.047	34	0.019	14
Acetone	1.99	1.95	98	1.25	63	0.55	28
Methyl ethyl ketone	0.78	0.49	62	0.33	42	0.11	14
Diacetyl	0.61	0.64	106	0.41	68	0.24	40
2,3-Pentanedione	0.64	0.67	106	0.40	63	0.11	17
Furan	0.11	0.045	40	0.026	23	0.004	4
Methyl furan	0.29	0.078	27	0.039	14	0.008	3
Hydrogen sulfide	0.14	0.060	43	0.054	39	0.010	7
Dimethyl sulfide	0.12	0.063	52	0.020	17	0	0
Methyl mercaptan	0.12	0.056	48	0.053	45	0.022	19
Methyl formate	0.32	0.22	69	0.13	41	0.02	6
Methanol	0.78	0.83	106	0.46	60	0.03	4
Ethanol	0.03	0.032	108	0.022	73	0	0
Isoprene	0.026	0.0026	10	0.0015	6	0	0
Total	9.50	7.63	80	5.20	55	2.01	21

[1] Rhoades (1958).

noticeably in very freshly roasted and ground coffee. It can be recognized at the coffee grinder where most of the very volatile coffee constituents are freed. Rhodes' (1958) chromatographic analyses of commercial instant coffees show a high (100 ppm) acetaldehyde content relative to that occurring in roast coffee. This might mean that acetaldehyde is produced in the hydrolysis of roast coffee. It is equally interesting that the acetaldehyde is retained in the spray dried powder. This can be demonstrated by adding that level of acetaldehyde to the extract before spray drying which will result in 100 ppm in the powder and comparing the resulting powder with a control sample. Acetaldehyde smooths the instant coffee cup flavor, gives noticeable aroma, but is not strikingly beneficial. It certainly is a part of coffee aroma and flavor. Acetaldehyde has also been reported quantitatively in coffee aroma by Merritt, C. et al. (1957) and Zlatkis and Sivetz (1960).

Propionaldehyde is the next higher homologous aldehyde and boils at 120 F (49 C). It, too, occurs in many fruits and has an aroma suggesting prunes or overripe apples. When added to extract or powder solubles, its presence is noted at less than 50 ppm. Rhoades (1960), Merritt and Proctor (1959), and Zlatkis and Sivetz (1960) analyzed the volatiles of roast and instant coffees and showed that propionaldehyde is present at about 20 ppm in roast coffee and somewhat less in soluble coffees. It is a normal contributor to coffee aroma and flavor, but is not a particularly outstanding flavor note.

Butyraldehyde is the next homologous aldehyde and has two isomers—the normal straight chain, bp 169 F (76 C), and the iso-branched chain, bp 147 F (64 C); the ratio of the iso- to the normal isomer is over 5 to 1 which is usual in natural sources of aldehydes. Butyraldehydes have characteristic odors which one associates with dairy products, particularly sour milk and blue cheese. The odors also resemble butyric acid in the basic pungent odor. It occurs in roast coffees at about 30 ppm, as reported by Rhoades (1958 and 1960) and Zlatkis and Sivetz (1960). Its odor and taste are detectable at that level. Soluble coffee flavor benefits greatly from the retention of several ppm of butyraldehyde. A genuinely desirable cup smoothness and natural coffee aroma and flavor are contributed by concentrations ranging from barely detectable to several times higher.

Valeraldehyde is the next homologous aldehyde and has, besides the normal straight chain configuration, the 2-methyl and the 3-methyl isomers. According to Zlatkis and Sivetz (1960), the isomers occur in about equal quantities and together are about 20 per cent of the volatile coffee essence. This would mean a concentration of about 60 ppm in roast coffee, and a fraction of this in soluble coffee. These aldehydes boil at 217 F (103 C) for normal, and 199 F (93 C) for iso-. They contribute a heavy, yet not undesirable flavor note; they are a significant part of the coffee aromas and flavor. The threshold of detection is less than 10 ppm equivalent in R & G coffee. With a vapor pressure like water, its flavor contribution is noticeable but not prominent. The valeraldehydes represent a large fraction of the volatiles in roast coffee. Their taste and aroma properties can be studied by making additions of about 50 ppm to coffee extract before drying. Merritt and Proctor (1959) report several-fold higher levels of valeraldehydes than Zlatkis and Sivetz (1960), and Rhoades (1960) reports lower valeraldehyde levels.

Furfural occurs in a great many natural plants, notably corn and other grains. It is also produced during destructive distillation of grains and coffee. Hughes and Smith (1949) report the following amounts of furfural at the corresponding roasting losses: 90 ppm at 15.7 per cent loss, 22 ppm at 18.2 per cent, 11 ppm at 19 per cent. They reported no loss of furfural from the roast coffee after six weeks in spite of its instability and volatility, bp 324 F (162 C). Stale samples over two years old had about 50 ppm furfural. The importance of furfural is its very characteristic odor, resembling benzaldehyde, yet more like an odor from a hay stack. It is not an appealing odor. It also occurs in soluble coffees at up to 100 to 200 ppm and is directly related in some instances to the hydrolysis yield of solubles originating in the percolators. About 10 to 20 per cent of furfural loss was noted in brew preparation.

Furfural is formed commercially from pentosans by acid hydrolysis; acid hydrolysis of pentosans also occurs in roasting and percolator hydrolysis. Higher levels of furfural which do not make for desirable flavors denote a high hydrolysis yield of coffee solubles. Quaker Oats Co. manufactures furfural from corn cobs and oat hulls and has amassed a great deal of knowledge regarding its chemistry. Furfural turns yellow brown on exposure to air and light and polymerizes becoming resin-like. It is readily steam distilled. It is widely used in furfural-phenol plastics, for accelerating rubber vulcanization and in the preparation of furan derivatives, all of which aspects are reflected in the chemistry of coffee. It may cause irritation of mucous membranes, act on the central nervous system and also cause headaches. It is a five-membered ring with four carbons and one oxygen; the aldehyde group is next to the oxygen. Formula: OC_4H_3CHO. Moncrieff (1946) likens the odor of furfural in dilute concentrations to that of bran and new bread, in both of which it is present.

Ketones

Acetone, bp 135 F (57 C), occurs in roast coffee at about 20 per cent of the coffee essence level as reported by Zlatkis and Sivetz (1960) and Rhoades (1958 and 1960). Merritt and Proctor (1959) report much less. It has a characteristic solvent odor, sweet and pungent, like fingernail polish, airplane cement, or rubber cement. Rhoades (1958) found about 50 ppm acetone in both roast and instant coffees, which is in agreement with Zlatkis and Sivetz (1960). Addition of acetone to coffee extracts and cups at these and lower levels gives sweetness and smoothness, but not any exceptional aroma and taste values beyond this. Rhoades (1960) and Hughes and Smith (1949) show acetone at 30 to 60 ppm in roast coffee with the higher acetone concentrations at the darker roasts.

Diacetyl, bp 190 F (88 C), occurs at about 7 per cent of essence level or about 20 ppm of roast coffee; this is in general agreement with Rhoades (1960), Zlatkis and Sivetz (1960), and Merritt, C. et al. (1957). Diacetyl has a sweet, buttery aroma and flavor. It is definitely an important part of coffee flavor because of its desirable, rich note. Diacetyl is used to accentuate butter flavor at up to 100 ppm in butter, baked goods, margarine, and other dairy products. Spray drying extract with less than 100 ppm diacetyl in the coffee solubles leaves a notable aroma and taste impression (smoother cup). Rhoades (1960) found that diacetyl/acetyl propionyl ratios rise to 1.7 in darker roast coffees. Hughes and Smith (1949) report that diacetyl flavor is detectable at 1 to 2 ppm in roast coffee.

In two-month old roast coffee samples there was a reduction of about half the diacetyl to acetyl methyl carbinol.

Acetoin or Acetyl Methyl Carbinol, bp 298 F (148 C), having the formula $CH_3CHOHCOCH_3$, when oxidized becomes diacetyl having the formula $CH_3COCOCH_3$. It is used as a butter flavor at less than 100 ppm in baked goods, butter, and margarine. A related compound, acetyl carbinol, bp 295 F (146 C), has somewhat of a "cockroach" odor.

Methyl ethyl ketone, bp 176 F (80 C), occurs in roast and soluble coffee at 10 to 20 ppm, as reported by Rhoades (1960), Zlatkis and Sivetz (1960), and Merritt, C. *et al.* (1957). It has an odor similar to acetone and behaves similarly except for its lesser volatility.

Alcohols

Methyl alcohol, bp 147 F (64 C), occurs in roast coffee at a few ppm, according to Zlatkis and Sivetz (1960) and Merritt and Proctor (1959). Its taste is detectable at this concentration.

The foregoing list of carbonyls and alcohols shows that none, individually, is a major coffee flavor contributor, except diacetyl, butyraldehyde, and valeraldehyde; the other aldehydes contribute a general fruity to sweet background aroma and smooth flavor in the cup.

The following **esters** are similar to the extent that they are pleasant odors and each contributes a type of dark roast flavor.

Esters

Methyl Formate, bp 90 F (32 C), is reported by Rhoades (1960), Zlatkis and Sivetz (1960), and Merritt and Proctor (1959) at about 4 per cent of coffee essence, hence at 10 to 20 ppm in roast coffee.

Ethyl Formate, bp 129 F (54 C), is reported by Zlatkis and Sivetz (1960) at about 0.3 per cent of coffee essence, hence about 2 ppm in roast coffee.

Methyl Acetate, bp 135 F (57 C), is reported by Merritt, C. *et al.* (1957) and Zlatkis and Sivetz (1960) at 2 to 5 per cent of coffee essence, hence 10 to 20 ppm of roast coffee.

Heterocyclic Compounds.—Furan, bp 90 F (32 C), and **methyl furan,** bp 145 F (63 C), are reported by Merritt, C. *et al.* (1957), Zlatkis and Sivetz (1960), and Rhoades (1960) in coffee essence at 3 to 5 per cent or 10 to 20 ppm of roast coffee. Furan resembles benzene in odor and is not unpleasant. Methyl furan has a similar but perhaps less pleasant odor. The physiological properties of furan are such that low levels cause marked disturbances in the body such as loss of appetite, reduced blood pressure and slower pulse. The aldehyde of furan is **furfural,** bp 323 F (162 C), which is unpleasant when smelled at the cap of the bottle, but sweet and pleasant in dilute concentrations. It is similar to the odors of bread, hay, and bran.

When the five-membered ring of furan has sulfur substituted for its oxygen, it is called **thiophene**, bp 183 F (84 C), and was reported by Zlatkis and Sivetz (1960) in coffee essence at about 0.1 per cent or 1 to 2 ppm in roast coffee. Thiophene, although a sulfur compound, does not have very much odor.

When the furan oxygen is substituted by —NH we have **pyrolle**, bp 266 F (130 C), which has a very nauseating odor. It is reported at 0.5 per cent in coffee aroma or at about 2 ppm by Merritt, C. *et al.* (1957).

When the pyrolle group is attached to **pyridine** it becomes **nicotine**, bp 475 F (246 C), which has a rank, offensive tobacco odor. The following structural formulas relate the nitrogen aromatics.

Structural Relation Between Trigonelline, Pyridine, Nicotinic Acid, and Nicotine

Trigonelline   Nicotinic acid   Pyridine

Nicotine

Pyridine, bp 239 F (115 C), has a repulsive odor. It occurs in roast coffee at about 200 ppm. It is a six-membered ring resembling benzene but with a nitrogen substituted for a CH group. When the meta position of the ring has a carboxyl (—COOH) group, it is nicotinic acid or the vitamin niacin. It occurs in coal tar and in wood distillation. It has a sharp taste. It forms an azeotropic mixture with 3 mols of water to boil at 199 F (93 C). Hughes and Smith (1949) report that pyridine and nicotinic acid are produced during roasting by the decomposition of trigonelline. A high pyridine content is a characteristic feature of highly roasted coffee. Pyridine odor can be detected readily in roast coffee. There is no change in pyridine content of roast coffee when held for 7 months. A good part of the sickening odor of stale coffee may be due to the loss of flavorful volatiles leaving behind the pyridine to be prominently displayed. In addition to pyridine, there are methyl homologues which would contribute similar flavors and aromas. Moncrieff (1946) associates pyridine with burnt odors and attributes a burning, bitter taste to its derivatives. Odor threshold is about 3 ppb in air.

Trigonelline is a white crystalline solid occurring at about 1.0 to 1.3 per cent in green coffee and 0.9 to 1.2 per cent in roast coffee. It has a bitter taste, about one-fourth as bitter as caffeine. Since about 10 per cent of trigonelline is decomposed during roasting (more in darker roasts) its decomposition product flavors are of interest. It occurs in seeds of numerous plants, in the sea urchin and jelly fish, but is not readily available commercially.

Niacin or nicotinic acid is developed in roasting; it occurs at about 100 ppm in light roasts and 400 ppm in Italian roasts. Each cup of coffee has only one-tenth of human daily dietary requirements.

Other vitamins in coffee are: thiamine, 2 ppm in green coffee, none in roast coffee; Riboflavin, 2 to 3 ppm; pantothenic acid 10 to 23 ppm; choline 600 to 800 ppm; folic acid 0.2 ppm; B_6 about 1.4 ppm; and B_{12}, negligible. None is of dietary importance (see Teply and Prier 1957).

Sulfur Compounds

The sulfur compounds occur in roast coffee and coffee aroma essence at very low concentrations. However, these sulfur compounds are very volatile, have potent odors and hence, have very low thresholds of odor detections. Therefore, the volatile sulfur constituents of coffee aroma play a major part in characterizing the pleasant aroma and flavor of coffee.

The odor of **Dimethyl sulfide**, bp 100 F (38 C), is detectable in air at ppb concentrations. Its potency becomes overwhelming at moderately higher concentrations. Although sulfurous odors are often objectionable to humans because they are often a part of odors from rot or decay, dimethyl sulfide odor in the parts per billion (ppb) magnitude in the atmosphere and coffee cup impart the essential properties of high grown, high quality mild coffees. Oddly enough, DMS is also the essential part of odors of some fish, and of clams and molasses. As one becomes sensitive to and acquaints oneself with this DMS odor, it is easily recognizable in these and other commonly used foods.

Volatile sulfur compounds are not found in the dry distillation of wood. The volatile sulfur constituents of coffee come from sulfur-containing proteins common to many plants. The sulfur-containing amino acids are methionine, cystine, and cysteine, and are exceptional because the most abundant proteins do not contain sulfur.

Rhoades (1958) found about 2 ppm DMS in roast coffee. This finding compares well with the findings of Zlatkis and Sivetz (1960): 4 ppm in roast coffee or about 1 per cent of the recovered coffee essence.

Merritt, C. *et al.* (1957) found about the same amount. Its delectable aroma may be recognized in cups of high grown Colombian coffees. Rhoades (1960) reported its absence in instant coffees. However, DMS carry-through from coffee extract to powder in spray drying at less than 10 ppm in the coffee solubles is easily noticeable and markedly improves the cup flavor and aroma. Brazilian coffees appear to contain no DMS as evidenced from odor and taste, as well as by Rhoades (1958).

Methyl Mercaptan, bp 46 F (8 C), odor is detectable in air at a few ppb concentrations. Like other volatile sulfides, mercaptans have an overwhelming odor at moderately higher concentrations. Its threshold of detection in water is about 2 ppb, while that of dimethyl sulfide is 12 ppb. Methyl mercaptan is reported in coffee essence at 0.1 per cent by Zlatkis and Sivetz (1960) or about 3 ppm in roast coffee, in agreement with Rhoades (1960). The Merck Index (1960) states that CH_3SH occurs in urine after ingestion of asparagus. It also occurs in coal tar and in the intestinal tract from the action of anaerobic bacteria on albumin. Methyl mercaptan odor is best associated with that of rotten cabbage which, oddly enough, is a constituent of coffee aroma experienced after percolator vent gases pass dry ice or liquid nitrogen traps with only partial condensation of coffee aroma. Table 84 gives the mass

TABLE 84

FRESH CABBAGE VOLATILES COMPOSITION

Analyses By Mass Spectrometry[1,2]

Compound	Mol Percentages (dry basis)	
CO_2	93.3	. . .
Water	4.08	. . .
Acetaldehyde[3]	1.46	56.2
Carbonyl sulfide, COS	0.36	13.8
Methanol[3]	0.28	10.7
Dimethyl sulfide[3]	0.22	8.5
3-Butene nitrile	0.15	5.8
Allyl isothiocyanate	0.07	2.8
Carbon disulfide, CS_2 [3]	0.010	0.40
Propanol	0.006	0.24
Ethanol	0.005	0.20
Butylisothiocyanate	0.005	0.20
Residual Pattern Suggests		
Methyl isothiocyanate	0.010	0.40
Crotonaldehyde	0.001	0.04
Methyl mercaptan[3]	0.003	0.12
Ethyl mercaptan	0.020	0.80
Ethyl propylsulfide	0.005	0.04
Total	2.605	100.34

[1] Merritt (1957), Qm Research and Engineering Center, Pioneering Research Division, Natick, Mass.
[2] Total condensables, October 21, 1957.
[3] Also found in coffee volatiles.

spectroscopic analyses of fresh cabbage volatiles. It shows methyl mercaptan as well as dimethyl sulfide and several other volatiles which also occur in coffee aroma. The mercaptan odor by itself is not an agreeable one, yet it is a part of coffee aroma and flavor. In its usual low concentrations and blended with other odors, it may be pleasant.

Hydrogen sulfide, bp 76 F (60 C), is best characterized as the odor of rotten eggs; it also occurs commonly in some well water, gas wells, coal pits, sulfur springs, near volcanoes, and in decaying organic matter. Hughes and Smith (1949) report about two ppm H_2S in roast coffee; PbS forms when coffee roasting gases react with $Pb(NO_3)_2$. Segall (1957) in studies on coffee brew found no free H_2S, nor did Merritt, C. *et al.* (1957) nor Zlatkis and Sivetz (1960). However, H_2S is not important in coffee aroma and flavor. If present, it appears to contribute more of a disagreeable taste sensation. An interesting odor sensation created by H_2S at less than one ppm levels in coffee solubles is the distinct aroma of "pop corn," no doubt its characterizing odor.

Carbon disulfide, bp 115 F (46 C), is reported by Zlatkis and Sivetz (1960) and Merritt, C. *et al.* (1957) at 0.2 per cent of coffee essence or about 1 ppm of roast coffee. Although CS_2 does not have as strong an odor as the organic sulfides or mercaptans, it is still an aroma contributor. Merritt (1957) confirmed the presence of CS_2 in cabbage odor; some elements of cabbage odor are also in coffee odor. CS_2 may be considered a foul odor.

Hydrocarbons

Pentadiene, bp 108 or 122 F (42 or 50 C), depending on isomer, also called isoprene, has the formula $(CH_2)_5$. It is also called methyl butadiene. It has a fresh petrol or aromatic odor of low intensity. It was reported by Zlatkis and Sivetz (1960) at 3 per cent of coffee essence level or about 12 ppm of roast coffee. It is probably not an important aroma or direct flavor contributor. However, since it polymerizes to form rubber (having two open reactive groups), it is a reactive component in the coffee pyrolysis chemicals mixture. Not infrequently a rubbery-to-burnt odor is encountered in roast coffee. This unsaturated volatile could readily cause such a result. Rhoades (1960) reported about 1 ppm isoprene in roast coffee.

NON-VOLATILES

Caffeine

Caffeine occurs at about 1 per cent in Arabica and about 2 per cent in Robusta coffees. Thus the corresponding cups of coffee have 100 and 200 mg caffeine. It is a white crystalline substance quite bitter in taste with no aroma, and slightly soluble in cold water, 2 per cent at 68 F (20 C), 18 per cent at 176 F (80 C), and 40 per cent at 212 F (100 C). It sublimes at 352 F (178 C) and accumulates in roaster stacks. It often can be seen as a white crystal on the surface of a roasted coffee bean, especially in the crevice. It is considered an alkaloid, a basic nitrogenous plant product having marked physiological action. Caffeine is much less active than other alkaloids like nicotine, atropine, cocaine, and adrenaline. Its chemical structure is related to theobromine which occurs in cocoa beans; methylation of theobromine produces caffeine. The structural formulas of uric acid, caffeine and theobromine are similar and are illustrated here. Some people are much more sensitive to the action of caffeine than others. Thus the popularity of decaffeinated coffees has grown since their development in Germany beginning about 1907.

Structural Relation Between Uric Acid, Caffeine and Theobromine

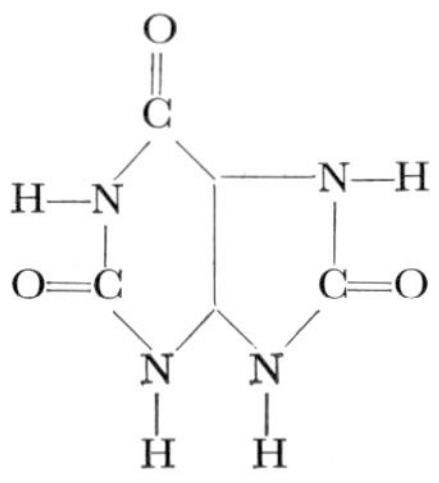

Uric acid

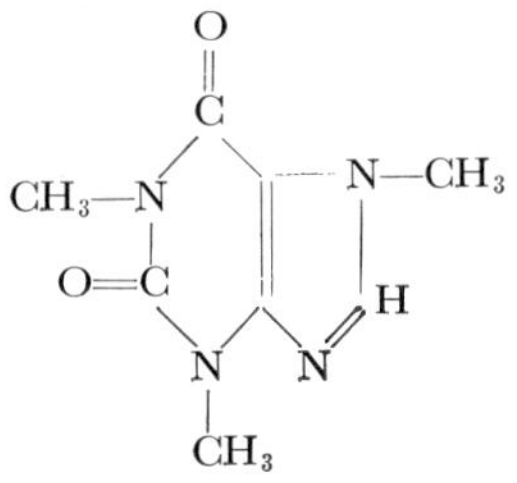

Caffeine

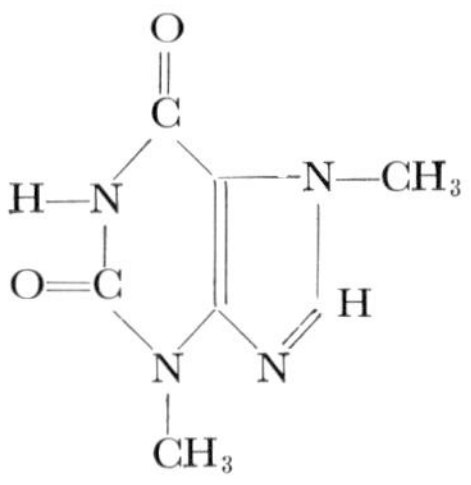

Theobromine

Caffeine relieves headaches caused by high blood pressure and fatigue by increasing the amount of urine flow. Coffee is a mild stimulant for the heart and kidneys. Caffeine stimulates many functions of the human body without causing a depressing after-effect as other alkaloids do. Excessive intake of coffee, however, can have over-stimulating, even toxic, effects. It is important to note that many of the volatile active substances in coffee also have physiological effects; hence the effects caused by coffee cannot always be entirely attributed to the caffeine. Proper movement of fluids through the body are important in minimizing edema and removing poisonous waste products from the blood stream, hence the "lift." The difference between oral and intravenous use of caffeine is that, for equal dosage, the latter is immediately physiologically effective whereas the reaction to oral use takes longer but also lasts longer and does not achieve the height of action of the intravenous dose. Under medical direction for special purposes, 200 to 400 mg caffeine dosages are not uncommon.

Chlorogenic Acid occurs at about $4^1/_2$ per cent in roast coffee and is reduced from about 8 per cent in green coffee. Chlorogenic acid largely undergoes hydrolysis to caffeic acid and quinic acid during roasting. Since quinic acid occurs at about 0.5 per cent in roast coffee, the hydrolyzed acids undergo further chemical change. The chemical formulations for chlorogenic acid hydrolyzing to caffeic and quinic acids are shown below:

Hydrolysis of Chlorogenic Acid to Caffeic and Quinic Acids

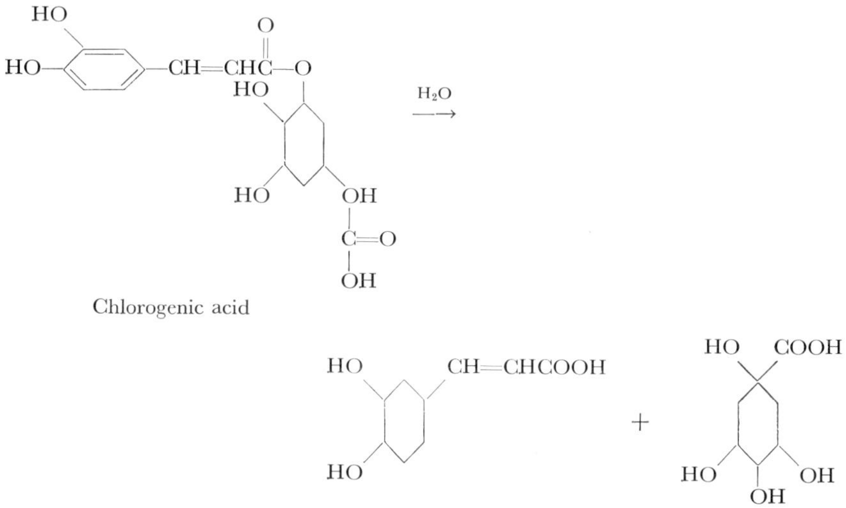

Chlorogenic acid

Caffeic acid   Quinic acid

These substances are referred to as acids since they have the carboxylic acid groups. Their tastes, however, are more bitter and astringent than acidic since the cyclic group is phenolic. A number of phenolic type compounds have been identified in roast coffee, and some of these have originated from chlorogenic acid. Properties and analytical procedures for chlorogenic acid have been reported by Moores (1948), Karrer (1950), Barnes (1951), and Lee (1962).

Non-Volatile Coffee Acids—Oxalic, Malic, Citric, Tartaric, and Pyruvic

These acids are all white crystals when pure and are non-aromatic. They occur in green and roast coffee at 0.2 to 0.5 per cent, which concentrations are sufficient for them to be detected by taste.

Oxalic Acid is a strong reducing agent, and in large quantities a poison although it occurs in rhubarb and in wood sorrel having sour juice. It is a dibasic acid having the formula $(COOH)_2$ and melts at 365 F (185 C) with sublimation and some decomposition.

Malic Acid is a hydroxy dibasic acid with the formula $(CHOHCOOH)$-(CH_2COOH). It occurs in unripe fruits such as gooseberries, rhubarb stalks, grapes, cherries, and tomatoes. It is also called hydroxysuccinic acid and melts at 212 F (100 C).

Citric Acid is common to all citrus and many other fruits, and its acid taste is easily recognized. Its formula is (CH_2COOH)-$(CHOHCOOH)$-(CH_2COOH). With one molecule of hydration, it melts at 212 F (100 C).

Tartaric Acid $(CHOHCOOH)$-$(CHOHCOOH)$, occurs as the monopotassium salt crystal in wine casks and when purified is known as "cream of tartar."

Pyruvic Acid $(CH_3COCOOH)$ occurs at 0.05 per cent only in roast coffee. It has an irritating odor. It melts at 284 F (140 C) and boils at 329 F (165 C). It oxidizes to acetic acid and is formed from acetol, CH_3COCH_2OH or methyl glyoxal, CH_3COCHO.

Phenols

These have pungent and antiseptic properties. They are an important part of wood smoke, especially in their ability to diffuse through meats in smokehouse curing. The phenolic content of the smoke helps to govern the flavor and aroma imparted to the meats being smoked. Phenols are also found in the condensed tars from the dry distillation of wood. Phenol is a benzene ring containing one hydroxyl group; **catechol** has two adjacent hydroxyl groups; **resorcinol** has two hydroxyl groups in meta position; and **hydroquinone** has two hydroxyl groups in para position. These phenols may be obtained from distilled coal tars. The white crystals of phenol will redden on exposure to air much as do the dry vacuum aroma distillates from coffee; phenol must be protected from light. Phenols react to form resins like phenol-formaldehyde. Coffee solutions and distillates contain many aldehydes and phenols. The phenols are readily steam distilled. Catechol, resorcinol, hydroquinone, cresols (ortho, meta, and para methyl group to phenol hydroxyl), guaiacols and eugenol all change from yellow to red and then darken further on exposure to air and light. They all react with ferric salts to give brown colorations which are the bases for analytical determinations. There are similarities of chemical structure between lignin, eugenols, and vanillin that indicate a high probability that they and related compounds form in the roasting process. These formulas are shown below. Guaiacol occurs in large quantities in wood tar, melts at 82 F (28 C), and has a characteristic pleasant odor.[1]

Caffeic acid, cumaric acid, and proto-catechuic acid formulas are also shown below since they relate to the compounds under discussion. They are aromatic acids widely found in plants associated with benzoic acid, salicylic acid, and gallic acid.

The structural relation between lignin, eugenols, and vanillin and also common aromatic acids in plants are:

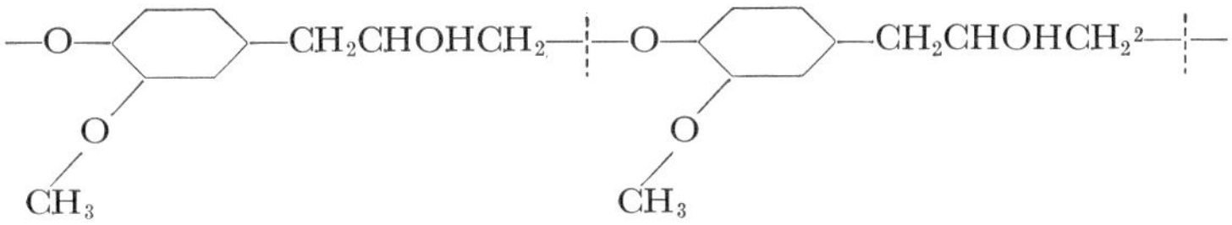

$$-O-\bigcirc-CH_2CHOHCH_2-|-O-\bigcirc-CH_2CHOHCH_2{}^2-|-$$

$$O \quad\quad O$$
$$CH_3 \quad\quad CH_3$$

Lignin structural unit—common in plants

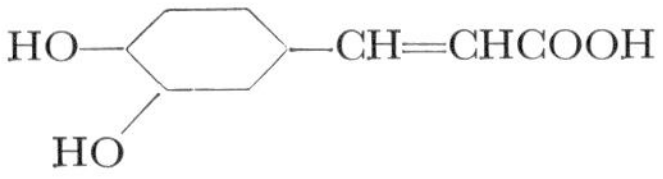

$$HO-\bigcirc-CH{=}CHCOOH$$
$$HO$$

Caffeic Acid—common in plants

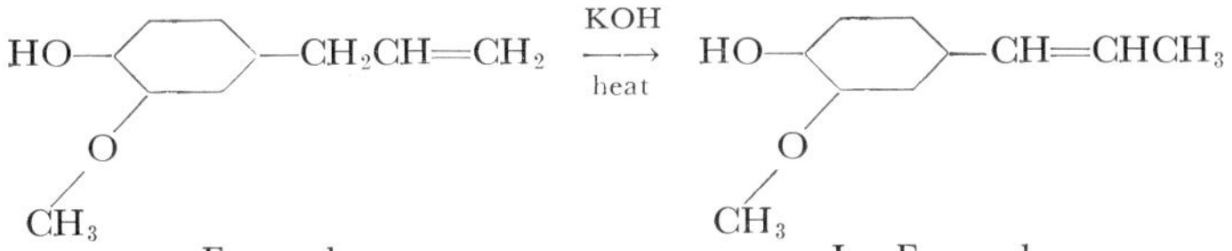

$$HO-\bigcirc-CH_2CH{=}CH_2 \xrightarrow[\text{heat}]{\text{KOH}} HO-\bigcirc-CH{=}CHCH_3$$

$$O \quad\quad O$$
$$CH_3 \quad\quad CH_3$$

Eugenol   Iso-Eugenol

$$HO-\bigcirc-CHO \quad\quad HO-\bigcirc$$

$$O \quad\quad O$$
$$CH_3 \quad\quad CH_3$$

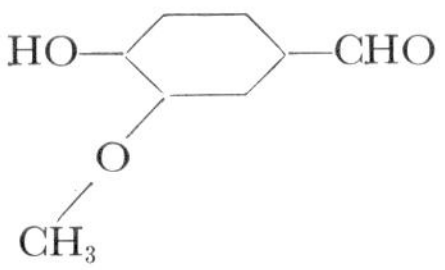

Vanillin—from oxidation of iso-eugenol 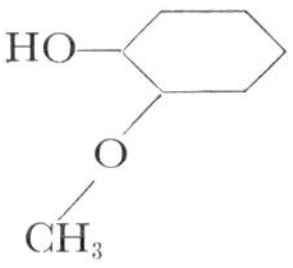   Guaiacol

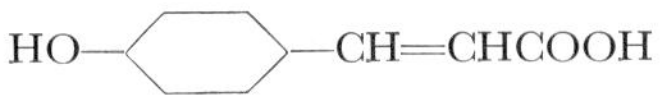

$$HO-\bigcirc-CH{=}CHCOOH \quad\quad HO-\bigcirc-COOH$$
$$HO$$

Cumaric Acid 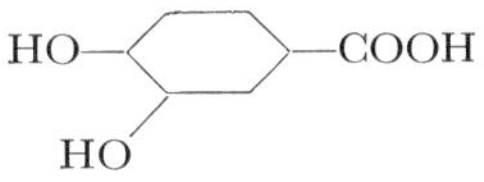   Proto-catechuic Acid

---

[1] Pyrogallol or pyrogallic acid $C_6H_3(OH)_3$ (1,2,3,) is not prepared from coal tar. Gallic acid, $C_6H_2(OH)_3COOH$, is prepared by the hydrolysis of tannins. When heated above 392 F (200 C), it loses carbon dioxide and forms pyrogallol, which is readily oxidized in air. Ferric salts color tannins blue or black. Tannins in solution with proteins form voluminous precipitates.

[2] Broken down by hydrolysis to lower polymers at linkage points indicated by vertical dotted lines.

The polyhydroxy aromatics are widely distributed in nature, often as glucosides. Many complex substances are derived from the polyhydroxy compounds of tannins. There are few references to work done in phenols in coffee and, considering the importance of phenolic flavors in coffee, much more data is needed.

Protein content of green coffee is about 14 per cent. Practically all coffee proteins are denatured with correspondingly reduced water solubilities after roasting. Although few protein compounds are lost during roasting, there is a large decrease in basic and non-basic fractions extractable with water as reported by Underwood and Deatherage (1952). Their study of amino acid stability under roasting conditions shows that many acids undergo decomposition. Proteins, due to their insolubility after roasting, have little taste influence except for whatever proteins are carried over into the brew to give a colloidal smooth texture to the cup. Water extractables from Brazilian green coffee contain about 7.5 per cent protein or half of bean content. Water extractables from the same roast coffee are about 4 per cent protein (based on nitrogen content multiplied by 6.25). Soluble coffees have about 6 per cent protein due to additional solubilization of grounds by protein hydrolysis. Analytical work reported on coffee protein is meager and often does not indicate whether allowances have been made in discounting other sources of nitrogen (such as caffeine and trigonelline which together account for 2 per cent of roast coffee).

Clements and Deatherage (1957) make a notable observation in regard to the behavior of acidified brewed coffee giving a flocculent brown precipitate. These are largely proteins and similar colloidal matter such as occur in the more spent acid hydrolysis stages of the percolation process. These protein substances are soluble in alkali (ammonia), but not in water or aqueous acids. They are reprecipitated from alkaline solutions upon acidification. This is a pH phenomenon and the transition pH is about 4.5; pH's as low as 3.8 occur in the most spent coffee of the percolation system. Acid hydrolysis of these protein insolubles yielded ten amino acids. A large portion of the insolubles did not dissolve on acid refluxing. This analytical procedure has its parallel in the percolators. The hydrolysates coagulate to leave tars in the coffee extract which are about half protein in nature. The remainder is mostly occluded extract and fine roast coffee particles. See bibliography of Chapter 17.

Water soluble proteins and amino acids are not strong flavor contributors to foods. However, the decomposition products of amino acids and proteins can be quite odorous in forms such as volatile amines and possibly some aminated organics. Cysteine is an amino acid with a mercaptan group. It occurs in green coffee and readily undergoes decomposition during roasting to release volatile mercaptan and amine groups of highly odorous potency. Cysteine has the formula, CH_2SH-($CHNH_2$)-COOH.

Amines are formed in roasting and in particularly dark roast coffees to the extent that their odor is prominent and recognizable. Ammonia, methylamine, dimethylamine, and trimethylamine are products of wood distillation and also of coffee roasting. Ammonia odor is typically pungent and easily identified; methylamine is most similar in odor to ammonia. Trimethylamine is least similar to ammonia and has more of a fishy odor. This fishy odor is noticeable from dark roast coffees. Amines are all very volatile substances; ammonia boils at -27 F (-33 C), methylamine at 21 F (-6 C), and trimethylamine at 39 F (3.5 C). Amines are odor detectable at a few ppb level of concentrations in the air. Amines are also formed from bacterial decomposition of proteins and other nitrogenous compounds. Merck Index (1960) states that trimethylamine is formed during the distillation of sugar beet residues which contain betaine. Trigonelline is the methyl betaine of nicotinic acid, so this may be the source of some amines from coffee. Taking a coffee extract and making it alkaline with sodium hydroxide, distilling off a major fraction of the water into a hydrochloric acid solution, for example, and then removing the chlorides on an anion resin column reveal a definite amine odor in the effluent. This is only about 20 to 40 ppm of roast coffee but will vary with degree of roast and type of coffee.

Caramelized sugars represent about 4 per cent of solubilized substances from roast coffee and 14 per cent of solubilized substances in soluble coffees. Most of the increased solubles yield are carbohydrates from darker roast coffees. Under the conditions of roasting, the few per cent of reducing sugars and about 8 per cent of sucrose in the green coffee bean undergo pyrolysis to produce some of the delightful coffee aromas and aldehydes. The solubles form caramel. Commercial caramel manufacture patents by Cleland and Shively (1955), Longnecker and Cleland (1953), and Fetzer (1962) usually heat sugar to concentrate the solution so as to dehydrate it. Thereafter, when the temperature rises close to 380 F (193 C), the caramelization reaction becomes exothermic. The rapid heat evolution is accompanied with darkening of the solution. If, during this heat production period, the solution is not immediately cooled, the reaction will proceed too far, and the whole melt will polymerize into a solid. The nature of the caramelization reaction is similar to what happens when coffee is roasted. The resulting caramel is a strong coloring agent typical of coffee color, and is used to color food products including cola beverages commercially. Caramel has a bitter and not very pleasant taste. It contributes flavor to coffee as well as other foods in which this similar cooking process occurs. Normally caramelization occurs without any addition to the sugars. However, a trace of nitrogenous matter like ammonia or amines accelerates the reaction. Proteinaceous matter is normally present even in refined sugars. Carmelization reduces the pH of sugars from neutral to about 5.0 or somewhat less, depending on the means of preparation. The presence of proteins can markedly influence the course of caramel-polymerizing reactions. The flavors developed during caramelization are important to the baking and beer industry. Browning reactions of amino acids with reducing sugars occur during roasting and percolation of coffee as they do during malt kilning and wort boiling in beer preparation. There are malanoidin or Maillard type reactions where carbonyl-amino types react, e.g., aldehydes and ketones and sugars with amines, amino acids, peptides, and proteins. True caramelization occurs when poly-hydroxy carboxylic compounds like sugars are heated without amino type compounds.

Oils are about 14 to 17 per cent of roast coffee, depending on the variety and the degree of roast. These are a mixture of vegetable oils commonly associated with plants and seeds. Their chemistry and composition will be discussed in Chapter 17. These oils have little to do with the taste of roast coffee and even less to do with the taste of unaromatized soluble coffee. The oils are coffee aroma carriers, and instant coffees taste better with than without oils. In coffees brewed from finely ground roast coffee, the colloidal oil contents are high. This can be evidenced by the heavy turbidity and colloidal content of the brew. The oil content in cases like this can run as high as 10 per cent oil in water solubles. Coarser grinds may free about 3 per cent of oil in water solubles. The flavor effectiveness of oils in both roast and soluble coffees comes from the fatty acid fraction associated with the oil. Fatty acids have a marked influence on reducing brew surface tension and hence impart a noticeable smooth texture effect in the mouth. The oil-fatty acid portion helps to carry through volatile flavors in the spray drying of instant coffee.

Mineral content of green coffee as determined by sulfated ash is about 4 per cent. According to Winton and Winton (1939) about 60 per cent of the ash is potassium oxide, 10 per cent magnesium oxide, about 5 per cent calcium oxide, 1 per cent silica, and 1 per cent ferric oxide. If the ash oxide is 4.5 per cent, then the pure elements are about 4.0 per cent. In addition, there is about 13 per cent of phosphorus and traces of sodium, manganese, copper, aluminum, and other elements. On this basis, there would be 200 mg potassium per cup of coffee if all the potassium were free to dissolve. According to Winton and Winton (1939) most of the ash is water soluble. This appears to be true from ash analyses of soluble coffees, which run at 10 to 12 per cent, depending on yield of solubles from roast coffee. Combustion of spent coffee grounds after percolation leaves only a negligible amount of ash, most of which is carried up the flue. At the 200 mg per cup level (2,000 ppm), the ash constituents may contribute some flavor; however, no such taste studies have been reported.

Gialluly (1958) reported taste results on coffee grown with different fertilizer formulations. The mineral composition of fertilizer regarding nitrogen, potassium, phosphorus, and magnesium was related to flavor properties. More data is needed in this type of work.

Broido (1961) and Broido and Martin (1962) have shown in preliminary work that the ash content and composition of sugars and carbohydrates exercise an important influence catalytically on the course of pyrolysis temperatures, time, and volatile products. This work would appear to be very pertinent to similar reactions in roasting coffee.

Neutron activation of green coffee beans or ash would give a good decay curve for accurate and rapid ash analyses.

BIBLIOGRAPHY

ALLISON, V. C. and KATZ, S. H.   1919.   An investigation of stenches and odors for industrial purposes.   J. Ind. Eng. Chem. *11*, 336–338.

AMERINE, M. A., PANGBORN, R. M., ROESSLER, E. B., and SIMONE, M.   1962.   Sensory analyses of foods.   Univ. of California, Davis, Calif. (To be published.)

ANON.   1959.   Glossary of sensory terms.   Food Technol. *13*, 733–736.

ANON.   Merck Index.   1960.   Merck and Company, Rahway, N.J.

BARNES, A.   1951.   Iso-chlorogenic acid.   J. Am. Chem. Soc. 72, 4178.

BRESSANI, R. *et al.*   1961.   Effect of coffee processing on niacin.   Food Technol. *15*, No. 6, 306–308.

BROIDO, A.   1961.   Effect of fire extinguishing agents on combustion of sucrose.   Science *133*, No. 3465, 1701–1702.

BROIDO, A., and MARTIN, S. B.   1962.   Effect of potassium bicarbonate on the ignition of cellulose by thermal radiation.   Technical Report 536.   U.S. Navy Research and Development Laboratory, San Francisco.

CHENEY, R. H.   1947.   Biology and economics of the beverage industry.   Econ. Botany *1*, 243–275.

CHENEY, R. H.   1960.   Chemical and physiological truisms of tea and coffee.   World Coffee and Tea *1*, No. 2, 82–83.

CHENEY, R. H.   1934.   Relation of caffein and coffee to human efficiency.   J. Am. Pharm. Assoc. Sci. Ed. *23*, 143–147.

CLELAND, J. E., and SHIVELY, L. R.   1955.   Manufacturing high tinctorial caramel.   U.S. Pat. 2,701,768, Feb. 8.

CROCKER, E. C.   1945.   Flavor. 172 p.   McGraw-Hill Book Company, New York.

DAWSON, E. H. *et al.*   1951.   Sensory methods for measuring differences in food quality.   U.S. Department of Agriculture, Bull. No. 34, Aug., Washington, D.C.

DOMINO, E. F.   1960.   Measuring effects of caffeine.   Univ. of Michigan Medical Center.   Coffee and Tea Inds. *83*, No. 7, 23.

DRAVNIEKS, A.   1961.   Armour research foundation lays groundwork for synthetic nose.   Chem. and Eng. News *39*, No. 14, 56.

DU PONT.   1958.   Physiological properties of furan.   Bull. FC 1-751.   Electrochemicals Department; *also* Furan.   New Products Bull. No. 7.

FETZER, W.   1962.   Caramel manufacturing.   U.S. Pat. 3,020,157.   Standard Brands, Feb. 6.

FOX, S. W., and FOSTER, J. F.   1957.   Introduction to Protein Chemistry.   John Wiley and Sons, New York.

GATES, R. R. 1946. Human Genetics. Vol. II. The Macmillan Company, New York.

GEMMILL, A. V. 1959. Gas chromatography, striking new guide to better foods. Food Eng. *31*, No. 5, 77–83.

GIALLULY, M. 1958. Factors affecting the inherent quality of green coffee. Coffee and Tea Inds. *81*, No. 11, 127–132.

GNAGY, M. J. 1961. Chlorogenic acid in coffee and coffee substitutes. J. Assoc. Official Agri. Chem. *44*, No. 2, 272–275.

GOLDSTEIN, A. 1961. Human sensitivity to caffein; an inherited character. Stanford Univ. Coffee and Tea Inds. *84*, No. 5, 29.

GUY, P. 1950. Odors and sense of chemical smell (bibliography to 1947). Airchem. Inc., 241 East 44 Street, New York.

HAARER, R. J. 1962. Modern Coffee Production. Leonard Hill Ltd., London.

HEYMAN, W. A. 1956. Aroma and flavor in instant coffee. Coffee and Tea Inds. *79*, No. 9, 59.

HOWARD, L. B. 1959. The flavor of food technology. Food Technol. *13*, No. 5, 8–15.

HUGHES, E. B., and SMITH, R. F. 1949. Volatile constituents of roasted coffee. J. Soc. Chem. Ind. *68*, No. 11, 322–327.

JACOBS, M. B. 1949. Coffee flavor. Am. Perfumer Essent. Oil Rev. *53*, 141–142.

JACOBS, M. B. 1949. Coffee flavor components. Am. Perfumer Essent. Oil Rev. *53*, No. 3, 231–232.

KARE, M. R., and HALPERN, B. P. 1961. Physiological and behavioral aspects of taste. University of Chicago Press, Chicago.

KOEHLER, F. A. 1950. Coffee for the armed forces. Historical study, Series II, No. 5, U.S. Army Qm. Corps, Washington, D.C.

KRISCHBAUM, E., and SCHMIDT, H. 1953. Coffee flavor change with grinds. Chem. Ing. Tech. *25*, No. 10, 598–600.

LEE, S. 1960. Carbon dioxide in tea and coffee. Tea and Coffee Trade J. *119*, No. 6, 36–39.

LEE, S. 1962. Chlorogenic acid in coffee. Tea and Coffee Trade J. *123*, No. 1, 13, 39–42.

LEVISALLES, J. 1958. Chemistry of naturally occurring furans. Part I. Perfumery Essent. Oil Record *49*, No. 9, 504–510.

LITTLE, A. D. and ASSOCIATES. 1958. Flavor Research and Food Acceptance. Reinhold Publishing Corporation, New York.

LONGNECKER, J. B., and CLELAND, J. E. 1953. Caramel color compositions. U.S. Pat. 2,651,576, Union Starch Company, Sept. 8.

MABROUK, A. F., and DEATHERAGE, F. E. 1956. Organic acids in brewed coffee. Food Technol. *10*, No. 4, 194–197. *Also* Coffee Brewing Institute (C.B.I.) publication No. 12.[1]

MAITLAND, R. 1936. Alkaloids and tannins in tea and coffee. Analyst *61*, 288–293.

MERRITT, C. 1957. Fresh cabbage volatiles composition; analyses by mass spectrometry. U.S. Army Qm. Corps Research and Eng. Center, Natick, Mass.

MERRITT, C., SULLIVAN, J. H., and RORERTSON, J. H. 1957. Volatile components of coffee aroma. Analytical Report No. 12. U.S. Army QM Corps, Natick, Mass.

MERRITT, M. C., and PROCTOR, B. E. 1959. Effect of temperature during the roasting cycle on selected components of different types of whole bean coffee. Food Research *24*, 672–680. *Also* Coffee Brewing Institute (C.B.I.) publication No. 46.[1]

MIHOLIC, S. S. 1934. Pharmacology and chemistry of coffee drinks. Bull. Soc. Chim. Roy. Yougoslav. *5*, 41–46 (English 46–47).

MINER, C. S. 1934. Acidity of roasted coffee. Nat'l Fed. of Coffee Growers of Colombia, May 25, 120 Wall Street, New York.

MINER, R. W. 1954. Basic odor research correlation. Annals, New York Acad. Sci. *58*, 13, 260.

MONCRIEFF, R. W. 1943. Flavor and food. Food Manufacture *18*, Oct., 342–343.

MONCRIEFF, R. W. 1946. Chemical Senses. John Wiley and Sons, New York.

MONCRIEFF, R. W. 1951. The aroma of coffee. Coffee and Tea Inds. *74*, No. 2, Part I, 11; No. 3, Part II, 17.

MONCRIEFF, R. W. 1958. Olfactory discrimination. Perfumery Essent. Oil Record *49*, No. 1, 27.

MONCRIEFF, R. W. 1950. The aroma of coffee. Food *19*, No. 4, Part I, 124–126; No. 5, Part II, 176–179.

MOORES, R. G. 1948. Chlorogenic acid. Anal. Chem. *20*, 620.

MOORES, R. G., and GRENINGER, D. C. 1951. Determination of trigonelline in coffee. Anal. Chem. *23*, No. 2, 327–331.

NATIONAL COFFEE ASSOCIATION. 1957. Coffee blends for institutions. Coffee and Tea Inds. *80*, No. 5, 12, 37, 49.

PAPASHVILY, H. 1962. Handbook of coffee. Holiday *31*, No. 2, 117–120.

PERYAM, D. R. *et al.* 1957. Food Acceptance Testing. U.S. Armed Services Food and Container Institute, Natick, Mass.

PUNNETT, P. W. 1952. Soluble vs regular coffee. Tea and Coffee Trade J. *102*, No. 2, 15, 29–30, 102.

RHOADES, J. W. 1960. Analysis of volatile constituents of coffee. Agri. and Food Chem. *8*, No. 2, 136. *Also* Coffee Brewing Institute (C.B.I.) publication No. 32.

RHOADES, J. W. 1958. Sampling method for analysis of coffee volatiles by gas chromatography. Food Research *23*, No. 3, 254–261. *Also* Coffee Brewing Institute (C.B.I.) publication No. 34.[1]

RITTER, R. B. 1960. Aroma, key to increased soluble sales. Tea and Coffee Trade J. *119*, No. 3, 24, 28, 87, 94, 95.

ROSENTHAL, J. 1957. Importance of taste in coffee. Tea and Coffee Trade J. *112* No. 2, 18.

SCHWEISHEIMER, W. 1956. Coffee and kidney stones. Tea and Coffee Trade J. *111*, No. 4, 22, 34.

SCHWEISHEIMER, W. 1958. Coffee and the heart. Coffee and Tea Inds. *81*, No. 10, 16, 43.

SCHWEISHEIMER, W. 1956. Effect of caffein on the heart. Tea and Coffee Trade J. *111*, No. 2, 12.

SCHWEISHEIMER, W. 1956. Effects of stimulant beverage. Tea and Coffee Trade J. *111*, No. 3, 18, 38.

SCHWEISHEIMER, W. 1956. Role of caffein in relief of headaches. Tea and Coffee Trade J. *110*, No. 6, 24.

SEGALL, S. 1959. Influence of high temperature holding upon components of coffee brew. Food Technol. *13*, No. 5, 266–270. *Also* Coffee Brewing Institute (C.B.I.) publication No. 41.[1]

SEGALL, S., and PROCTOR, B. E. 1959. Influence of high temperature holding upon components of coffee brew. Food Technol. *13*, No. 12, 679–682. *Also* Coffee Brewing Institute (C.B.I.) publication No. 49.[1]

SIVETZ, M. 1961. Coffee flavor identity and aroma-taste response. Tea and Coffee Inds. *84*, No. 8, 9–10.

SIVETZ, M. 1949. Role of acids in soft beverage flavor. Food Ind. *21*, No. 10, 74–75.

STONE, H., OUGH, C. S., and PANGBORN, R. M. 1962. Determination of odor difference thresholds. J. Food Sci. *27*, No. 2, March–April.

TAYLOR, N. W. *et al.* 1930. Quantitative measurement of acid taste. Protoplasma *10*, 84–97.

TEPLY, L. J., and PRIER, R. F. 1957. Nutritional evaluation of coffee including niacin bioassay. J. Agri. and Food Chem. *5*, No. 5, 375–377. *Also* Coffee Brewing Institute (C.B.I.) publication No. 24.[1]

UKERS, W. A. 1922 and 1935. All about coffee. Tea and Coffee Trade J., 79 Wall Street, New York.

---

[1] See listing of other C.B.I. publications in Chapter 19 Bibliography.

UNDERWOOD, G. E., and DEATHERAGE, F. E. 1952. Amino acids of green and roast coffee. Food Research *17*, No. 5, 425–432.

URIBE, A. 1955. Brown Gold. Random House, New York.

WENZEL, B. M. 1948. Differential sensitivity to olfaction. Thesis, Columbia Univ., New York.

WENZEL, B. M. 1955. Olfactometric method. Science *121*, 802–803.

WENZEL, B. M. 1948. Techniques in olfactometry. Psychol Bull. *45*, 231–247.

WILLIAMS, R. J. 1947. Biochemical individuality and its implication. Chem. and Eng. News *25*, No. 16, 1112–1113.

WINTON, A. L., and WINTON, K. B. 1945. Analysis of Foods. John Wiley and Sons, New York.

WINTON, A. L., and WINTON, K. B. 1939. Structure and Composition of Foods. Vol. IV. John Wiley and Sons, New York.

ZLATKIS, A., and SIVETZ, M. 1960. Analysis of coffee volatiles by gas chromatography. Food Research *25*, 395–398.

CHAPTER 16

Physical Properties of Coffee

A knowledge of the physical as well as chemical properties of coffee at all stages of processing is necessary: (1) to design process equipment; (2) to make material balances for coffee solubles and insolubles; (3) to make heat balances for heat and temperature distributions in the process; and (4) to control and develop processing conditions and products for desired coffee flavor and uniformity.

Quality control tests are closely associated with coffee properties. As coffee is a natural substance, its properties are variable, and it is frequently necessary to state ranges of properties rather than exact figures for constituent concentrations.

The manner of presentation in this chapter is to take the property as, for example, density, and to review densities of coffee from green coffee through roast coffee beans and grind to powder and spent grounds. Extract densities are covered under coffee extract.

This chapter covers coffee densities, light reflectance or color, particle size distribution, granular fluidity, thermal properties, swelling of grounds and water adsorption, solubles availability and extraction, moistures, instant coffee powder solubilities and, finally, extract properties. In addition, there is the factor of cleanliness of the cup of instant coffee as it is affected by sediment, floating specks, dirty cup rings, and oily droplets or films.

DENSITIES

Cherry

The coffee cherry, when it is picked red, has a bulk density of about 50 lb per cu ft; after pulping and fermentation, but while the green beans are still wet (50 per cent moisture), they retain a bulk density of about 50 lb per cu ft. When the green coffee bean in pergamino or hull is dried to about 13 per cent moisture, its bulk density is about 25 lb per cu ft. The dry, hulled, polished green coffee bean has a bulk density of about 44 lb per cu ft.

A recapitulation of the bean weight yield relations from cherry are: 550 lb fresh cherry give 225 lb wet pergamino, which yield 120 lb dry pergamino, and this yields 100 lb dry hulled and polished green coffee beans (wet processing). In dry processing, 550 lb fresh cherry give 200 lb dry cherry and then 100 lb dry hulled and polished green coffee beans.

Green Beans

The absolute dry green bean specific gravities vary from 1.30 for high grown mild coffees to 1.25 for lower grown mild coffees and 1.20 for Brazilian and Robusta coffees.

Roast Beans

Absolute specific gravities will depend on the bean type and the rate and degree of roast, but they are about 60 per cent of the original green bean specific gravities for palatable light roasts, and 50 per cent for medium to dark roasts. Robusta coffees do not swell in volume quite as much as mild coffees on comparable roast colors. The absolute bean specific gravities of Portuguese West African Robusta are more similar to high grown mild coffees than to Grazilian or low grown mild coffees. For example, the denser beans are about 0.1 specific gravity unit more dense before and after the same type roasting. Treatment of green coffee beans, for decaffeination before roasting, causes them to swell less, resulting in greater bulk densities. For example, instead of 18 to 22 lb per cu ft, decaffeinated coffee may be 22 to 26 lb per cu ft, over a comparable roast color range. These swelling differences may be related to differences in chemical composition and physical structure of these beans. Darker roasts, in general, give lighter bulk densities for a given coffee or blend. For example, a 23 lb per cu ft bulk density for a given blend at the lightest roast that is palatable may give 18 lb per cu ft at a dark palatable roast.

Ground Roast Coffee

Grinding invariably raises the bulk density of roast coffee. A more uniform particle size and a more uniform particle size distribution in the bed or column also gives higher bulk densities. Vibration, vacuum loading and other techniques for settling the particles among themselves to minimize void, increase the bulk density of ground roast coffee. For example, vacuum loading R & G coffee into a percolator column increases column loadings about 10 per cent, compared to a natural fall fill. Lower bulk densities occur in smaller diameter vessels (e.g., less than 1 ft) than in larger diameter vessels. This is due to greater wall support for the granular coffee bed in the smaller diameter column. Vibrated coffee beds may increase 15 per cent in bulk density. Finer grinds give denser beds. For example, a coarse grind (25 per cent on 8 mesh) may give 19 lb per cu ft, but a home use regular grind gives 23 lb per cu ft, while a fine grind gives 24 or 25 lb per cu ft. Too fine a grind may become less dense due to its fluffy nature, i.e., entrained air. Moisture content of the roast coffee will affect bulk density. For example, R & G coffee with 6 per cent

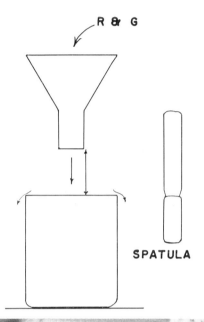

Fig. 273. Apparatus for Density Measurement
of Ground Coffee

moisture is more dense than R & G coffee with no moisture. Localization of chaff can cause very low bulk densities and occurs when fines and chaff accumulate in bin corners. Uniform particle distribution (across the bed diameter of a 2 or 3 ft diameter percolator column) increases loading densities 5 to 10 per cent, and finer grinds may increase loading densities 10 to 15 per cent.

Fine grind coffees give bulk densities of 25 to 30 lb per cu ft, and after vibratory settling, these will rise to 27 to 33 lb per cu ft.

Bulk densities of whole beans can be measured by natural fill or vibratory weight fill of a cubic foot box of beans leveled off at the top or in a large steel beaker (see Fig. 273). Usually natural fall fills are taken be-

Courtesy Syntron Company

FIG. 274. VIBRATING TABLE FOR POWDER BULK
DENSITY MEASUREMENTS

cause that is the way beans or R & G coffee are collected in bins or columns.

In Fig. 273 R & G coffee falls freely from funnel into beaker and overflows. The bottom of the funnel is about 4 to 6 in. above the top of the beaker. Beaker must be of rigidly dimensioned stainless steel, weighed with and without the coffee. The spatula is for leveling the freely fallen pile of grounds on top of the beaker.

Instant Coffee Powder

This bulk density is an important property that is continually monitored and controlled in the spray drying of extract. It can be measured in various ways. The volume of powder sample must be sufficient to give an accurate result. For example, 100 gm of powder are weighed and put into a 1,000 ml accurately indexed Pyrex graduate. The graduate is then placed on a vibratory table or tamping mechanism (see Fig. 274) to obtain the settled powder volume in 15 sec. If this settled powder volume is 500 ml, then the bulk density is 0.20 gm per ml or 12.5 lb per cu ft. Powder bulk densities of 14 to 15 lb per cu ft are used with present packaging practices. Low extract concentrations, low oil contents, and high carbohydrates give powder bulk densities of 10 or 11 lb per cu ft. In the case of extracts heavily laden with oils and fatty acids, bulk densities of 27 lb per cu ft may occur. Packaged instant coffee powders (which have undergone much particle breakage) are about 18 lb per cu ft in the jar. Powder bulk densities are invariably the result of the coffee extract

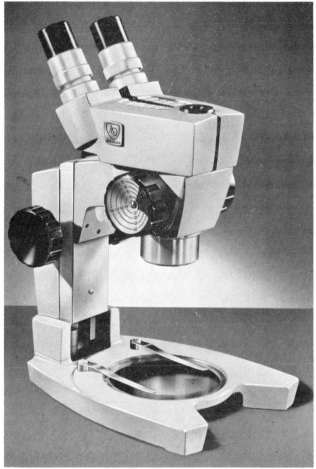

Courtesy American Optical Company

FIG. 275. STEREO-MICROSCOPE

properties. The appearance of the particles (and their screen analysis) can be seen under a stereo-microscope, see Fig. 275. High powder bulk densities due to fines give the powder poor fluidity. Low bulk densities with discrete beady particles usually have good fluidity. Agglomerated particles give lower powder bulk densities and poor fluidity. Figure 276 shows one means of measuring powder fluidity.

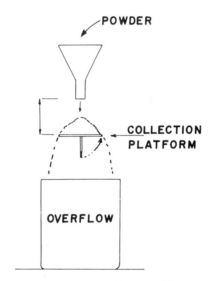

FIG. 276. APPARATUS FOR FLUIDITY MEASUREMENT
OF GRANULAR MATERIAL

Powder falls freely from a funnel onto an accurately leveled and dimensioned disc. The less fluid the powder, the more it accumulates on the disc. Powder density variations must be taken into account. The bottom of the funnel and the accumulating disc must be maintained at a set distance. The accumulated powder is tipped into a collection cup for weighing to obtain the fluidity index.

COLOR: ROAST, GROUND, AND INSTANT COFFEES

Ever since green coffee beans have been roasted, the degree of coffee flavor development in the roaster has been judged by the color reaching the eye. And, in fact, roast bean color by eye is a fair criterion of coffee flavor development, especially when one is working with a given green coffee. Since the end of World War II, there has been some use and limited acceptance of reflectance of light from ground, screened, and smoothed surface roast coffee particles as measured by a photoelectric cell. Lockhart (1960A), Little and Mackinney (1956), Little, Mackinney, and Chichester (1958 and 1959), and Little (1960) describe the work done on coffee color. Brody and Bedrosian (1959) use light reflectance measurements on other foods. In brief, the light intensity cell transforms the reflected light into an electrical voltage and is at least as sensitive as the eye; it gives a numerical reflectance value as a point of reference useful for day-to-day, month-to-month control. The eye cannot give a numerical reference point. The one limitation to an economical light intensity measurement is the color spectrum being examined. Roast coffee beans have different colors, depending on blend, age, moisture, and other factors. Therefore, to obtain a comparable light intensity measurement for varying colors, the light source must be a compromise representing the majority of the coffee roast colors encountered. This is not accurately possible. However, the Photovolt Corporation of New York has made a tri-stimulus glass filter to give an acceptable light spectrum for such practical work. The light reflectance measurements are useful and accurate as long as reference coffee sample measurements are made frequently enough.

A major problem in applying light reflectance measurements lies in the preparation of the ground coffee samples. The outside surfaces of roast beans are not a good index of the degree of bean roast. They can be dark on the outside but much lighter on the inside, as well as the reverse. For color comparison by eye, the bean sample must be ground and spread on a tray next to the control sample, preferably in daylight. Since some fluorescent lighting does not give a natural light spectrum, comparisons of grounds by daylight are invariably better than by electric lights at night.

For the light reflectance meter it does not matter whether the surroundings are day or night. Figure 277 shows the instrument and the reflectance probe. Usually a porcelainized plate of suitable reflectance is used as a standard.

For duplication of reflectance results, the ground coffee should be screened to obtain a uniform particle size; for example, through 30 mesh, on 40 mesh. Furthermore, the selected grounds fraction should be gently purged with air to remove any chaff, which is light colored and will give a high reflectance reading. Then the screened fraction which is free of chaff is compressed to about 1,000 psig on a Carver press (Fig. 278) to form a disc 2 in. in diameter and about $1/4$ in. thick in a steel plate. Compression of the fine particles orients them and forms a smooth reflecting surface. Compression must not be so great that oil is released to the surface of the particles for this will cause a low reflectance reading. The reflectance probe is placed directly on the smooth coffee grounds surface for the reading. The probe lens should have no fines or dust to interfere with the passage of reflected light. Care should be taken to have fresh reference coffee samples because oil comes to the surface of roast beans that are stored for several days. Roast coffee reflectance standards are altered to accommodate the best flavor results as well as changes in blend and moisture.

The preparation and measurement of reflectance color by this means takes some effort and time. But in any medium to large roast coffee operation where uniformity is important, this method is useful. For example, in instant coffee processing, a small darkening in the roast can increase fatty acid content of extract and change atomizing performance.

Roast colors will vary from any single roaster, but color variations are

Courtesy Photovolt Corporation

FIG. 277.   LIGHT REFLECTANCE PROBE AND INSTRUMENT

somewhat greater with batch than with continuous roasters. The objective is to prevent the range of roast color variance from being so great that taste differences are noted. A deviation of one shade from standard reflectance is not too serious, but two shades definitely reveals flavor changes.

The equipment for taking roast coffee light reflectance measurements are: (1) Model 610 Photovolt reflection meter with amber tri-stimulus filter and calibrated standard enamel reflector. (2) A Carver laboratory press, with a 2-in. diameter by 1-in. high cylinder of steel. (3) Several dozen steel blocks $3/8$ in. deep, with $2^1/_{16}$ in. circle, $1/_4$ in. deep. (4) W. S. Tyler Ro-Tap or equivalent with 30 and 40 mesh screens (see Fig. 279).

(5) Laboratory grinder and chaff air blower. Spatula for leveling R & G coffee.

The same reflectance probe and instrument can be used to measure the reflectance of spray dried instant coffee powder. Since such powders are dusty, however, the powder is placed in a clean glass beaker with flat bottom and the sample in the beaker is placed on the upright probe. Care must be taken that no fine dust disproportionately adheres to the bottom glass surface, because this causes more light reflectance.

Powder light reflectance as a numerical index of color is measured to determine uniformity of production as well as to compare reflectance in

Courtesy Fred S. Carver Inc.

FIG. 278.   CARVER HYDRAULIC PRESS

color with competitors' products. Here again, reflectance is measured by the tri-stimulus light source, and does not indicate differences in coffee color spectrum. For example, some instant coffee powders are reddish while others are tan; such light spectrum differences are not differentiated on this instrument. Redness may reveal itself only as a darker color with less light reflectance.   The oil-surfaced instant coffee powders are much darker than those to which oil is not added.   Powders, before oil addition, that are light in color usually have many fines.   Instant coffee powder color or light reflectance is *not* an indication of roast color but only of the physical particle size of the spray dried powder.   For example, a dark roast instant coffee may have a very light powder color because the particles are fine.   Nescafé has been an example of this type of instant coffee. On the other hand, a light roast instant coffee may form dark beady particles.

Courtesy W. S. Tyler Company

FIG. 279.   SCREENING ROTARY TAPPING MACHINE

The crushing of beady particles results in more light reflectance, and consequently lighter colored powders.   Screening of particles shows the fines to be light colored and the coarse beady particles to be dark.   The public tends to prefer darker powders, possibly because they resemble the familiar appearance of roast coffee.   Agglomerates of fine particles give a light appearance.   An oily fine powder may be darker than a non-oily large beaded powder.   High carbohydrate content as from a 100 per cent Robusta instant coffee at a 40 per cent solubles yield from R & G coffee gives lighter particles and more light reflectance than similar sized particles from lesser yields and other blends. Light powder densities of 12 lb per cu ft are smashed to 17 lb per cu ft which results in very light colored, dusty powders. Selgin (1962) has placed on the market a 3-color line spectrum recorder which is useful for confirming color contours of color lithographed labels, caps, and so on. Figure 280 shows the Photovolt unit being used for the same purpose.

Courtesy Coffee & Tea Industries magazine

FIG. 280. LIGHT REFLECTANCE FROM COLORED LABEL

PARTICLE SIZE DISTRIBUTION

Green Coffee Bean Sizes and Shapes

Bean sizes and shapes vary as discussed in Chapter 7 in the section on green coffee. In Brazil, coffees are classified by screens. No. 20 is a very large bean; No. 19 is an extra large bean; No. 18 is a large bean; No. 17 is a bold bean; No. 16 is a good bean; No. 15 is a medium bean; and Nos. 13 and 14 are small beans. Figure 271 in Chapter 15 shows the actual hole sizes and dimensions. Pea-berries are classified over slotted screened holes, Nos. 9 to 13, as shown in Fig. 271. Other coffee growing countries have their own bean size standards. Mild coffee beans are, in general, larger in size than Brazilian beans. Bean lengths are 7 to 11 mm; widths are 6 to 7 mm; boldness is 3 to 5 mm with most beans close to 4 mm. Beans weigh 0.1 to 0.2 gm each, averaging about 0.15 gm, see Haarer (1962) p. 258.

Roasting coffee causes about a 16 per cent weight loss and a 50 to 80 per cent increase in bean volume. The resulting bean dimensions may be determined from this volume increase.

Ground Coffee

Figure 281 shows cumulative screen analyses of grinds ranging from cracked beans to those used in commercial percolation as well as in the home. Figure 282 shows the weighing of screened fractions of roast coffee. Knowledge of ground coffee screen analyses is important in the processing of soluble coffee to guard against excessive pressure drops in the water flow through the percolator bed.

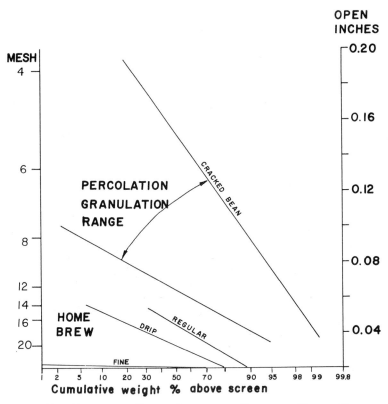

FIG. 281. CUMULATIVE SCREEN ANALYSES OF DIFFERENT COFFEE GRINDS

Figure 279 shows the RO-Tap machine used for screen analyses. Three screen fractions such as on 8 mesh, and through 20 mesh are sufficient to know the quality of the grind. If, for example, there are 5 or more per cent through 20 mesh in a grind used for plant percolation, this may cause some flow difficulties depending on process conditions. Usually a 3-min rotary tapping of a 50 gm ground coffee sample gives the desired weight fractions. Grinder samples should be run every few hours. The

U.S. Department of Commerce lists standard coffee grinds in Table 41, Chapter 8, Vol. I.

Instant Coffee

A similar screen analysis can be made using finer screens for instant coffee powder; for example, 40 and 80 mesh. Beady spray dried powders have 10 to 35 per cent on 40 mesh and up to 10 per cent through 80 mesh. After jar packaging by vacuum tamping this same powder analysis is only about 1 to 10 per cent on 40 mesh and as much as 30 per cent through 80 mesh.

Courtesy National Coffee Association—U.S.A.

FIG. 282. WEIGHING SCREENED FRACTIONS OF ROAST COFFEE

To evaluate spray drying results and possible influences of extract properties, screen analyses of powders while spray drying give useful data in conjunction with powder bulk densities and microscopic examination of particles. Agglomerated particles give high on 40 mesh weight fractions, but the quality of the particles and fluidity must be examined. The 40 mesh opening corresponds to about 350 mu and the 80 mesh opening to about 180 mu.

An example of a beady spray dried powder is about 5 per cent of 600 mu, 10 per cent of 500 mu, 20 per cent of 400 mu, 25 per cent of 300 mu, 25 per cent of 200 mu, 10 per cent of 100 mu, and 5 per cent of 50 mu and less.

An intrinsic property of fine particles is their large surface per unit weight; 1 gm of powder averaging 200 mu in diameter has a total surface of about 1 sq meter. Hartman (1939) states that as particles are made finer, their physical and chemical nature changes markedly when the ratio of surface to apparent volume exceeds 10,000. Soluble coffee particles are in this order of magnitude. It is simple to demonstrate that (1) on 40 mesh, (2) through 40 mesh on 80 mesh, and (3) through 80 mesh, instant coffee powders each taste different.

INSTANT COFFEE POWDER SOLUBILITY

Until 100 per cent coffee in the form of spray dried beady particles was placed on the market in 1951, the extracted coffee solubles were called "soluble coffee product." They were termed "soluble" because they were water soluble—slowly, not instantly—and "coffee product" because they had about 50 per cent carbohydrates. However, when the 100 per cent beady powder appeared, it was named instant coffee because it dissolved in boiling water in a few seconds, while the earlier powders did not. Instant coffees from spray driers dissolve quickly down to 150 F (66 C). Some instant coffees dissolve fairly quickly at 120 F (49 C), but none except the foam or pseudo-freeze dried flakes dissolves instantly in 60 F (16 C) water. Normally, if an instant coffee dissolves in less than 10 sec upon addition of boiling water, it is considered fast enough. But sometimes instant coffees do not dissolve in 30 sec, or a minute, or even longer. To dissolve the powder, it should be placed in the cup and boiling water should be poured over it. The powder is not to be placed in the boiling water because more lumps may form.

If the water has not boiled, it contains dissolved air. This gives the resulting instant coffee a flat taste, and it also makes rapid and complete solubility more difficult. The undissolved particles absorb moisture and trap air bubbles which prevent some powder from being wetted. These clumps of powder float about the cup without dissolving and often leave a residual foam. High percentages of fines also hold air so that they do not wet and dissolve. Poor solubility is often caused, in part, by high carbohydrates (high hydrolysis yields) and low fatty acids. The latter help to break up the foam.

Agglomerated fine particles dissolve quickly because they are fused together. The thicker walled larger beady particles also dissolve well since they have less surface per unit weight for air adsorption. Shutdown powders[1] which have high carbohydrate contents usually have poor water solubility. Mixing powders with good and poor solubility does not improve the poorer solubility fraction very much. Powders resulting from extracts with concentrations over 30 per cent usually have better solubilities than those from extracts containing less than 30 per cent solubles due to the thicker walls and larger sizes of particles formed. Powders that have had considerable particle breakage and increase in bulk density during packaging usually have poorer solubilities. Reworking powders with poor solubility usually is at less than 20 per cent and often at less than 10 per cent levels. This is, the normal product will tolerate only these levels of reworked substandard powder without noticeable damage to quality.

WATER SOLUBLES FROM GREEN AND ROAST COFFEE

The fraction of coffee solubles that will dissolve in boiling water from green and roast coffees varies somewhat with type of coffee and degree of roast. Even different lots of the same variety of green coffee or lots with different moistures give somewhat different yields of solubles. Green coffees contain about 26 per cent solubles and Robustas, about 2 per cent more. Water extraction of green coffee is slow; grinding of the green beans hastens the operation.

Grinding Roast Coffee Finely

The fineness of roast coffee grind influences the solubles yield due to the increased release of oily-proteinaceous colloids from exposed surfaces. However, in darker roasts, coffee solubles decrease 2 or 3 per cent from about 26 per cent in the palatable range of roasts. Decaffeinated coffees due to solubles losses during decaffeination give 2 to 3 per cent less solubles than before decaffeination. Before attaining very dark roasts, solubles yields rise about 1 per cent before they fall. This might be partly caused by resolubilization of celluloses, carbohydrates, and denatured proteins. Darker roasts have less volatile and titratable acidity. This can be discerned from odor, pH measurements, and taste.

Breakdown of roast coffee bean cells speeds up solubles extraction and increases solubles yields. For example, boiling water can remove 35 per cent solubles from pulverized roast coffee beans. The increased solubility is due to the breakdown of the coffee bean cell structure, allowing free solution without the necessity for diffusion of molecules and colloids out of the cells.

---

[1] Powder obtained when stopping the operation.

Molecular Size of Solubles

The coffee bean cells are about 30 mu in diameter. The boiling point temperature rise and freezing temperature depression for coffee extract solubles are quite small. This means that most of the solubles have rather high molecular weights. The concentrated, cold extracts are viscous. Some hydrolyzed solubles have large molecular weights also. This can be measured by diffusion experiments through calibrated permeable membranes such as Visking plastic dialysis sheets.

When considering water solubility data, the grind and modes of extraction are important. Some water soluble molecules are within the particle cells, but are too large to diffuse out rapidly, if at all. These large molecules can be dissolved only by opening the cell walls. The greater the number of cell walls opened, the greater the solubles yield without hydrolysis. The finer the grind, the greater is the percentage of cells ruptured. Figure 145 (Chapter 10) shows the percolation concentration profile and gradual transition from hydrolysis to extraction with finer grinds.

Because of the buildup of non-diffusible water soluble molecules (too large to diffuse readily into the coffee cell) in the extract moving from water feed, there are more large molecules in the extract solubles outside the roast coffee particles than within. This phenomenon can be measured by mixing a dextrose (30 D.E.) solution and coffee grounds. The dextrose portion is diffusible; the partially hydrolyzed large starch molecules are not as diffusible. Dextrose has a molecular weight of 198 and is 10 A long, while caffeine has a molecular weight of 194 and is 15 A long.[2] The 30 mu cell is 30 by 10^4 A but permeability through the cell wall, i.e., the size of the cell openings, may be only a fraction of this or a few hundred Angstroms. The caramelized molecules and hydrolyzed molecules are hundreds of Angstroms in size.

Temperature and time of extraction are not important variables with pulverized roast coffee. Temperature and time of diffusion of solubles are important variables with coarser particles.

Ternary Equilibrium Diagram for Water Solubles and Insolubles

Solubles equilibrium between coffee grounds and extract is a physical phenomenon. This has been covered in Chapter 10. It is amplified in this section to show that perhaps 50 per cent of the coffee solubles will not diffuse back into the grounds. This results in a higher solubles concentration outside the coffee grounds. Solubles equilibrium occurs with the wet (not dry) coffee grounds (see Fig. 283). The equilibrium line

---

[2] For unit conversion factors, see Table 104, Appendix III.

varies slightly with the amount of non-diffusibles solubles in the free extract and with the grind used. Solubilization of large molecules, such as those of corn syrup and coffee extract, forms a true solution. Solubles yield is increased by several per cent by the presence of colloids. Before molecular solubles (large or small) or colloids can move away from the ground coffee particles, the roast cell walls must be wet and absorb about one-third their roast weight in water.

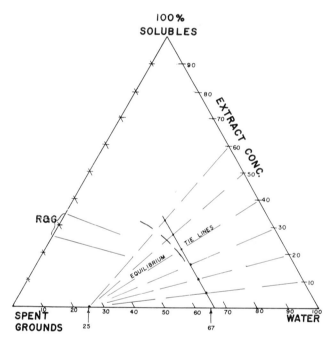

FIG. 283. TERNARY EQUILIBRIUM DIAGRAM FOR WATER AND COFFEE

Wetting

Selective water absorption concentrates the adjacent extract. The adjacent extract is concentrated in three ways: (1) by selective water absorption; (2) by the inability of non-diffusible solubles to enter the cells; and (3) by the surface contribution of non-diffusible solubles. Selective water absorption by coffee grounds is about four times greater from a sucrose solution than from a salt solution. Salt ions hold water more strongly. Selective water absorption by the coffee grounds in the percolator accounts for about a 3 per cent concentration rise which would otherwise not occur. The wetting and swelling give off a little heat and cause about a 7 per cent increase in roast coffee particle size. This can be seen under a microscope with a calibrated slide. In a coffee bed, this particle swelling fills the interstitial void.

Hardness of Wet Coffee Particles

Compressibility of a bed of grounds is related to the fineness of grind and the degree of breakdown of the cellular wall structure. The bed of wet coffee grounds is more compressible with finer grinds, darker roasts, and higher hydolysis yields of soluble components. Easier compressibility results in reduced interstitial voids for extract flow with subsequent cumulative sealing off of flow passages. Such compressive forces of granular beds become effective with fine grinds at 50 psig differentials. Brown, (1950) covers some of these flow and pressure differential factors.

MOISTURES: GREEN, ROAST, AND INSTANT COFFEES

Green coffee contains about 13 per cent moisture when it leaves the coffee growing country and usually a few per cent less when it is processed in the consuming country. Punnett (1959, 1961, and 1962) has measured the equilibrium moistures of green, roast, and instant coffees at various air relative humidities, and these are listed in summary form in Table 85. The rates of moisture absorption and liberation vary with

TABLE 85

RELATIVE HUMIDITY OF AIR VS MOISTURES FOR GREEN, ROAST, AND SOLUBLE COFFEES[1]

Relative Humidity of Air	Per Cent Moistures at 68 to 78 F (20 to 26 C)		
	Green Beans	Roast Beans	Soluble Coffee Powder
95	25 to 28	25	. . .
84	16 to 19	17	25
76	13 to 16	9	20
66	11 to 14	9	15
55	10 to 12	6.7	12
43	8 to 11	5.1	10
33	7.5 to 11	4.3	6
23	6.7 to 7.4	3.6	5.5
9	4.7 to 6.3	3.1	5.2
0	3.2 to 4.2	1.7	3.9

[1] Summarized data of Punnett, P. W. (1959). Tests were carried out over a three month period.

temperature, air circulation, and other factors. Soluble coffee absorbs moisture up to equilibrium in hours to days and roast coffee does this in days to weeks. Green coffee equilibrates more slowly. The rates of moisture absorption are usually much faster than the rates of desiccation. With greater water holding capacity in air at warmer temperatures, faster rates of moisture absorption occur. Green coffee, that has been stored for months to years in a lower temperature and lower relative humidity than those in equilibrium with twelve per cent moisture will have its moisture reduced to perhaps 8 per cent. New crop coffees have the highest moisture consistent with safe bagging and exporting. Past crop coffees are bleached or dark and much lower than 10 per cent in moisture if storage conditions have been dry.

Measuring Moisture

To obtain green coffee moistures from whole beans is a slow process. Therefore, it is usually desirable to grind the coffee before making oven moistures or toluene distillations. There are several instruments that are used for measuring moisture of grains and these usually work by measuring dielectric strength. They should be calibrated against toluene or oven moistures periodically. Once calibrated, they give quick and reasonably reliable results. Some of these instruments are Seedburo or Steinilite, Moisture Register or Tagliabue, Division, Weston Instruments. The Universal measures the conductivity of a pellet compressed in a standard manner, and the Alladin II by Klock, Incorporated, uses a direct weighing and the infra-red heating of a small ground sample to obtain results in a few minutes. As it is not uncommon even with toluene and oven moistures to obtain somewhat variable moistures, moisture allowances and the use of sample references are always good practice.

Roast coffee moistures are also run by toluene reflux (1 to 2 hr) or oven (24 hr). With heater standardization coffee grounds can have their moisture measured on an Ohaus electric coiled balance (see Fig. 284) or Genco Infra-red lamp balance in 20 to 30 min.

Courtesy Ohaus Scale Corporation

Fig. 284. Moisture Balance

Roasted coffee normally has hardly any moisture unless it has been water quenched. Some vacuum packed coffees have up to 3 per cent moisture, which causes them to stale faster once the can is opened. Some soluble coffee processing operations use even higher roast coffee bean moistures to keep fines low during grinding as well as to pre-moisten the particle fibers for better wetting during percolation. The 20 to 30 min heat balance moisture methods are accurate enough for such moistures. This method can also be used on partially dried spent coffee grounds, but may need the full 30 min heating on the balance. The heat balances can usually be adjusted so that the rate of heating can be altered to suit the sample being dried. For example, soluble coffee would have a gentle rate of heating, while moist spent grounds would have a higher rate. Drying rate curves can be run to set the best rate of heating without carbonizing or liberating bound moisture. Soluble coffee powders usually have less than 4 per cent moisture. Spent coffee grounds may have 70 per cent moisture initially and as low as 15 per cent after drying. Soluble coffee powder moistures can also be measured by benzene or toluene reflux in cases of verification (see Association Official Agricultural Chemists, A.O.A.C.). Duck and Gross (1957) and Elder (1949) consider humidity-carbohydrate moisture equilibria.

Spray dried powders should have their moistures recorded about once an hour even if drier operating conditions appear normal. At comfortable temperatures the relative humidity in the room where moistures are measured must be less than 40 per cent. Otherwise the powder during sampling and weighing absorbs enough moisture to give high results as, for example, 4.0 per cent when moisture is really 3.0 per cent.

Depending on moisture and composition, instant coffee powders can fuse at temperatures above 145 F (63 C) in a few hours. Fusion may occur in less than an hour at 160 F (71 C). Temperatures of 130 F (54 C) may cause instant powder fusion in less than 24 hr. Powder fusion in a glass jar causes the fused mass to shrink and pull away from the wall. It is possible to use two per cent calcium gluconate or "Micro-cel" (calcium silicate) for moisture absorption in instant coffee powders (see Denboske, 1962).

THERMAL PROPERTIES OF COFFEE

Design of any equipment that heats or cools coffee requires a reasonable knowledge of the associated thermal changes. Many of these have already been covered under roasting and spray drying, but the thermal properties will be summarized here.

Heat of Wetting.—Coffee moisture is mostly free, but since heat is liberated in wetting dry green, dry roast, and dry solubles, it indicates that some percentage of the coffee holds the water in strong physical or chemical combination (bound water). Hougen and Watson (1936) give about 2 to 5 cal per gm (4 to 9 Btu per lb) for heat of wetting of cellulose.

Heat Capacity.—For green or roast coffee, heat capacity can be taken as about 0.4. Coffee compositions and (specific heats) are: $1/10^3$ water (1.0); $1/10$ oil (0.45); 0.4 cellulose (0.32); and 0.3 carbohydrate (0.3). Extract specific heat can be approximately calculated by using (0.4) for solubles and (1.0) for water at different concentrations.

Heat of Pyrolysis.—The heat liberated in roasting pyrolysis can be approximated from the amount of CO_2 liberated (for example, 4.0 per cent, or about 100 cal per gm green coffee or 180 Btu per lb green coffee). The exothermic heat depends on the degree of roast. Darker roasts may give up 300 Btu per lb. Roasting coffee is mainly pyrolysis, not oxidation.

Heat of Combustion.—Burning of spent coffee grounds is oxidation. The heat liberated per unit weight can be estimated from the constituents of the grounds: 15 to 20 per cent oil; the rest is mostly cellulose. This gives about 9,000 to 10,000 Btu per lb dry grounds, based on 18,000 Btu per lb for oil and 8,000 Btu per lb for cellulose.

Heats of Solution.—Carbohydrates liberate about 3 to 5 cal per gm (5 to 9 Btu per lb) of solubles. It is about the same for coffee solubles, depending on the degree of dilution. Since the initial water added to carbohydrates is held more securely, there are higher heats of solution evolved from higher concentration extracts (e.g., 30 to 40 per cent) than lower concentration extracts (e.g., 0 to 10 per cent). This means dilution would absorb heat slightly or cool the solution.

CLEANLINESS OF CUP OF INSTANT COFFEE

Some general articles on this subject have been published by Daly (1955) and Iacano (1957). Instant coffee in the cup is expected to be clear with no floating nor sedimentary particles, no oil slicks and no cup rings. Also, the beverage should not be turbid nor foamy. To meet all these requirements is sometimes difficult and some allowances have to be made.

Floating Oil Slicks.—These are undesirable, but with many of the coffee oil "aromatized" instants, tiny oil droplets are characteristic of the beverage cup. Dark roast coffees and fine grinds sometimes allow enough oil into the extract to cause small slicks. This oil carries considerable amounts of coffee flavor through spray drying.

---

[3] Ten per cent coffee, 90 per cent water.

Floating Specks.—These are usually black and are most often due to powder buildup on the drier walls which has been burnt or carbonized. Direct-fired carbonized fuel may also cause floating specks. The black carbon specks, and sometimes coffee powder agglomerates are objectionable foreign matter. They are especially noticeable in a cup of coffee with cream or milk. These specks usually do not alter coffee flavor and often are very minute. Inspection of spray dried powder for such floating specks by addition of milk to the cup is a routine test.

Foam.—This is often due to high hydrolysis solubles yields and low oil content. Robusta coffees are often associated with a foamy cup on pouring. Foam that disappears in 5 to 10 sec is not objectionable, but is undesirable when it lasts for several minutes. Foam that persists on cups of espresso coffee is sometimes sought; otherwise it is undesirable. Even in an espresso cup, foam is undesirable in taste and appearance when Robustas are in the blend. A foamy extract spray dries to give golden specks in the powder.

Turbidity.—This is seldom encountered in soluble coffees unless it is contributed by (1) the oil content or dark roasts; (2) oil add-back in aromatized coffee; or (3) freeze dried brew colloids.

Cup Ring.—This is frequently related to foam. It is a surface tension phenomenon that seems to draw insoluble substances to the cup wall. Removal of extract tars by centrifuging also removes oils (and flavor), results in excessive foam, and gives light bulk powder densities.

Foam and Cup Ring.—Cup rings are not infrequently associated with foamy rings. The tars tend to cling to the cup wall presenting an unsightly appearance. The cup rings are often very difficult to wash out. Tars can be minimized by (1) taking lesser hydrolysis yields; (2) eliminating Robustas from the blend; and (3) settling out the tars. Centrifuging to remove the tars usually removes most of the coffee oil but tars settled in extract can minimize the cup ring yet not remove so much cup flavor. Settled tars can represent several per cent of extract volume. Some tars are oily and occlude air so that they float on the extract. Complete tar and oil removal causes poor powder solubilities and foams. Foam color can be tan to black. The tan foams are usually associated with Robusta blends. Black particulate tar rings may occur in any blend. Blends and light roasts that will contribute to instant coffee foaming can often be anticipated from brews prepared from the same roast coffee. A high ferric iron contamination also causes a black cup ring. Foam and cup rings are sometimes contributed by a cumulative series of circumstances. For example, separate factors such as high extract drawoff temperatures, channeling of extract, or too short a settling time for the extract before spray drying may cause tar rings on the cup.

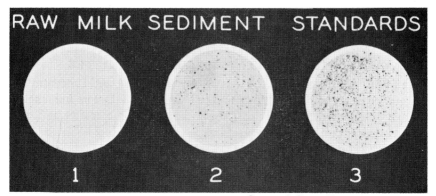

Courtesy Sediment Testing Supply Company

FIG. 285. SEDIMENT DISK FILTER STANDARDS

Sediment in the Cup.—This is usually due to fine particles of roast coffee and is sometimes due to tars. A good procedure for measuring sediment content is to filter instant coffee through milk disk filter paper under aspirator suction. Insolubles are caught on the filter paper disk, and the number and size of particles can be compared to the milk standard disks 1, 2, and 3. Instant coffees should be like standard disk 1, seldom like 2, and never like 3. Figures 285 and 286 show the standard

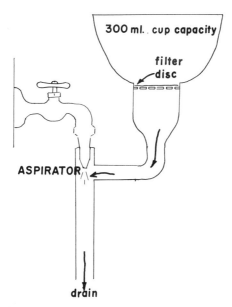

FIG. 286. APPARATUS FOR PREPARING VACUUM FILTER
SEDIMENT DISK

paper filter disks and the filter cup apparatus. There is a distinct difference between specks that float and are examined on a milk and coffee surface and sediment that settles to the bottom of the cup.

LIGHT TRANSMISSION THROUGH BREWED COFFEE

This will be influenced by the degree of roast, blend, and concentration of solubles in the cup. Turbidity and pH will also be factors influencing the amount of light transmission. Dark roasts have less acidity and give a much darker cup color. Robusta coffees, which are less acid, also give a much darker cup color.

The visible light transmission spectrum for coffee solubles, regardless of the source of coffee, is similar. The color spectrum is also similar to that for caramel and amber glass (Amerine and Cruess, 1960). Figure 287 illustrates such a curve in the visual spectrum from red (7,000 A)

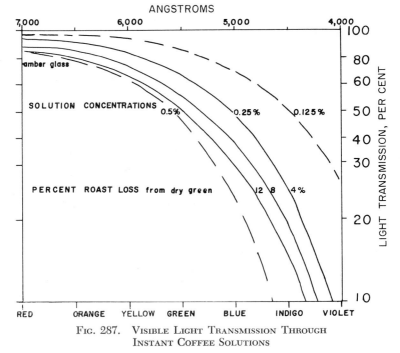

Fig. 287. Visible Light Transmission Through Instant Coffee Solutions

to violet (4,000 A). Since brown is the dominant color of coffee, most of the transmission of light wave lengths occurs in the red to yellow region with least light transmission in the violet to blue region. The roasted coffee with only 4 per cent dry weight loss allows more light through than the coffee with 8 per cent dry weight loss, which in turn allows more light through than the 12 per cent dry weight loss. This corresponds to weight losses from "as is" green beans of 14, 18, and 22 per cent, respectively. There is a pH change which is about 5.0, 5.15, and 5.30, respectively. The magnitude of change in per cent light transmission with such differences in roast weight losses is small and varies over the spectrum. It is equivalent to about one-third to one-half of the effect of doubling solubles concentration from the median value (0.25 per cent solubles) of 4 per cent dry weight loss.

Deschreider and Driessche (1946) describe an empirical technique for measuring the degree of roast loss by light transmission, and show a good correlation. Menezes (1955), Gal (1959), and Mossel (1947)

Courtesy Klett Manufacturing Company

Fig. 288.   Light Transmission Comparator (Dual Tube)

discuss similar roast loss measurement methods. Deschreider's coffee extraction technique takes a little longer than measuring light reflectance of R & G coffee as described earlier, but is certainly a practical method. A standard coffee solution is used as reference in Deschreider's Stammer colorimeter which is similar to a Klett or du Bosque comparator as shown in Fig. 288. This type of comparator colorimeter is used in the sugar refining and caramel manufacturing processes for color control purposes. In the case of a Beckman spectrophotometer, light transmissions can be made at any wave length from a rotating prism. In most instances, coffee solution light transmission measurements at 1 wave length in the portion of highest light absorption area may be sufficient, з.g., blue at 510 mmu or 5,100 A or 430 mmu indigo-violet. Using 1 wave length of light (filter) simplifies the measurement. An economical instrument that can be used for this purpose is shown in Fig. 289; others are made by Bausch & Lomb Optical Company, Klett Manufacturing Company, and Photovolt Corporation.

The use of glass color standards is not accurate unless the glass spectrum standard corresponds reasonably well with the spectrum of coffee. Such a glass standard can be prepared by the manufacturer at nominal cost. Glass color standards have been prepared for caramel which has a slightly different spectrum from coffee, depending on its mode of preparation.

Courtesy Bausch & Lomb Inc.

FIG. 289.   MONOCHROMATIC LIGHT TRANSMISSION INSTRUMENT
(340 TO 950 MMU)

Most instant coffees at a concentration of $1/4$ per cent at 430 mmu wave length allow 18 to 22 per cent light transmission, whereas at 510 mmu at $1/4$ per cent there is about 50 to 60 per cent light transmission. Such light transmission measurements can be useful in comparing competitive brew cup color intensities. For example, for lower priced instant coffees (used in some vending machines and under private labels) a dark beverage color is desired with the least weight of instant coffee. A dark roast coffee can easily effect a solubles reduction in the cup of 25 per cent as far as matching beverage light transmission is concerned. Such competitive light transmissions of beverage are also influenced by pH; Robustas are less acid and darker in cup. High hydrolysis yields of soluble components increase light transmission by dilution of the light absorbing constituents.

Beer's law (Glasstone, 1940), in regard to transmitted light, states that halving the brew concentration (or thickness) doubles the per cent of light transmitted.

LIGHT REFRACTION

Light is refracted in passing through a sucrose solution or a coffee extract solution. For sucrose degree Brix (density) is the same as per cent sucrose in solution and can be read also from a refractometer. For coffee solubles in extract, degree Brix readings from a refractometer are about 15 per cent higher. That is, 30° Brix is closer to 25.5 per cent coffee solubles, or 60° Brix is closer to 51 per cent coffee solubles. The degree Brix-per cent solubles relation does not vary much for all practical purposes with different blends, roasts, and yields. At any rate, no such exhaustive study has yet been reported. Accountability of coffee solubles in process is very much dependent on this relationship. Figure 116 shows a hand refractometer for 0 to 60° Brix; Fig. 117 (Chapter 9) shows an in-line refractometer. There are also recording instruments that will record soluble solids from continuously monitored extract flow streams, but these units cost around $5,000, and the expense is seldom justified.

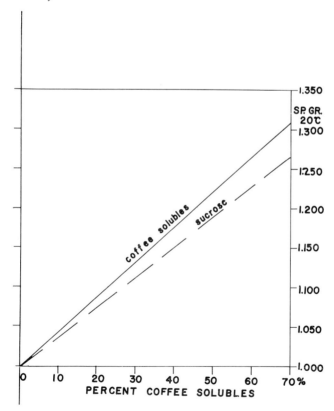

FIG. 290. SPECIFIC GRAVITY OF SUCROSE AND COFFEE SOLUTIONS

SPECIFIC GRAVITY OF COFFEE EXTRACT

This is a function of the solubles content and is about 1.5 to 2.5 per cent higher than sucrose. This means that the water is held more tightly. For example, a 27 per cent sucrose solution has a specific gravity of 1.100 at 60 F (16 C), but 1.115 for coffee solubles. A 53 per cent sucrose solution has a specific gravity of 1.200 at 60 F (16 C), and 1.230 for coffee solubles.

Specific gravity can be readily calculated from cumulative composition. For example, a 32 per cent coffee solubles solution using a 1.60 specific gravity for pure coffee solubles (or carbohydrates) will give 0.20 ml gravity equivalent for solubles. The 0.68 ml water with the same gravity equivalent gives a total of 0.88 ml or a specific gravity of

TABLE 86

COFFEE EXTRACT CONVERSION TABLE—ABBREVIATED

°Brix	Per Cent Solubles	Specific Gravity, 60 F (16 C)	Weight Ratio, Water/ Solubles	Extract Weight, per gal	Weight Powder, lb per gal	Gal Water	Ml Extract for 2 gm Solubles
2	1.8	1.009	54.5	...	...	...	...
4	3.4	1.016	28.3	...	...	...	...
6	5.0	1.024	19.0	8.53	0.43	0.97	39.0
8	6.5	1.030	14.4	8.58	0.56	0.96	30.0
10	8.3	1.037	11.0	8.62	0.72	0.95	23.2
12	9.6	1.043	9.4	8.68	0.83	0.94	20.0
14	11.4	1.050	7.8	8.75	1.00	0.93	16.7
16	13.0	1.056	6.7	8.79	1.14	0.92	14.6
18	14.8	1.064	5.8	8.86	1.31	0.91	12.7
20	16.5	1.071	5.1	8.93	1.47	0.90	11.3
22	18.2	1.079	4.5	8.99	1.64	0.88	10.2
24	20.0	1.087	4.0	9.05	1.81	0.87	9.2
26	21.5	1.093	3.7	9.11	1.96	0.86	8.5
28	23.2	1.101	3.3	9.16	2.12	0.85	7.8
30	25.0	1.106	3.0	9.21	2.30	0.83	7.2
32	26.6	1.115	2.8	9.26	2.47	0.82	6.7
34	28.5	1.123	2.5	9.35	2.67	0.80	6.3
36	30.2	1.130	2.3	9.41	2.84	0.79	5.9
38	32.0	1.139	2.1	9.48	3.04	0.77	5.5
40	33.8	1.148	1.96	9.55	3.23	0.76	5.2
42	35.5	1.155	1.32	9.62	3.42	0.75	4.9
44	37.2	1.164	1.69	9.70	3.61	0.73	4.6
46	39.0	1.173	1.56	9.78	3.82	0.72	4.4
48	41.0	1.183	1.44	9.86	4.04	0.70	4.1
50	42.8	1.190	1.34	9.92	4.25	0.68	3.9
52	44.6	1.198	1.24	9.97	4.45	0.66	3.7
54	46.5	1.207	1.15	10.1	4.70	0.65	3.6
56	48.3	1.216	1.07	10.1	4.88	0.63	3.4
58	50.0	1.224	1.00	10.2	5.10	0.61	3.3
60	52.0	1.232	.92	10.3	5.36	0.59	3.1
62	54.0	1.240	.85	10.3	5.57	0.57	3.0
64	56.0	1.248	.79	10.4	5.83	0.55	2.9
66	58.0	1.255	.72	10.5	6.08	0.53	2.8
68	60.0	1.261	.67	10.5	6.30	0.51	2.6
70	62.0	1.278	.61	10.6	6.60	0.48	2.5

1.00/0.88 = 1.135. A 50 per cent coffee solubles solution has a 0.31 ml equivalent volume for solubles and a 0.50 ml equivalent volume for water, making a total of 0.81 ml or a specific gravity of 1.00/0.81 = 1.230. Figure 290 gives specific gravities for sucrose and coffee solutions. Table 86 is an abbreviated coffee extract conversion table which can be interpolated. Other items in the table that are useful are weight of water per unit weight of solubles, milliliters of coffee extract needed for 2 gm of solubles when cupping, and weight of extract, solubles, and water per gallon.

Some plants use hydrometers for measuring specific gravity of coffee extracts. Accurate hydrometer readings can take $^{1}/_{4}$ to $^{1}/_{2}$ hr due to occlusion of air in foam. The hydrometer rises continually as gases escape. Also glass hydrometers break and are a continual expense, and there is an extract loss from samples which are not returned to production. Each 10 F (5.6 C) temperature change in the commercial range of percolation concentrations from 40 to 80 F (4 to 27 C) causes about a 0.002 specific gravity change. For example, 35.0 per cent coffee solubles at 50 F (10 C) is 1.160, or 1.156 at 70 F (21 C). Sometimes °Baumé or °Twaddell degrees are used instead of specific gravity, and these are related as follows:

Per Cent Solubles	Degree Brix	Specific Gravity at 60 F (16 C)	Degree Baumé	Degree Twaddell
0	0	1.00	0	0
11.4	14.0	1.05	7	10
23.2	28.0	1.10	13	20
34.0	40.0	1.15	19	30
44.5	52.0	1.20	24	40
56.5	64.2	1.25	29	50

VISCOSITY OF COFFEE EXTRACTS

As discussed in Chapter 14, the important property of viscosity of coffee extract can easily be measured at various temperatures by pipette or viscosimeter and a reference standard such as sucrose solutions. Figure 291 shows a plot of viscosity (log scale) vs the reciprocal of absolute temperature (1/K). The radiating lines are for different concentrations of coffee solubles. The 0 to 10 per cent viscosities are similar to water. The 20 to 30 per cent viscosities are similar to sucrose solutions, while the viscosities for 40 per cent and higher are like corn syrup. The 10 to 30 per cent radial lines can be defined by one equation. The 40 to 60 per cent lines can be defined by another equation. In the first case the angle with the horizontal is thirteen degrees plus the concentration minus ten divided by two; in the second case the angle is thirteen degrees plus the concentration divided by two. The X intercept, 0.0011, is somewhat of a focal point for the radiating lines corresponding to a temperature of 450 F (232 C). Neither the reasons for the radial pattern nor the focal intercept temperature are significant to the author. Sucrose and other solutions have similar patterns. Perhaps the meaning of this pattern will be clarified sometime. The fact that the two similar equations relating temperature and viscosity are separated between 30 and 40 per cent solubles may be significant because extract properties do change

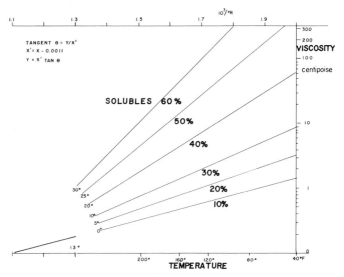

FIG. 291.   VISCOSITY OF COFFEE EXTRACTS VS TEMPERATURE

in this region. This has been observed in atomizing coffee extracts containing over 33 per cent solubles to produce large, beady particles and better flavor retention.

Plotting the viscosities for 33 dextrose equivalent (D.E.) corn syrup (Miller *et al.*, 1942) shows that the corn syrup viscosities are somewhat less than viscosities of corresponding 40 and 60 per cent coffee solubles solutions. This means that coffee solubles have a viscosity corresponding to less than 33 D.E. or perhaps 20 D.E. which is a 20 per cent conversion of the starch to dextrose. The 20 D.E. corn syrup has larger molecules than the 33 D.E. corn syrup.

SURFACE TENSION

For water, surface tension is 75 dynes/cm; for coffee extract, it will vary primarily with fatty acid and oil content. Tension is usually reduced by surface concentrating organic compounds to about 40 dynes/cm or less. Increased temperatures reduce extract surface tension according to the Eotvos equation (Glasstone, 1940); or its variant: $\sigma = \sigma_0 (1 - T/T_c)^n$ where n is about 1.21, σ_0 depends on critical constants of the liquid, T_c is the critical temperature of water and T is the temperature of interest; both are absolute temperatures. As T rises, surface tension decreases. Extract solubles concentration seems to have little influence on surface tension.

ELECTRICAL CONDUCTANCE OF COFFEE EXTRACTS

There are indications that coffee solubles ionize. Specific electrical conductance is directly related to solubles concentration up to about 10 per cent solubles. At this point the proportionality deviates. There is reduced ionization in more concentrated solutions, e.g., acetic acid. The fact that this deviation from linear relation occurs markedly at about 15 per cent solubles could be related to the disappearance of brew colloids during percolation at this electrolytic density. Related to the ionization of extract constituents is the pH of extracts and brew cup strength (Stokes and Stokes, 1956).

HYDROGEN ION CONCENTRATION (ACIDITY)

The pH of coffee extract is higher than the cup of instant coffee prepared from it. For example, a 35 per cent solubles extract pH of 5.20 may correspond to a 1 per cent solubles cup pH of 4.85. The sugar or caramel binding of water must reduce H ion dissociation. The pH of a cup from extract (e.g., 4.85) is more acid than the cup from spray dried powder (e.g., 4.95) because volatile acids are lost. The extract has about 0.9 per cent of acetic acid relative to coffee solubles plus volatile acids formed in hydrolysis. The cup pH rising from 4.85 to 4.95 makes a noticeable taste difference. Cups of coffee from extract taste and are more acid (with bite and bitterness) than those from powder. Table 87 shows the relation of pH to acidity and alkalinity. The pH of brewed coffees is about 5.1 depending on blend and roast (e.g., Robustas are higher at about pH 5.4). Instant coffees are about pH 4.9 but may be higher with Robusta blends. Holding brewed coffee hot in the presence of air causes acidity to rise as long chain compounds break down to form shorter chain acids.

CURDLING OF MILK OR CREAM

Milk or cream, added to a cup of hot coffee, may curdle if the cup pH is too low (acid). This sometimes happens to restaurant coffee that is held hot for several hours. Curdling can occur with cups of instant coffee that have a high hydrolysis solubles yield (acids). Such an acid instant coffee can usually be detected before real harm is done by adding milk or cream to hot water-diluted extract. Since the diluted extract cup of coffee is about 0.10 pH unit lower than powder, if the extract does not cause curdling, the dried powder will be safe. Remedial steps in processing can be taken before curdling occurs in the dissolved powder. In a borderline

TABLE 87

THE MEANING AND MEASUREMENT OF pH[1]

Water is seldom neutral. Usually it is alkaline and occasionally it is acid. The amount of alkali or acid present can be determined by analysis and is reported as total alkalinity or total acidity. In addition to the quantity measurement, however, there is also an intensity measurement of acidity and alkalinity; this is called the "pH value" of the solution.

A neutral condition exists when this pH value is 7.0; i.e., the solution is neither acid nor alkaline. When the pH value falls below 7.0, it indicates a greater *intensity* of acidity. When this value exceeds 7.0, it indicates a greater *intensity* of alkalinity. Thus, pH is a number which indicates the *intensity* of either acidity or alkalinity of a water solution.

A—Showing the variation in pH when 100 ppm of different materials are added to pure water

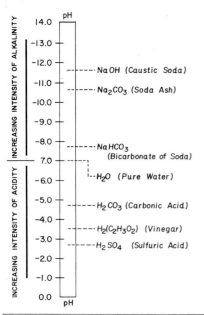

To illustrate that pH is not a quantity measure, Table A shows different pH values of common acids and alkalies—all at concentrations of 100 ppm. As an example, a solution containing 100 ppm of carbonic acid has a pH of 4.6, whereas a solution with the same amount of sulfuric acid has a pH of 2.8. This difference is due to the fact that sulfuric is a "stronger" acid than carbonic. Likewise it can be seen that a solution containing 100 ppm of bicarbonate of soda has a pH of 7.7, whereas the same quantity of caustic soda in solution has a pH of 11.4. This shows that caustic soda is a "stronger" alkali than sodium bicarbonate.

This scale adopted to show intensity of acidity or alkalinity (pH value) is somewhat misleading, for a change of 1.0 pH actually means that the intensity (either acid or alkaline) is multiplied by ten. This is more clearly shown by Table B, in which pH 7.0 is given a value of one.

B—Intensity of Hydrogen Ion Concentration

pH Value	Values Showing Intensity		
14	10,000,000		
13	1,000,000		
12	100,000		
11	10,000		
10	1,000		
9	100		
8	10		
neutral 7	——Alkalinity	Acidity	
6		10	
5		100	
4		1,000	
3		10,000	
2		100,000	
1		1,000,000	
0		10,000,000	

case, curdling may not occur at 150 F (66 C), but will take place at temperatures of over 178 or 180 F (81 or 82 C). Milk and cream are also contributing factors. Drinkable, yet slightly sour, milk as well as slightly acid cream may cause curdling. It is of prime importance to avoid packaging and releasing to the consumer instant coffee powder that will curdle because this can damage a firm's reputation.

The transition point at which milk or cream can curdle relates to a very small difference in pH. For example, the 100 ppm alkalinity of tap water may be sufficient to prevent curdling under some conditions. This is another good reason for using distilled water in testing instant coffee powders; it allows a margin of safety. Natural waters are normally slightly alkaline.

An extract with pH 4.8 may have a 4.65 pH when diluted in distilled water. The same coffee extract diluted to cup strength in 100 ppm alka-

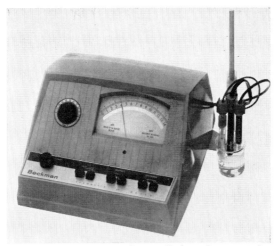

Courtesy Beckman Instruments Inc.

FIG. 292.   pH METER

line water may have a 4.75 pH. The instant coffee powder dissolved in distilled water may have 4.80 pH and in 100 ppm alkaline water a 4.9 pH. Curdling may occur at 4.65 pH, but it will not occur at 4.75 pH. Processors of soluble coffee, using moderate solubles yields and with considerable Robusta coffee in their blends, at a dark roast seldom have a milk curdling problem. Instant coffees produced from one plant are usually very constant in the cup pH; for example, a pH of 4.90 may result in the cup for many months, perhaps years, with a deviation of only ±0.05 pH.

It is not possible to determine by taste the point at which curdling will occur. Figure 292 shows a pH meter with electrodes.

More alkaline cups of coffee appear darker in color. For example, a cup of Robusta coffee may have a pH of 5.30 and will allow about 25 per cent less light transmission than a cup of mild Brazilian coffee of the same solubles concentration at 5.00 pH. For the same reason, a cup of coffee brewed in the Midwest of the United States with alkaline water is not only flat-flavored, but has a pH well above 5.00 even with a mild acidy coffee blend.

BIBLIOGRAPHY

AMERINE, M. A., and CRUESS, W. V. 1960. Technology of Wine Making. AVI Publishing Company, Westport, Conn.

ANON. 1948. Coffee Grinds. Simplified Practice R 231-48. U.S. Department of Commerce. Superintendent of Documents, Washington, D.C.

ANON. 1962. Factors influencing foam stability in beer. Food Eng. 34, No. 6, 95.

ANON. 1960. Revised every 5 years. Official Methods of Analysis. Association of Official Agricultural Chemists (A.O.A.C.), Washington, D.C.

BRODY, A. L., and BEDROSIAN, K. 1959. Spreads cooled for quality reflectance colors. Food Eng. 31, No. 11, 98.

BROWN, G. G. 1950. Unit Operations. 210–213. John Wiley and Sons, New York.

CONANT, J. B. 1939. Chemistry of Organic Compounds. The Macmillan Company, New York.

DALY, T. 1955. Variations in soluble coffee products. Tea and Coffee Trade J. 109, No. 4, 88, 90.

DENBOSKE, J. V. 1962. Silicate keeps hygroscopic foods free flowing. Food Eng. 34, No. 6, 89–90.

DESCHREIDER, A. R., and DRIESSCHE, S. V. D. 1946. Study of the roasting and coating of coffees. Rev. de Fermentations et Ind. Aliment. 1. 222–229. Paris.

DUCK, W. N., and GROSS, R. C. 1957. Relative humidity limit for hard candy work. Candy Ind. and Confectioner's J. 109, Aug. 6, 13–14, 16, 31–32.

ELDER, L. W. 1949. Functional package design. Chem. and Eng. News 27, No. 38, 2682–2686.

FERRAZ DE MENEZES. 1955. Control of coffee infusion by densitrometry. Rev. Inst. Adolfo Lutz 15, No. 1, 135–151, Sao Paulo, Brazil.

GAL, L. 1959. Analyses of coffee mixtures. J. Sci. and Food Agri. 10, 11, 269.

GETMAN, F. H., and DANIELS, F. 1937. Theoretical Chemistry. John Wiley and Sons, New York.

GLASSTONE, S. 1940. Physical Chemistry. D. Van Nostrand Company, Princeton, N.J.

HAARER, A. E. 1962. Modern Coffee Production. Leonard Hill Ltd., London.

HARTMAN, R. J. 1939. Colloid Chemistry. Houghton Mifflin Company, Boston.

HOUGEN, O. A., and WATSON, K. M. 1936. Industrial Chemical Calculations. John Wiley and Sons, New York.

IACANO, P. 1957. Quality standards for soluble coffee buyers. Tea and Coffee Trade J. 113, No. 2, 26.

LITTLE, A. C. 1960. Collaborative study of the measurement of color of ground coffee. Tea and Coffee Trade J. 118, No. 3, 18, 38, 51–52. Also Coffee Brewing Institute (C.B.I.) publication No. 51.[4]

LITTLE, A. C. and MACKINNEY, G. 1956. On the color of coffee. Food Technol. 10, 503. Also Coffee Brewing Institute (C.B.I.) publication No. 17.[4]

---

[4] See listing of other C.B.I. publications in Chapter 19 Bibliography.

LITTLE, A. C., CHICHESTER, C. O.. and MACKINNEY, G. 1959. On the color of coffee. Part II. Food Technol. *12*, 505–507. *Also* Coffee Brewing Institute (C.B.I.) publication No. 37.[4]

LITTLE, A. C., CHICHESTER, C. O., and MACKINNEY, G. 1959. On the color of coffee. Part III. Food Technol. *13*, 684–688. *Also* Coffee Brewing Institute (C.B.I.) publication No. 48.[4]

LOCKHART, E. E. 1958. Analysis of coffee grinds. Publication No. 32. Coffee Brewing Institute (C.B.I.), 120 Wall Street, New York.[4]

LOCKHART, E. E. 1959A. Coffee grinds. Part II. Classification and analysis. Food Research *24*, No. 1, 91–96. *Also* Coffee Brewing Institute (C.B.I.) publication No. 30.[4]

LOCKHART, E. E. 1960A. Roasted coffee. Color measurement and classification. Food Technol. *14*, 597. *Also* Coffee Brewing Institute (C.B.I.) publication No. 53.[4]

LOCKHART, E. E. 1959B. The coffee hydrometer. Coffee and Tea Inds. *82*, No. 6, 50–51, 68, 70; *Also* Tea and Coffee Trade J. *117*, No. 2. *Also* Coffee Brewing Institute (C.B.I. publication No. 43).[4]

LOCKHART, E. E. 1960B. Words for coffee men; roast color. World Coffee and Tea *1*, No. 2, 67.

MEYER, L. H. 1960. Food Chemistry. AVI Publishing Company, Westport, Conn.

MILLER, B. S. *et al.* 1942. Viscosity of corn syrups. Corn Industries Research Foundation, Purdue University, Lafayette, Ind.

MOSSEL, D. A. A. 1947. Determination of degree of roast of coffee. Pharm. Weekblad *83*, 591–594.

PUNNETT, P. W. 1962. Measuring weight loss in roast coffee. Tea and Coffee Trade J. *122*, No. 2, 16, 52.

PUNNETT, P. W. 1961. Moisture content of green coffee. Tea and Coffee Trade J. *121*, No. 4, 14, 18.

PUNNETT, P. W. 1959. Moisture-R. H. equilibria of coffee. Tea and Coffee Trade J. *117*, No. 6, 124, 126, 128.

SELGIN, P. J. 1962. Automatic color recorder. Business Week No. 1717, 122.

SHREVE, R. N. 1945. Chemical Process Industries. McGraw-Hill Book Company, New York.

SIVETZ, M. 1949. Acids in soft beverage flavor. Food Eng. *21*, No. 10, 75–76.

STOKES, J. M., and STOKES, R. H. 1956. The conductances of some simple electrolytes in aqueous sucrose solutions at 25 C. J. Phys. Chem. *60*, 217–220.

---

[4] See listing of other C.B.I. publications in Chapter 19 Bibliography.

CHAPTER 17

Chemical Properties of Coffee

The best sources of published information on coffee chemistry and composition are the bulletins of the Coffee Brewing Institute and reports of their research as listed in the bibliography (1952 to date, Chapter 19). Earlier analytical coffee work is reported by Winton and Winton (1939) and Elder (1949). Caffeine is discussed by Walters (1949), and Levenson (1960) describes the soluble coffee manufacturing process. There is more knowledge of the chemistry and analysis of coffee and its constituents in a Coffee Brewing Institute punch card file, a coffee literature survey from 1925 to 1954 carried out by the Food Technology Department of the Massachusetts Institute of Technology (1955). Continuing articles since 1954 are available from coffee, food, and related industry journals, especially foreign journals from coffee-growing countries. In recent years, a great deal of analytical data about coffee has been reported from India. Germany has always been a highly interested and productive source of coffee investigation and publications. Brazil, with its large coffee surpluses, has done a great deal of work in attempting to use coffee beans for varied purposes. It was only after 1958 that truly significant quantitative analyses of coffee aroma volatiles were made. The processing of soluble coffee since World War II has revealed much about coffee; also, a great many new questions have arisen. Many chemists and chemical engineers were hired to operate, design, and develop soluble coffee process plants and processes. Since 1950, the chemistry of coffee has received more investigation and more constructive analytical work and processing experience than in all previous years of roasting and grinding coffee. Parallel progress has been made in determining the chemistry of other natural flavor substances with the application of improved analytical instruments.

General analyses and reports on coffee have been made by Chandrasekharn and Narayanan (1953), Casares and Yguaran (1954), Hughes and Wise (1955), Mani *et al.* (1954), Prescott (1924), Merritt, C. *et al.* (1957), Lockhart (1957), Elder (1949), Schwartz and Wagner (1935), Winton and Winton (1939), Tate (1941), and others.

Variation and Chemical Complexity of Natural Products

One problem in evaluating reported chemical analyses (aside from the variance in composition of green coffees and degree of roast influences) is that chemical analyses for class compounds are obscured by the complexity of chemical combinations in nature. This is frequently why analyses of natural substances cannot be duplicated exactly.

Carbohydrates.—For example, carbohydrates vary from simple sugars to disaccharides, to trioses, etc. There are starches in the green coffee bean and dextrins (heat solubilized starch) in the roast coffee bean. Larger carbohydrate molecules are pentosans which yield mannose and galactose on hydrolysis. Pentosans are part of a larger group of polysaccharides called hemi-cellulose which are soluble in alkali. Then there are the holo-celluloses insoluble in alkali. Lignin, the binding agent for the celluloses, is an amorphous material of high molecular weight which is also soluble in caustic or bisulfite. The chemical formula for lignin is related to caffeic acid or coniferyl alcohol. Lignin is also related to vanillin as cinnamic acid is to benzaldehyde, and lignin can occur as a glucoside (see page 119 for structural formulas). The holo-cellulose is soluble in concentrated sulfuric acid and yields glucose. Then there are other types of celluloses designated as cellulose and alpha-cellulose. Cellulose is soluble in ammoniacal copper hydroxide. Woldron *et al.* (1960) did a recent carbohydrate study on coffee, as did Natarajan *et al.* (1955A). Absolute or definitive chemical analyses are difficult to make when there is such a complexity of compounds as well as variation in chemical compound size and molecular structure.

Furthermore, there are glucosides of proteins, and proteins are associated with oils or lipids. For example, a petroleum ether or hexane extraction of roast coffee removes fatty acids and oils, plus a significant percentage of phosphoproteins. Thus there results some variation in the amount and composition of chemical class analyses. Results often depend on the procedure of analysis. Man has categorized each class of chemical compounds to find a useful work pattern. But natural phenomena and substances are not quite so sharply delineated in some cases. There are interlocking and overlapping of chemical substances and these confound analyses and the analyst.

Proteins.—These are no less complicated than carbohydrates. Proteins are the source of much coffee flavor as derived in the pyrolysis volatiles from roasting. Proteins have a range of molecular size and properties resembling, in some ways, the carbohydrates. Some proteins are water soluble; they are the small molecules whose basic unit is the amino acid. Large molecules of protein are hydrolyzed with acids to make smaller water soluble molecules of amino acids. Some protein molecules are so large that they are insoluble in water and dilute acids. Proteins in food chemistry are discussed by Fox and Foster (1957) and Meyer (1960). Amino acid analyses by Underwood and Deatherage (1952) and Clements and Deatherage (1957) show many of the commonly recognized natural proteins present. Natarajan *et al.* (1955B and 1956) have compared proteins of different coffees.

Some of the identified proteins in coffee are methionine and cysteine, see Barbera (1956). These contain sulfur which occurs in mercaptan groupings. Elder (1949) reports about 0.1 per cent sulfur in both a green and roast Colombian coffee sample. Proteins are a source of nitrogen compounds in pyrolysis. Some of the pyrolysis products formed in roasting have nitrogen in the cyclic group structures, for example, proline and pyrrole. Tryptophane and indole are also found which are not unlike pyridine in odor. Roasting green coffee denatures most of the protein. Roasting renders protein less water-soluble and amorphous. Some large protein molecules partly break down. The protein reactions are largely irreversible. These phenomena partly explain why water extract of green coffee gives higher solubles yields with room temperature water than with boiling water, e.g., 32 vs 27 per cent solubles yield.

Phosphates.—The integrated relationship between the classes of chemical compounds in coffee can be seen from the fact that phosphorus, as phosphate, is associated both with lipids and glucosides. There are phospholipids, phosphoproteins, and phosphatides like fatty glycerides as lecithin. See Rewald (1946) and Bengis and Anderson (1934).

Mineral Constituents.—These play an important part in the structural growth of the plant and seed. They are part of the chemical structures of carbohydrates, lipids, and proteins.

Winton and Winton (1939) report many ash analyses of green coffee, as do Lockhart (1957) and others. Ash is not lost in roasting. Ash can be separated from the roast coffee in parts as water solubles and insolubles. Muller (1958), Haarer (1962), and Gialluly (1958) discuss the importance and adequacy of various minerals to coffee plant development and growth deficiencies as well as to roast bean flavor and physical properties of the bean. It is well established that many coffee trees can be grown successfully in mineral solutions of phosphates, nitrates, ammonium or urea, sulfates, ferric, potassium, calcium, and magnesium ions. Trace elements are often required for plant health and good yield of cherry. Muller (1958) cites manganese, boron, zinc, copper and other trace elements as important.

ANALYSES

Green Coffee

Hence, the coffee bean is a complex chemical composition and as variable as nature and man's attendance to its cultivation. Although a critical examination of the published chemical analyses of coffee will not be made here, an approximate illustration of the chemical composition of green, roast, and soluble coffee is offered.

Table 88 gives the approximate chemical composition of green coffee. Coleman *et al.* (1955) discuss pectic acid from cherry mucilage. The table is arranged to show what is water soluble and what is not. Carbo-

TABLE 88

CHEMICAL COMPOSITION OF GREEN COFFEE[1]
Dry Basis—Approximate

	Classes and Components	Water Solubility	Per Cent of Green Coffee		
			Item	Total	Soluble
1.	Carbohydrates			60	
	Reducing sugars	Soluble	1.0		
	Sucrose	"	7.0		
	Pectins	"	2.0		
			10.0		10
	Starch	Easily solubilized	10.0		
	Pentosans	" "	5.0		
			15.0		..
	Hemi-celluloses	Hydrolyzable	15.0		..
	Holo-cellulose	Non-hydrolyzable fiber	18.0		
	Lignin	" " "	2.0		
			20.0		..
2.	Oils	Insoluble		13	..
3.	Protein (N × 6.25)	Depends on per cent denatured		13	4
4.	Ash as oxide	Depends on per cent hydrolyzed		4	2
5.	Non-volatile acids				
	Chlorogenic	Soluble	7.0		
	Oxalic	"	0.2		
	Malic	"	0.3		
	Citric	"	0.3		
	Tartaric	"	0.4		
			8.2	8	8
6.	Trigonelline	Soluble		1	1
7.	Caffeine (Arabica 1.0%, Robusta 2.0%)	Soluble		1	1
				100	26

[1] Data averaged from Elder (1949), Lockhart (1957), Mabrouk and Deatherage (1956), Merritt, C. *et al.* (1957), Moore and Heininger (1951), Winton and Winton (1945), and others.

hydrates are listed in general categories from completely water soluble to practically water insoluble. Carbohydrates represent the largest portion of the green coffee bean—about 50 to 60 per cent—whereas carbohydrates are only about 40 per cent of the water solubles.

The coffee oil is insoluble in water as are most of the proteins. However, the portion of the proteins that dissolves is dependent on the fineness of the coffee particle during extraction, the temperature of the extracting water, and the exhaustiveness of the extraction. Although 26 per cent solubles are shown from green coffee, over 30 per cent can be attained by variations of the above procedures. In addition, the amounts of carbohydrates solubilized depend on the fineness of grind.

The fiber portion under carbohydrates is taken as 20 per cent and consists of holo-cellulose and lignin; hemi-celluloses are considered hydrolyzable.

Discrete chemical substances like caffeine, trigonelline, and chlorogenic acid are the most accurately defined. Robustas have twice the caffeine content of Arabica mild, or Brazilian coffees. The oil fraction is fairly accurate but varies with coffees. Some of the colloidal proteins and phosphatides are removed with the water soluble fraction and petroleum ether fraction. Usually there are more minerals in the water soluble portion than in the water insoluble portion, but more minerals are water soluble after roasting.

Roast Coffee

A comparison of the analyses of the green and roast coffee compositions shows what happens to the chemical classes (see Table 89).

Some of the carbohydrates are destroyed in the roasting process. Almost all the sucrose disappears. Since the pyrolytic chemical reactions are complex, the water soluble portion of the carbohydrates is simply designated caramelized (browning type compounds). The water soluble and insoluble portions of caramelized carbohydrates are shown in a range related to (1) fineness of grind and (2) degree of hydrolysis. This shows a solubles yield of 27 per cent from roast coffee with normal grinds and boiling water and 35 per cent solubles yield from pulverized grinds.

Composition of the Water Solubles of Coffee Powder

Table 90 lists the resulting chemical compositions. The composition of extracted and hydrolyzed spent coffee grounds are also listed. The composition will vary plus or minus about 15 per cent with different blends, roasts, and extraction yields. The caffein content of Robusta coffee is double that of the Arabicas. Chlorogenic acid is reported to vary in a few coffees. Soluble coffee composition can be evolved from the roast coffee composition. Over 90 per cent of the soluble substances will be removed from the R & G coffee. For example, if caffeine is 1.0 per cent in green coffee, and there is a 16 per cent roast loss, then there is 1.2 per cent caffeine in the roast coffee. Hardly any caffeine is lost in the roast-

TABLE 89

CHEMICAL COMPOSITIONS SOLUBLE AND INSOLUBLE PORTIONS OF ROAST COFFEE
(APPROXIMATE, DRY BASIS)[1]

	Per Cent	
	Solubles	Insolubles
1. Carbohydrates (53%)		
Reducing sugars	1–2	. . .
Caramelized sugars	10–17	7–0
Hemi-cellulose (hydrolyzable)	1	14
Fiber (not hydrolyzable)	. . .	22
2. Oils	. . .	15
3. Proteins ($N \times 6.25$); amino acids are soluble	1–2	11
4. Ash (oxide)	3	1
5. Acids, non-volatile		
Chlorogenic	4.5	. . .
Caffeic	0.5	. . .
Quinic	0.5	. . .
Oxalic, Malic, Citric, Tartaric	1.0	. . .
Volatile acids	0.35	. . .
6. Trigonelline	1.0	. . .
7. Caffeine (Arabicas 1.0, Robustas 2.0%)	1.2	. . .
8. Phenolics (estimated)	2.0	. . .
9. Volatiles		
Carbon dioxide	Trace	2.0
Essence of aroma and flavor	0.04	. . .
Total	27 to 35	73 to 65

Note.—Volatiles may be classed chemically as acids, amines, sulfides, carbonyls (aldehydes and ketones), and others. Non-volatiles may be classed chemically as acids, carbohydrates, proteins, oils, phospholipids, minerals, and others.

[1] Data averaged from Elder (1949), Lockhart (1957), Mabrouk and Deatherage (1956), Merritt, C. et al. (1957), Winton and Winton (1945), and others.

ing. Caffeine crystals sublimed into roaster stacks are accumulations from minute continual roaster losses. With a 38 per cent solubles yield from R & G (dry) coffee, the caffeine content of the instant coffee (dry) is 1.2/0.38 or 3.2 per cent. Similar calculations can be made for the non-volatile acids, trigonelline and ash. Over 90 per cent of the ash constituents are water soluble; the spent grounds have only a few tenths of one per cent ash, depending on efficiency of extraction. Some caffeine and other water solubles are lost with the spent grounds. This is an index of the inefficiency of extracting the truly water soluble portion of grounds.

Coffee Ash

In green coffee (Winton and Winton, 1939) ash is about 60 per cent K_2O, 15 per cent P_2O_5, 15 per cent CaO and MgO (in a ratio of about 1 to 2), and $^1/_2$ per cent Na_2O. The anions are about 5 per cent SO_3, 1 per cent SiO_2, and 1 per cent chlorides. The ash contains about 1 per cent iron and traces of other metals. Thus sulfates and chlorides appear in

TABLE 90

CHEMICAL COMPOSITION OF COFFEE SOLUBLES AND SPENT GROUNDS (INSOLUBLES)
(*Approximate, Dry Basis*)[1]

		Per Cent	
	Chemical Compound or Class	Solubles	Spent Grounds
1.	Carbohydrates (3 to 5 per cent reducing sugars)	35.0	65
	(browning complexes)	15.0	. . .
2.	Oils (and fatty acids)	0.2	18
3.	Proteins (amino acids and complexes)	4.0	15
4.	Ash (oxide)	14.0	Fraction of 1%
5.	Acids non-volatile		
	Chlorogenic	13.0	. . .
	Caffeic	1.4	. . .
	Quinic	1.4	. . .
	Others	3.0	. . .
6.	Trigonelline	3.5	Few tenths per cent
7.	Caffeine		
	(Arabicas)	3.5	" " " "
	(Robustas)	(7.0)	. . .
8.	Phenols (estimated)	5.0	" " " "
9.	Volatiles		
	Before drying—acids and essence	(1.1)	Nil
	After drying	Nil	Nil
	Total	100	98+

[1] Averaged and calculated from data of Elder (1949), Lockhart (1957), Mabrouk and Deatherage (1956), Merritt, C. *et al.* (1957), Winton and Winton (1945), and others.

TABLE 91

ESTIMATED COFFEE ASH DISTRIBUTION[1]

	Green Coffee	Roast Coffee	Soluble Powder	Dry Spent Grounds
Dry weight relations[2]	1.176	1.000	0.380	0.620
Per cent ash content, dry basis	4.00	4.71	10.00	1.47
Weight ash per unit weight roast coffee, dry basis	0.0471	0.0471	0.0380	0.0091

Percentage distribution of ash components

Mineral Oxide	Per Cent of Total				
	Green, Roast Ash	Solubles Ash		Grounds Ash	
	%	% Tot.	% Sol.	% Tot.	% Grds.
K_2O	62.5	52.0	75.59	10.5	33.65
P_2O_5	13.0	3.0	4.36	10.0	32.05
CaO	5.0	2.0	2.90	3.0	9.62
MgO	11.0	8.0	11.63	3.0	9.62
Fe_2O_3	1.0	0.4	0.58	0.6	1.92
Na_2O	0.5	0.4	0.58	0.1	0.32
SiO_2	1.0	. . .	. . .	1.0	3.21
SO_3	5.0	2.0	2.90	3.0	9.61
Cl	1.0	1.0	1.46	. . .	. . .
	100.0	68.8	100.0	31.2	100.0

[1] Winton and Winton (1945).
[2] Assuming 15 per cent weight loss on roasting.

soluble coffee at several tenths per cent. Table 91 shows the estimated ash distribution on green and roast coffee, solubles, and spent grounds.

The function of minerals and their precise composition in the bean have been grossly overlooked since they have much influence on the course of the thermal pyrolysis during roasting. For example, Broido and Martin (1961 and 1962) point out how the presence of mineral salts in wood reduce pyrolysis temperature and markedly influence the composition and amount of volatile organic substances formed. Gialluly (1958) fertilized coffee trees and followed through to cupping brew from the roasted beans. A marked difference in coffee flavors was noted with different fertilizer formulas.

Coffee Volatiles Composition and Staling

Reichstein and Staudinger (1955) in the 1920's in Europe pioneered the first prominent work on the chemical nature of coffee aroma and flavor. Yet it is a complex subject. There are numerous volatiles—some very volatile, some subject to rapid oxidation, and others to polymerization. Other volatiles are subject to resinification and precipitation. Recent work using gas chromatography and infra-red absorption and/or mass spectroscopy have provided more accurate data about these coffee aroma volatiles. Table 82 (Chapter 15) lists the results of coffee essence composition by Rhoades (1958 and 1960), Zlatkis and Sivetz (1960), and Merritt, C. et al. (1957). Table 83 (Chapter 15) lists the gas chromatographic analyses of R & G coffee volatiles by Rhoades (1958). Hughes and Smith (1949) report on coffee volatiles stability. Natarajan et al. (1956), Greenbaum (1955), and Farber (1958) have reported on volatile reducing substances of coffee. Lee (1960), Cartwright and Snell (1947), and Bredt (1934) report on roast coffee gases.

The data are in reasonably good agreement. They show that about 50 per cent of the volatiles are aldehydes, about 20 per cent ketones, about 8 per cent esters, about 7 per cent heterocyclic, about 2 per cent dimethyl sulfide, and lesser amounts of other organic and odorous sulfides. There are also small and fractional percentages of nitriles, alcohols, and low molecular weight saturated hydrocarbons and unsaturated ones like isoprene. There are also furans, furfurals, acetic acid, and homologues. These are as volatile as water but not so volatile as to contribute much coffee aroma at 50 ft.

No one has yet marketed a synthetic coffee aroma. None of the commercial flavor houses in the world has ever prepared an acceptable sample to simulate coffee aroma. One reason is that flavor houses in general have been awed by coffee aroma as being too complex and chemically unstable to support investments to investigate it thoroughly. Further, flavor houses have in general very little practical working knowledge of coffee. Coffee is not one of their normal commercial products. The addition of individual identified chemical components to coffee extract or brews definitely enhances the cup flavor. Success in this field will be achieved in time through reasonable effort in systematic investigation of the aroma and flavor contributions of each chemical component. Data are needed on combinations of chemical components in influencing aroma and flavor. Eventually, acceptable coffee flavors, perhaps even better than natural, can be formulated. Such a study would probably also explain the cause of staling.

TABLE 92

ANALYSIS OF A COFFEE AROMA ESSENCE[1]

	Mol Wt	Per Cent	Bp		Relative Flavor Importance[2]
			C	F	
Acetaldehyde	44	19.9	21	70	1
Acetone	58	18.7	56	133	2
Diacetyl	86	7.5	88	190	1
n-Valeraldehyde	86	7.3	102	216	2
2-Methylbutyraldehyde	86	6.8	91	196	2
3-Methylbutyraldehyde	86	5.0	91	196	2
Methylfuran	82	4.7	63	145	2
Propionaldehyde	58	4.5	49	120	2
Methylformate	60	4.0	32	90	2
Carbon dioxide	44	3.8	−78	−108	. . .
Furan	68	3.2	32	90	1
Isobutyraldehyde	72	3.0	63	145	1
Pentadiene (isoprene)	68	3.0	30	86	2
Methylethyl ketone	72	2.3	80	176	2
C_4–C_7 paraffins and olefins	. . .	2.0	35	95	2
Methyl acetate	74	1.7	57	135	2
Dimethyl sulfide	62	1.0	38	100	1
n-Butyraldehyde	72	0.7	75	167	1
Ethyl formate	74	0.3	54	129	2
Carbon disulfide	76	0.2	46	115	2
Methyl alcohol	32	0.2	65	149	3
Methyl mercaptan	48	0.1	6	43	1
		100.0			

[1] Zlatkis and Sivetz (1960).
[2] 1, large; 2, medium; and 3, small.

Some volatiles are more odorously important than others in formulating the coffee aroma. On the other hand, some identified volatile components of coffee aroma are not odorously important at all. Known facts about coffee aroma come close to an explanation of staling. Given the chemical nature of coffee solubles and the coffee aroma portion, certain chemical reactions probably occur in staling. First, R & G coffee loses the low boiling volatiles of coffee aroma. The important dimethyl sulfide, acetaldehyde, propionaldehyde, and aromatic esters volatilize in a few minutes to a few hours. The boiling temperature of each volatile component identified is listed in Table 92. The R & G coffee absorbs water from the surrounding air.

Staling

Moisture absorption (or water addition from quench) needs only to be 1 per cent of R & G coffee to effect noticeable staling in less than an hour on a tray spread with ground coffee. After a vacuum coffee can is open for a day, the same stale flavor will be apparent. Staleness is a coffee taste term not yet defined by chemical composition change. Lockhart (1957) shows a gas chromatograph analysis of a fresh R & G coffee sample. The loss and alteration in volatiles composition is accounted for by simply holding the R & G coffee open to air 66 hr. Staling can be demonstrated by exposing ground coffee to air or to several per cent moisture (by adding water to the coffee) for minutes to an hour before preparing a vacuum brew type extraction compared to grinding the fresh roast bean coffee; the taste difference is obvious.

At one time staling was associated with coffee oil rancidity, but it is now known that rancidity has little to do with staling. Staling is the loss and alteration in composition of the volatile coffee aroma constituents. Under packaging, ample evidence has shown that the 29-in. Hg vacuum in the can is essential to preserve the coffee aroma. A 27-in. Hg vacuum allows sufficient coffee aromatics to be oxidized and the stale taste to be detectable in the resulting brewed cup. Thus the difference of a few milliliters of oxygen is enough to oxidize the aromatic aroma and flavor fraction of the 1 lb of roast and ground coffee in the can. Segall (1957) studied stability of hot coffee brews.

Aldehydes are known to be readily oxidizable, especially in sunlight (a can allows no light to enter). Dimethyl sulfide (DMS) is not only volatile but also readily oxidizes to methyl sulfoxide; this loss of a potently aromatic component will downgrade most coffee aroma and flavor. DMS is an exhilarating part of the coffee aroma; the sulfoxide is not very volatile nor odorous. The latter has little taste character at ppm levels. The sulfoxide is also susceptible to further oxidation and chemical reactions.

Staling of roast bean flavor is retarded by the cellular protection given the chemical constituents by the AA- or adsorbed CO_2 atmosphere. However, as moisture penetrates the bean, CO_2 and coffee aroma volatiles are released and altered. Beans are moderately stale in a week, more stale in two weeks, and quite stale in three weeks. Darker roasts stale differently than lighter roasts. Coffee staling rates can be retarded noticeably by storage of roast coffee beans or grounds in air-tight containers at cooler temperatures, 30 F (-1 C) or lower. Drip or vacuum preparation of coffees, which bring out coffee flavor better, reveals staling sooner than percolation, which distills off volatiles and leaves a carmelized brew. Extracts which have coffee volatiles stale rapidly. For example, extract held at 80 F (27 C) for 1 or 2 hr is noticeably inferior in flavor to extract held at 40 F (4 C). The greater the air exposure of extracts and the lower their solubles concentrations, the faster the staling and coffee flavor deterioration. Frozen extracts at −10 F (−23 C) will not deteriorate for many months, or perhaps years.

A source of deterioration in coffee extracts and distillates is the chemical reactions that occur. Aldehydes in extract do not evaporate so readily as from the R & G coffee, but the aldehydes can be precipitated by phenols which are present. Aldehydes will condense or polymerize by themselves in an acid medium. Moisture added to roast coffee releases some aromatics partially through hydrolysis reactions.

The vacuum pack of R & G coffee accomplishes adequate protection of the coffee aroma and flavor, and the subject of staling coffee has not been of much interest in recent years. Articles covering coffee staling have been prepared by Elder (1937 and 1940), Schuman and Elder (1943), Johnston (1939), Punnett (1930, 1938, 1958, 1960), Prescott (1924), Prescott et al. (1937), and others referred to in Chapter 14 bibliography.

Antioxidants are used largely to protect fatty substances from oxidation. There is no indication that antioxidants retard the staling of coffee.

Ascorbic acid is used in military specifications for instant coffee, but this is not so much to protect the instant coffee from oxidation as to provide vitamin C to the military personnel.

Instant coffee prior to aromatization by means of coffee oil (and other methods) underwent little flavor change from the day of preparation. After the initial coffee volatiles were lost and some oxidation occurred, the instant coffee powders were relatively the same in taste for many months, possibly up to a year or two. Any flavor changes in properly packed instant coffee from six months to several years would be nominal if sealed air-tight and stored at less than 70 F (21 C). But with coffee oil add-back and inert gas pack protection, staling of instant coffee is not uncommon before the product reaches the consumer. Staling after the jar is opened by the consumer occurs in a day or two but is not as objectionable as stale R & G coffee. Instant coffee stability in air storage, when not aromatized, is very good; when instant coffees are aromatized (carrying noticeable coffee flavor and aroma), the stale flavor change is easily noticed.

CLASSIFICATION OF COFFEE COMPOUNDS

In discussing the chemistry of coffee, there is always the problem of how to organize the material for study and understanding. Substances are found in the green coffee and are converted in the process of roasting. Thereafter, some of these are water soluble and some are not. Some are gaseous and very volatile under normal conditions. Some compounds are chemically stable; others are not. Combinations of some coffee substances are reactive.

Classification has already been made into generally recognized groups of organic compounds found in foods. These are carbohydrates, proteins, oil, and ash. Acids are an important part of coffee and are classified as volatile and non-volatile. These were discussed in Chapter 15. Chlorogenic acid has been studied by Hoepfner (1933). Phenols, as derived from chlorogenic acid, are classified because they are quite different in chemistry from other classes of compounds. Phenolic compounds are important chemically and tastewise. Phenols also represent as much as 5 per cent of the soluble coffee composition (Prescott *et al.* 1937).

Trigonelline and caffeine each occur at about 1 per cent in the green Arabica coffee beans. They are definite chemical compounds. Work with trigonelline was done by Hughes and Smith (1946 and 1949) and Moores and Greninger (1951). Nicotinic acid, pyridine, pyrolle, methyl pyrolle, etc., are undoubtedly derivatives from trigonelline, caffeine, or their precursors. Furan, methyl furan, furfural, thiophene, and related compounds, as well as pyrolles, are pyrolysis products of the bean, e.g., furfural from pentosan hydrolysis (Hughes and Smith 1949).

The chemistry of these nitrogenous compounds must be differentiated from the protein nitrogen compounds and amino acids.

Similarly the sulfur bearing compounds must be differentiated from their originating proteins.

Nitrogen compounds may be stable like caffeine, unstable like proteins, and volatile like amines. Hultin (1956) discusses nitrogen compounds in instant coffee. The sulfur compounds can be in solid (water soluble or insoluble) protein structures or in volatile sulfides and mercaptans.

The coffee oil fraction, least influenced by the other chemical changes in the coffee bean (because oil undergoes little change in roasting and extraction) can be examined almost as a physical and chemical composition that can be largely withdrawn from roast coffee or spent coffee grounds when desired. This subject will be developed on pp. 175 to 182.

The important subject of acidity has already been covered in some detail in Chapter 15 (Miner, 1934 and Mabrouk and Deatherage, 1956) as have many of the identified chemical constituents of coffee. These are aldehydes, ketones, esters, furans, sulfides, hydrocarbons, pyridine, trigonelline, niacin, vitamins, caffeine, acids, phenols, minerals, proteins, amines, and caramel.

Chaff-Composition

Chaff is the bean cavity parchment (similar to the outer hull) liberated during roasting. It has a chemical composition resembling the green coffee bean but has a bitter and poor flavor. It contains about the same caffeine content as the bean.

Cherry Composition

Nadal (1959) in studying coffee by-products reports that 40 per cent of the ripe cherry is pulp, 20 per cent mucilage, and 40 per cent bean and parchment. The pulp contains 60 per cent water, 28 per cent organic matter, of which 1.6 per cent is nitrogen (10 per cent protein equivalent), and has 1.3 per cent ash. It is high in phosphate and potassium. The dry pulp contains 2 per cent oil, about one-third fiber, 60 per cent nitrogen-free extract, 10 per cent protein, and 10 per cent sugars. Work has been done in the coffee-growing countries to find use for the pulp, mucilage, and hulls removed from the bean. In general, other than returning the mucilage and pulp to the land for mulching, and the burning of hulls, no significant industry has developed from these rejected substances. Pulp can be used to prepare vinegar or for cattle feed, but neither application is widely used.

Coffee Mucilage

This is about 85 per cent water. The 15 per cent solids are about 9 per cent protein and 4 per cent sugars with 1 per cent pectic acid and 0.6 per cent ash. Mucilage is high in calcium and sulfur with traces of manganese. The mucilage has a pH of 4.8 when ripe, 5.0 pH when green. The sugar content of mucilage solids is about 13 per cent in green fruit rising to 24 per cent in ripe fruit. Corresponding solids are 14 and 18 per cent. The gel structure of the mucilage is broken down by pectinases. Some sugar fermentation and protein decomposition also occur which lead to the potent odors around green coffee bean fermentation areas (Nadal 1959). The chemistry of mucilage fermentation is discussed in Vol. I, Chapter 3.

Chlorophyll has recently been synthesized by Woodward in the United States and by Fischer in Germany. Chlorophyll has a pyrrole chemical nature and magnesium within the structure. New crop coffee beans are often vividly green. The chlorophyll that the beans contain alters during the aging of coffees to give derivatives of chlorophyll.

Chemical Analyses of Coffee Constituents

These can be found and are carried out normally as detailed in the Assoc. Official Agric. Chemists manual methods, except where improved methods are reported in other specific publications. This book does not cover such analyses. Many references are given in each chapter to papers describing such analytical techniques. Many analytical methods recently applied, such as in gas, paper, and column chromatography, supersede earlier analytical procedures. Furthermore, the use of the mass-spectrometer, infra-red spectrometer, and the emission spectrometer have made possible accurate analyses not heretofore possible. The use of gas and solution adsorption columns has made possible isolations and separations of individual coffee constituents with techniques not known or seldom applied before World War II.

COFFEE OIL

Green or roast coffee bean oil has a chemical composition similar to many edible vegetable oils as shown in Table 93. It is liquid at room temperature and at 45 F (7 C), but will settle out fatty acid crystals

TABLE 93

CHEMICAL COMPOSITION OF FATS AND OILS (APPROXIMATE)[1]

Number Carbon Atoms	Tri- glyceride	Number of Double Bonds	MP F	MP C	Cof- fee	But- ter	Cot- ton seed	Soy- bean	Corn	Coco- nut	Tal- low	Olive	Lin- seed	Tung
8	Caprylic	..	61	16[2]	...	...	..	..	..	8	...	...	...	..
10	Capric	..	88	31[2]	...	...	..	..	..	7	...	...	...	..
12	Lauric	..	109	43[2]	...	...	..	..	..	47	...	...	...	..
14	Myristic	..	129	54[2]	3	...	1	..	..	18	...	...	...	..
16	Palmitic	..	145	63	28	28	21	7	7	9	35	15	4	2
18	Stearic	..	156	69	10	25	22	4	3	2	40	10	4	3
18	Oleic	1	57	14	21	39	29	32	43	6	25	70	18	13
18	Linoleic	2	32	0[3]	28	...	23	49	39	3	...	5	30	..
18	Linolenic	..	32	0[3]	...	...	..	2	..	...	...	...	...	(73)[4]
20	Arachidic	..	...	..	3	...	Tr.	1	1	...	...	...	...	..
	Other glycerides	..	...	..	...	8	..	..	..	...	...	...	44	9
	Non-saponifiables	..	...	..	7	...	..	..	..	...	...	...	...	..
	Total				100	100	96	95	93	100	100	100	100	99

[1] Conant (1939), Shreve (1945), and Eckey (1954).
[2] Melting points of the free acids which are usually within 1° C of those of the corresponding triglycerides.
[3] Below freezing.
[4] Eleo-stearic acid, isomer of linolenic acid.

slowly during storage. Roast coffee has more fatty acids than green coffee, and percolator hydrolyzed grounds have even more free fatty acids. Roast coffee may have 5 per cent free fatty acids in the oil.

Literature on Coffee Oil

This is mostly European, especially in regard to chemical analyses. Much work has also been done in Brazil in connection with using the coffee oil portion to recover some value from surplus coffees. Such work was carried on in Brazil from 1937 to 1940, and also about 1960.

Eckey (1954) devotes several pages to coffee oil. Coffee oil has a relatively large portion of unsaponifiables which are listed at about 7 to

12 per cent. Unsaponifiable contents are a function of the type of solvent used. The unsaponifiable portion contains sterols and sterol derivatives useful in pharmaceutical preparation. Analyses of coffee oil have been reported by Bauer and Neu (1938, 1942, 1943, 1944), Slotta and Neisser (1939), Noel (1929 and 1931), Hauptmann *et al.* (1939, 1942, 1943, 1946), Bengis and Anderson (1934), Wettstein *et al.* (1945), Polin *et al.* (1943), Chakiavorty (1943), and others. They have reported almost 1 per cent sterols in the coffee oil in assorted varieties; that is, ergo-, sito-, stigma-, and cafe-sterol. Angelo (1937) reports pigments in the unsaponifiable oil fraction. Resinous acids are reported by Descartes de Garcia (1943); resinols are reported by Bauer and Neu (1944), Bengis and Anderson (1934), Chakiavorty (1943), and Hauptmann *et al.* (1946). Bauer *et al.* (1944) reported finding a saturated hydrocarbon nonacosane $C_{29}H_{60}$ of MP 145 F (63 C). Ergosterol is chemically related to Vitamin D and is discussed by Munk (1933). Traces of Vitamin E, alpha-tocopherol, and Vitamin A have also been reported in coffee oil.

Oil Market

Coffee grounds even after soluble coffee extraction do not have as much oil content as other oil bearing seeds. For example, the following seeds have 50 per cent or more oil: babassu, castor bean, copra, peanuts (shelled), sesame seed, and tung nuts. Those seeds having more than 20 per cent oil are: corn (germ), flax, hemp, perilla, and rape. Cottonseed has 15 per cent oil; kapok seed has 18 per cent oil; and soybeans have 16 per cent oil. Green coffee beans have 11 per cent, and roasted have 13 per cent oil. Percolator extracted and hydrolyzed coffee has about 15 to 18 per cent oil.

Sale of vegetable oils is very competitive. Good prices for vegetable oil either for edible purposes or for fatty acids cannot be obtained, although the latter are higher priced. The chemical composition of the coffee oil largely determines its commercial use as well as the demand for a particular oil composition. There is no demand for new edible oils or soap stock. Use of sterols has not encouraged any pharmaceutical firm to draw on the coffee oil supply.

Solvent Extraction Plant

Coffee oil has not been available because every household discards its coffee grounds and, since 1955, most soluble coffee processors have been burning their spent grounds. For oil recovery by expelling or extraction, a sizable equipment investment is needed. The value of the product does not warrant building an oil recovery system unless there are at least 100 tons per day of dry feed coffee grounds and preferably 200 tons per day. Then the cost of extraction with a petroleum solvent like hexane may be 5¢ per lb of oil. Market prices in 1962 for good grades of edible oils are about 11¢ per lb. The plant investment would be at least $400,000. A factor in the cost of the plant is the amount of iron contacting the oil in process. Fatty acids attack bare iron, steel, brass, or copper. These metals have a degrading effect on oil flavor and color. Use of stainless steel is warranted in some of the oil handling equipment to avoid contamination. This brings a better price for the oil. Oils are frequently rated on properties such as clarity, odor, color, and fuming at elevated frying temperatures. Each property of coffee oil would have to be investigated before investing in a coffee oil recovery plant.

The coffee oil must have uniform properties if it is to be recovered for sale. It appears that differences are small in coffee oil composition for Arabica coffees with the limited data available. More data on coffee bean oil properties and composition are needed. Robustas are reported to have higher than average coffee oil content. More data would have to be obtained on coffee varieties to determine whether blend variations in a soluble coffee plant would cause significant enough variations in the recovered coffee oil to influence its end use. Depending on its use, such variations in oil properties may be important. There are several soluble coffee locations (such as metropolitan New York City and Houston, Tex.) that have sufficient spent coffee grounds to justify operating a 100 ton per day oil extraction plant for spent coffee grounds.

Another consideration that discourages the recovery of coffee oil is the fact that after percolation (hydrolysis) as much as 15 per cent of the saponifiable portion is in the fatty acid form. This means that if an edible oil were to be processed by removing the fatty acids (as for instance an ammonium salt by centrifuging) it would result in entraining an almost equal weight of neutral coffee oil. The fatty acid portion would be sold for soap stock at a very low price. Thus the total loss of oil would be about 30 per cent; 15 per cent for soap stock, 10 per cent unsaponifiables, and several per cent in "winterizing" acid and wax crystals. The light color of the oil is an important factor in selling. Coffee oil, due to the high reddish coloration from the grounds, is not as light in color as other vegetable oils. This may mean a lower selling price. Pre-rinsing the coffee grounds color bodies with water results in a lighter colored oil. Subsequent bleaching out or removal of color bodies from the oil with Fuller's earth and/or charcoal may be required. This means additional operating costs and oil yield losses. Glycerine has been manufactured synthetically for almost a decade now. The recovery of glycerine from oil splitting does not offer financial gain. Until there is some commercial recovery of coffee oil, it is unlikely that much of its chemistry and value to users can be realized.

Commercial Oil Recovery Equipment

Expelling coffee oil is probably the cheapest way to remove the oil from the spent grounds. Expelling carries out a great many substances with the oil that are not wanted, e.g., color and "foots" that must be centrifuged away. Expeller oil yields leave about 5 per cent coffee oil in the residual cake. Solvent extraction leaves only a few tenths of 1 per cent coffee oil in the granular stripped grounds. V. D. Anderson Company in Cleveland, Ohio, and French Machinery Company in Piqua, Ohio, make such expellers. Solvent extraction plants can be purchased from Allis-Chalmers in Milwaukee, Wis., Blaw-Knox, Chicago, Ill., V. D. Anderson, and other firms. Coffee oil has been used in specialty soaps. These have good lather and detergent properties. Possibly, it could also be used for cosmetics. Coffee oil may sell best as a fatty acid or for edible use. Once coffee oil is available, other users will draw on its unique properties.

Pilot Recovery of Coffee Oil

Preliminary development work can be carried out in bench top Soxhlet solvent extractors and pilot column extractors and pilot solvent strippers. When working with low boiling petroleum solvents, fire and explosion hazard is always present. The solvent can be thoroughly stripped from the coffee oil by heating the oil to at least 212 F (100 C) in a thin film at 29 in. Hg vacuum. Final solvent traces can be removed from the oil by placing the oil on a tray in a laboratory oven at 212 F (100 C) overnight.

Solvent extracted coffee oil is filtered to remove insolubles (phospholipids pink fluff). Coffee oils may result having 35 to 75 per cent light transmission in a 1 cm tube at 510 mmu wave length and may appear reddish to amber. Fine coffee grounds contribute more to coloration of solvent extracted coffee oils. Light amber oils with 80 per cent light transmission can be achieved by water rinsing the grounds first, screening off finer particles, and by taking the full 17 per cent oil yield. Lesser oil yields, such as 8 per cent, carry a full red color. Caustic refining causes the greatest color lightening of coffee oil but causes a 30 per cent soap stock loss. Refining losses according to the Assoc. Official Agric. Chemists Manual are 2.5 to 3 times the free fatty acid concentration. Hence, 14 per cent fatty acids would mean at least 35 per cent oil loss. Solvent extractions of coffee grounds with above room temperature hexane at, for example, 140 F (60 C) will cause cream colored crystals to deposit out from the oil overnight at 70 F (21 C); oil extractions at 80 F (27 C) give many fewer crystals.

Solvent Removal from Grounds

In commercial operations with rice bran and soybean, the solvent saturated fiber is heated in a screw jacket as the fiber tumbles forward until all solvent is removed. Moisture levels in entering oil laden coffee grounds should be less than ten per cent or the solvent will have difficulty penetrating the coffee cell structure. The bulk density of dry spent coffee grounds is 30 to 40 lb/cu ft. Coffee oil content of spent coffee grounds varies from about 15 to 18 per cent, depending on blend, roast, and solubles yields.

In handling combustible solvents, inert gas is used for purging. Inert gases are also used to cover oils during storage to avoid oxidation.

Since granular fiber has a specific gravity of about 1.6, a unit volume of extractor will hold 0.6 weight unit of dry spent grounds and 0.6 volume unit of solvent of which about one-third wets the coffee grounds.

Although oil extraction systems used are the Kennedy paddle type and Blaw-Knox rotary cell, the percolator column (as used for water extraction of coffee grounds) is well suited for solvent extraction of oil from the dry spent coffee grounds. It offers: (1) vacuum loading of granular coffee; (2) continuous operation of a battery of columns similar to percolation; (3) a minimum solvent to coffee grounds (or oil) ratio; (4) a closed solvent system which is safer, with no moving parts; moderate heating is possible; (5) steam purge which can be used to remove solvent from coffee grounds after oil extraction; and (6) solvent stripped coffee grounds which can be blown out of the percolator column at 10 to 15 per cent moisture ready for disposal or burning. The solvent percolation process for coffee oil is identical with water percolation.

Spent coffee grounds as discharged from the water percolation still have some hydrolyzed sugars which will ferment. Hence, fly and insect infestation and foul odors may result from storage of such wet grounds. Also, as the spent coffee grounds drain and dry partially, they are subject to spontaneous smouldering and possible combustion. For these reasons, special consideration and storage facilities must be provided if appreciable amounts of wet spent coffee grounds are to be stored.

Hexane extraction of freshly roasted and ground coffee gives a different oil than that from hexane extraction of percolated spent coffee grounds. The former oils are rich in coffee aroma, while the latter virtually have no desirable aroma. Fresh steamed R & G coffee after hexane extraction has no noticeable solvent residue. The condensed distillate of water and hexane, however, has a very strong coffee aroma. This strong aroma can be concentrated in a fraction of, for example, one-tenth or one-twentieth the hexane volume by coffee oil addition, followed by hexane evaporation.

The coffee aromatics are more strongly held in the coffee oil than in the hydrocarbon hexane. Hexane can be stripped from coffee oil at 122 F (50 C) in a rotary film vacuum evaporator. Similar extractions for oil and coffee aromatics concentration from steam distillates can be made with solvents such as Freon-11 which is non-flammable. Indications are that the R & G coffee steam distillates with solvent are richer in coffee aromatics than the solely solvent extracted coffee oil.

Commercial Solvent Extraction Process

The oil in solvent solution, which may contain 10 to 20 per cent oil, can, after filtration, have the bulk of the hexane solvent removed under vacuum (or atmospheric pressure using 20 psig steam) so that the coffee oil still retains about 10 per cent solvent. Various types of evaporators can be used such as a film type or a flash type. The coffee oil with 10 per cent solvent is now sent to a bubble cap distillation column. Oil enters at 230 F (110 C). Tower trays are heated with 20 psig steam. The tower is at about 20-in. Hg vacuum, and steam is purged into the bottom of the column so that steam distillation of hexane occurs. All noticeable hexane solvent is driven from the oil.

The solvent stripped oil is stored over a period of 3 to 6 days at about 40 F (4 C) in large tanks. This crystallizes out fatty acids and insolubles. This is called "winterizing"; insolubles are centrifuged or filtered out. The oil is then treated with ammonium hydroxide to neutralize the fatty acids which become the soap stock (creamy yellow precipitate) entraining about their own weight of neutral oil for centrifuge separation. The resulting clear oil is much lighter in color. This oil can be used for preparing margarine or other edible products. In order to use the oil at this point for deep frying or salad oil, it must be deodorized. This process is substantially a steaming of the hot oil under higher vacuum to remove volatiles and cooling before removing the oil from the deodorizer. Oxygen must be kept away from the hot oil to prevent off-flavor called "reversion." Bleaching of the oil with fuller's earth or a similar medium is then required to attain lighter colors.

General handling of coffee oil indicates that it is relatively stable chemically. Rancidity (oxidation of the unsaturated linkages) does not readily occur. However, oils that have been refined as described have also had most of their natural anti-oxidants removed. Such refined oils may be unstable and readily oxidized. For this reason refined oils are stored under inert gas (nitrogen) and anti-oxidants may be added back to them.

As an index of the importance of materials of construction in such an oil processing plant, a comparison of oil quality achieved in glassware and stainless steel vs carbon steel can be made. Invariably the glass and stainless steel system makes a better quality oil, of lighter color. Iron contamination gives the oil a greenish cast.

A projected use of coffee oil is to convert it to fatty acids by fat splitting. This is quickly accomplished by high pressure steam in a fractionating column. This step would separate out unsaponifiables. The fatty acids can then be separated by crystallization of stearic acid from methanol and/or vacuum distillation. Fatty acid sale value is almost twice that for edible oils. Fatty acids can also be separated by high vacuum distillation. Molecular stills are used to recover Vitamin D from cod liver oil, and similar separations have been considered for coffee oil but it is not rich enough in such vitamins to make it commercially attractive.

Oil Analyses

Acid Number is the percentage of free fatty acids. Oil in green coffees are said to have 1 to 2 per cent; oils in roast coffees have 3 to 5 per cent (depending on the degree of roast); and percolated coffees have up to 15 per cent (Lange, 1944 and Meyer, 1960).

Saponification Number is the number of milligrams of potassium hydroxide required to saponify 1 gm of fat or oil. For coffee oil it varies from 170 to 199, according to Eckey (1954).

Iodine Number is the number of grams of iodine combining with 100 gm of oil or fat. For coffee oil 95 to 100 is the range reported by Eckey (1954) and others.

The Reichert-Meissl Number is mostly used for butter. It is an index of volatile acids which is usually very low for coffee oil. There are other oil test numbers reported, such as for esters, hydroxyls, Hehner, Polenske, and thiocyanogen.

The subject of oils, their properties and analyses is a specialized field. Bailey (1951), Eckey (1954), Markley (1960), Gunstone (1958), and Jamieson (1943) should be referred to, as well as the publications of soap and oil associations and societies. The published literature on the chemistry of coffee oil remains sketchy.

Johnston *et al.* (1943), Polin *et al.* (1943) and Descartes de Garcia (1943) show that coffee oil has powerful anti-oxidant properties. This may explain why the normally unstable coffee aromatics are quite stable in the oil. Polin *et al.* (1940, 1942, and 1943) have various patents on coffee oil use.

Brown (1944), Kohle (1940), and Martinenghi (1939) discuss the advantage of coffee oil in hard and soft soap manufacture.

In the references to studies on unsaponifiables are some references on coffee waxes, but except for the confirmed observations that the surface of the bean has a high wax content, information is fragmentary.

Although waxes have physical properties and solubilities somewhat similar to fats, they have different chemical compositions and undergo different chemical reactions. Waxes are usually a mixture of higher alcohols, with some esters. Waxes are not made soluble by boiling caustic solution and appear in the unsaponifiable fraction of oils.

Probably the largest commercial production of coffee oil was in Brazil in 1937. Oil was extracted from 2,000,000 lb of green coffee, which would be about the equivalent oil from 150,000 132-lb, bags of green coffee.

Eckey (1954) points out that there are less phospholipids extracted with the oil from roasted coffee than from green coffee. Bengis and Anderson (1932 and 1934) show that coffee oils are not oxidized during roasting.

Some have expressed the opinion that coffee oil is not suitable for edible purposes because the glycerides hydrolyze during deodorization; this is a matter that would need to be determined experimentally.

Hydrogenated coffee oil has a very oily nature, due to the unsaponifiables, which hinders the making of good flakes. With the current trend toward the use of unsaturated oils, hydrogenated properties are less important. Coffee oil is about 53 per cent unsaturated and 39 per cent saturated.

The physical properties of coffee oil are similar to those of other vegetable oils. Coffee oil has a specific gravity of 0.9440 to 0.9450; a refractive index of 1.468 to 1.469; and a viscosity variation with temperature slightly higher than soybean or linseed oil.

BIBLIOGRAPHY

Chemical Properties

ANON. 1960. Revised every 5 years. Official Methods of Analysis. Association of Official Agricultural Chemists (A.O.A.C.), Washington, D.C.

BARBERA, C. E. 1956. Sulfur containing amino acids. Coffee and Tea Inds. 79, No. 1, 12, 79.

BARNES, H. M., FELDMAN, J. R., and WHITE, W. V. 1950. Iso-chlorogenic acid. J. Am. Chem. Soc. 72, 4178–4182.

BREDT, C. 1934. Roasted coffee gases. Food Inds. 6, 344–349, 386.

BROIDO, A., and MARTIN, S. B. 1962. Effect of $KHCO_3$ on ignition of cellulose by thermal radiation. U.S. Navy Radiological and Defense Laboratory. Technical Report 536. Oct. 2, San Francisco 24, California.

CARTWRIGHT, L. C., and SNELL, C. T. 1947. Gases from roasted coffee. The Spice Mill 70, No. 2, Part I, 16, 26; No. 3, Part II, 16, 24.

CASARES, R., and YGUARAN, F. R. A. 1954. Analysis de extractos de cafe. Anales. Bromatol. 6, 365–393, Madrid.

CHANDRASEKHARN, M. R., and NARAYANAN, B. T. 1953. Aspects of coffee chemistry. Sci. and Culture 18, No. 3, 386–387, Calcutta, India.

CLEMENTS, R. L., and DEATHERAGE, F. E. 1957. A chromatographic study of some of the compounds in roasted coffee. Food Research 22, No. 2, 222–232. Also Coffee Brewing Institute (C.B.I.) publication No. 26.[1]

COLEMAN, *et al.* 1955. Pectic acid from coffee cherry mucilage. Arch. Biochem. Biophys. *59*, 157–164.

ELDER, L. W. 1949. Coffee. In Encyclopedia of Chemical Technology. Vol. IV. Edited by R. E. Kirk and D. F. Othmer. 215–223. Interscience Division, John Wiley and Sons, New York.

ELDER, L. W. 1940. Staling vs rancidity in roasted coffee. Antioxygens produced by roasting. Ind. Eng. Chem. *32*, 798–801.

ELDER, L. W. 1937. Staling vs rancidity in roasted coffee. Oxygen absorption by the fat fraction. Ind. Eng. Chem. *29*, 267–269.

FARBER, L. 1958. Volatile reducing substances in the aroma of coffee. Food Research *24*, No. 1, 72–78.

FOX, S. W., and FOSTER, J. F. 1957. Introduction to Protein Chemistry. John Wiley and Sons, New York.

GIALLULY, M. 1958. Factors affecting the inherent quality of green coffee. Coffee and Tea Inds. *81*, No. 11, 127–132.

GIRAL, and FERNANDEZ. 1944. Aroma of roasted coffee. Anales. Inst. Invest. Cient. *1*, Univ. Nuevo Leon, Monterrey, Mexico.

GREENBAUM, F. R. 1955. Report of chemical process for testing coffee aroma and flavor. (Volatile reducing substances of coffee.) Tea and Coffee Trade J. *109*, No. 2, 40.

HAARER, R. J. 1962. Modern Coffee Production. Leonard Hill Ltd., London.

HESTER, A. S., and HIMMLER, K. 1959. Chemicals from acetaldehyde. Ind. Eng. Chem. *51*, 1424–1430.

HOEPFNER, W. Z. 1933. Chlorogenic acid in roasted coffee. Z. Untersuch. Lebensm. *66*, 238.

HUGHES, E. B. 1948. Chemistry of coffee. J. Soc. Chem. Ind. *29*, 462.

HUGHES, E. B., and SMITH, R. F. 1946. Nicotinic acid in coffee. J. Soc. Chem. Ind. *65*, 284.

HUGHES, E. B., and SMITH, R. F. 1949. Volatile constitutents of roasted coffee. J. Soc. Chem. Ind. *68*, 322–327.

HUGHES, E. B., and WISE, W. F. 1955. Estimation of coffee to chicory ratio in mixtures. J. Soc. Chem. Ind. *74*, 549.

HULTIN, H. O. 1956. Nitrogen compounds in instant coffee. (Thesis.) Mass. Inst. Technol., Cambridge, Mass.

HUSANI, S. A., and COOPER, G. E. 1957. Fractionation of wood smoke. Food Technol. 11, 499–502.

ISHLER, N. H., FINUCANE, T. P., and BORKER, E. 1948. Determination of caffeine. Anal. Chem. *20*, 1162.

IYENGAR, J. R., NATARAJAN, C. P., and BHATIA, D. S. 1955. Tannins in coffee Bull. No. 4, 259–261, Central Food Technology Research Institute, Mysore, India.

JACOBS, M. B. 1953. The Chemistry and Technology of Food and Food Products. Interscience Division, John Wiley and Sons, New York.

KARRER, P. 1950. Organic Chemistry. Elsevier Division, D. Van Nostrand Company, Princeton, N. J.

KOGAN, L., DICARLO, F. J., and MAYNARD, W. E. 1953. Determination of caffeine and trigonelline in coffee by paper chromatography. Anal. Chem. *25*, 1118.

LEE, S. 1960. Carbon dioxide in tea and coffee. Tea and Coffee Trade J. *119*, No. 6, 36–39.

LENTNER, C., and DEATHERAGE, F. E. 1959. Organic acids in coffee in relation to the degree of roast. Food Research *24*, 483–492. *Also* Coffee Brewing Institute (C.B.I.) publication No. 45.[1]

LENTNER, C., and DEATHERAGE, F. E. 1958. Phenolic acids in coffee. Chem. & Ind. 1331–1332. *Also* Coffee Brewing Institute (C. B. I.) publication No. 36.[1]

---

[1] See listing of other C.B.I. publications in Chapter 19. Bibliography.

LEVENSON, H. S. 1960. The manufacture of soluble coffee. *In* Encyclopedia of Chemical Technology. Vol. V. Edited by R. E. Kirk and D. F. Othmer. Interscience Division, John Wiley and Sons, New York.

LOCKHART, E. E. 1957. Chemistry of coffee. Coffee and Tea Inds. *80*, No. 9, Part I, 71, 73, 90, 97; No. 10, Part II, 21, 23, 25; No. 10, Part III, 16, 30. *Also* Coffee Brewing Institute (C.B.I.) publication No. 25.[1]

MABROUK, A. F., and DEATHERAGE, F. E. 1956. Organic acids in brewed coffee. Food Technol. *10*, No. 4, 194–197. *Also* Coffee Brewing Institute (C.B.I.) publication No. 12.[1]

MACRIS, and MARIS. 1956. Chromatographic examination of coffee extracts. Z. Lebensm-Untersuch. u-Forsch. *103*, 324.

MANI, G. S. *et al.* 1954. Chemical composition of coffee blends and adulterants. Indian Coffee *18*, 205–208.

MERRITT, C., SULLIVAN, J. H., and ROBERTSON, J. H. 1957. Volatile components of coffee aroma. Analytical Report No. 12, U.S. Army Qm. Corp., Natick, Mass.

MERRITT, M. C., and PROCTOR, B. E. 1959. Effect of temperature during the roasting cycle on selected components of different types of whole bean coffee. Food Research *24*, 672–680. *Also* Coffee Brewing Institute (C.B.I.) publication No. 46.[1]

MEYER, L. H. 1960. Food Chemistry. AVI Publishing Company, Westport, Conn.

MINER, C. S. 1934. The acidity of roasted coffee. Nat'l Fed. of Coffee Growers of Colombia. May 25, 120 Wall Street, New York.

MONCRIEFF, R. W. 1950. The Aroma of coffee. Food *19*, No. 4, Part I, 124–126; No. 5, Part II. 176–179.

MOORES, R. G., and GRENINGER, D. M. 1951. Determination of Trigonelline in coffee. Anal. Chem. *23*, 327–331.

MOORES, R. G., McDERMOTT, D. L., and WOOD, T. R. 1948. Determination of chlorogenic acid in coffee. Anal. Chem. *20*, 620.

MULLER, L. 1958. Detection and control of minor element deficiencies. Coffee and Tea Inds. *81*, No. 11, 71–77.

NADAL, N. G. M. 1958. Coffee byproducts. Coffee and Tea Inds. *81*, No. 8, 9.

NADAL, N. G. M. 1959. Coffee mucilage chemical composition. Coffee and Tea Inds. *82*, No. 8, 17–18.

NATARAJAN, C. P. *et al.* 1955A. Carbohydrates in green and roast coffee. J. Indian Chem. Soc., Indian News Ed. *18*, 9–12.

NATARAJAN, C. P. *et al.* 1955B. Comparison of proteins of different coffees. Bull. Cent. Research Inst. *4*, 260–261. Mysore, India.

NATARAJAN, C. P. *et al.* 1956. Volatile value (V.R.S.) of Indian coffee and substitutes. Bull. Cent. Research Inst. *3*, 307–309, Mysore, India.

NATARAJAN, C. P., IYENGAR, D. L., and BHATIA, D. S. 1957. Tannin-like constituents in coffee. J. Sci. Research *16*, 42.

PRESCOTT, S. C. 1924. Investigation of coffee. Jabez Burns and Sons, New York.

PRESCOTT, S. C. *et al.* 1937. The staling of coffee. Food Research *2*, No. 1, 1–20; No. 2, 165–173.

REICHSTEIN, T., and STAUDINGER, H. 1955. Coffee aroma. Perfumery Essent. Oil Record *45*, No. 3, 86; *also* 1955. Coffee and Tea Inds. *78*, No. 6, 91; *also* 1950. Z. Angew. Chem. *62*, 292.

RHOADES, J. W. 1960. Analysis of the volatile constituents of coffee. Agri. Food Chem. *8*, No. 2, 136. *Also* Coffee Brewing Institute (C.B.I.) publication No. 52.[1]

RHOADES, J. W. 1958. Sampling method for analysis of coffee volatiles by gas chromatography. Food Research *23*, No. 3, 254–261. *Also* Coffee Brewing Institute (C.B.I.) publication No. 34.[1]

SCHWARTZ, F. W., and WAGNER, F. E. 1935. Chemical changes in coffee roasting. Bull. Eng. Sci. No. 51, Rensselaer Polytechnic Institute, Troy, N. Y.

SEGALL, S. 1957. Chemical stability of coffee brew components. (Ph.D. Thesis.) Food Technol. Dept., Massachusetts Institute of Technology, Cambridge, Mass.

Tate, F. G. H. 1941. Chemistry of coffee. Chemical Age *44*, April 5, 185–186.
Underwood, G. E., and Deatherage, F. E. 1952. Amino acids of green and roast coffee. Food Research *17*, 425–432.
Walters, R. H. 1949. Caffeine. *In* Encyclopedia of Chemical Technology. Vol. IV. Edited by R. E. Kirk and D. F. Othmer. Interscience Division, John Wiley and Sons, New York.
Williams, R. J. 1956. Biochemical Individuality. John Wiley and Sons, New York.
Winton, A. L., and Winton, K. B. 1945. Analysis of Foods. John Wiley and Sons, New York.
Winton, A. L., and Winton, K. B. 1939. Structure and Composition of Foods. Vol. IV. John Wiley and Sons, New York.
Woldron, M. L., Plunkett, R. A., and Laver, M. L. 1960. Carbohydrates of coffee. J. Agri. Food Chem. 8, Jan.-Feb., 58–65.
Zlatkis, A., and Sivetz, M. 1960. Analysis of coffee volatiles by gas chromatography. Food Research 25, 395–398.

Coffee oil

Angelo, S. 1937. Pigments of coffee seed. Rev. Brasil Chim. *4*, 368–371; *also* 1938. Chemical Abstracts *32*, 1752.
Bailey, A. 1951. Industrial Oil and Fat Products. Interscience Division, John Wiley and Sons, New York.
Bauer, K. H., and Neu, R. 1938. Coffee oil. Fette und Seifen. *45*, Part I, 229–232; *also* 1938. Chemical Abstracts *32*, 9534.
Bauer, K. H., and Neu, R. 1942. Coffee oil. Fette und Seifen. *49*, Part II, 419–428; *also* 1943. Chemical Abstracts *37*, 5607.
Bauer, K. H., and Neu, R. 1943. Coffee oil. Fette und Seifen. *50*, Part III, 345–347; *also* 1944. Chemical Abstracts *38*, 3499.
Bauer, K. H., and Neu, R. 1944. Coffee oil. Fette und Seifen. *51*, Part IV, 343–347.
Bengis, R. O., and Anderson, R. J. 1932. The chemistry of the coffee bean. J. Biol. Chem. *97*, 99–113; *also* 1934. *105*, 139–151.
Brown, R. 1944. Coffee oil in soap manufacture. U. S. Pat. 2,354,686.
Chakiavorty, P. N. 1942. Coffee sterol. J. Am. Chem. Soc. *64*, 2235; *also* 1943. *65*, 929–932; *also* 1943. *65*, 1325–1328.
Conat, J. B. 1939. Chemistry of Organic Compounds. The Macmillan Company, New York.
Dannmeyer, F. 1930. The preparation of an activated substance from crude coffee. Chemical Abstracts *25*, 726; *also* Strahlentherapic *38*, 583–590.
Descartes de Garcia, P. R. 1943. Coffee oil. Anais. Assoc. Quim. Brasil *2*, 57–74; *also* 1944. Chemical Abstracts *38*, 1133.
Eckey, E. W. 1954. Vegetable Fats and Oils. Reinhold Publishing Corporation, New York.
Gunstone, F. D. 1958. Introduction to the Chemistry of Fats and Fatty Acids. Chapman and Hall, Ltd., London.
Hauptman, T. *et al.* 1939. Coffee sterol I. Z. Physiol. Chem. *259*, 245–250; *also* 1939. Chemical Abstracts *33*, 7813.
Hauptman, H. *et al.* 1943. Coffee sterol II. J. Am. Chem. Soc. *65*, 992–994; *also* 1943. Chemical Abstracts *37*, 1446.
Hauptman, H. *et al.* 1943. Coffee sterol III. J. Am. Chem. Soc. *65*, 81–85; *also* 1943. Chemical Abstracts *37*, 4122.
Hauptman, H. *et al.* 1942. Coffee sterol and derivatives. Bol. Fac. Fil. Cienc. Letras. Univ. Sao Paulo *14*, 181–188; *also* 1946. Chemical Abstracts *40*, 392.
Heller, H. 1940. Oil from coffee grounds. Seifensieder *67*, 192; *also* Chemical Abstracts *34*, 5306.
Jamieson, G. S. 1943. Vegetable Fats and Oils. Reinhold Publishing Corporation, New York.

JOHNSTON, W. R., GORE, H. C., and FREY, C. N. 1943. Preventing rancidity. (Standard Brands.) U. S. Pat. 2,314,968 and Canadian Pat. 412,131.

KAHN, N. A., and BROWN, J. B. 1953. Composition of coffee oil. J. Am. Oil Chem. Soc. 30, No. 12, 606–609

KIRCHENBAUER, H. G. 1960. Fats and Oils Chemistry and Technology. Reinhold Publishing Corporation, New York.

KOHLE, H. 1940. Oil from coffee grounds. Seifensieder 76, 162–163; also 1941. Chemical Abstracts 35, 3470.

LANGE, N. A. 1944. Handbook of Chemistry. 5th Edition. Handbook Publishing Company, Sandusky, Ohio.

LENDRICK, K. 1930. Volksernahr. 5, 310–312; also 1931. Chemical Abstracts 25, 4633.

MARKLEY, K. S. 1960. Fatty Acids. Interscience Division, John Wiley and Sons, New York.

MARTINENGHI, G. B. 1938. The fats of coffee grounds. Olii minerali, grassie saponi, colori e vernici 18, 112–114; also Chemical Abstracts 33, 1165.

MASSATSCH, C., and SCHNEIDER, E. 1935. Coffee fat and degree of roast. Deut. Nahr. Rundschau, p. 36; also 1937. Chemical Abstracts 31, 6755.

MUNK, F. 1933. Coffee bean fat and wax. Allgem. Oel-Und Fett.-Stg. 29, 13–15; also Chemical Abstracts 27, 1414.

NOEL, VON, L. 1929. Coffee Oil. Pharm Zentralhalle 70, 69–77; also Chemical Abstracts 23, 1718.

PATTISON, E. S. 1959. Industrial Fatty Acids and Their Applications. Reinhold Publishing Corporation, New York.

POLIN, H. S. et al. 1943. Byproducts from coffee oil. U. S. Pat. 2,314,393.

POLIN, H. S. et al. 1941. Industrial utilization of the coffee plant. Am. Chem. Soc. News Ed. 19, 877–881.

POLIN, H. S. et al. 1940. Plastic named Caffelite. U. S. Pat. 2,207,069.

POLIN, H. S. et al. 1942. Polymerization of coffee oil. U. S. Pat. 2,277,252.

REWALD, B. 1946. Phosphatides and coffee oil. Oil and Soap 23, 19–20.

SCHUETTE, H. A., COWLEY, M. A., and CHANG, C. Y. 1934. Composition of coffee oil. J. Am. Chem. Soc. 56, 2085–2086.

SHREVE, R. N. 1945. Chemical Process Industries. McGraw-Hill Book Company, New York.

SLOTTA, K. H., and NEISSER, K. 1938. Coffee sterol. Ber. 71B, 1991–1994; also 1939. Chem. Abstracts 33, 768; also 1938. Ber. 71B, 2342–2346; also 1939. Chem. Abstracts 33, 990; also 1938. Coffee sterol, Part V. Ber. 72B, 120–133; also 1939. Chem. Abstracts 33, 2604.

WETTSTEIN, A. et al. 1941. Coffee sterol. Helv. Chim. Acta. 24, 332–358.

WETTSTEIN, A. et al. 1942. Coffee sterol. Helv. Chim. Acta. 25, 718–731.

WETTSTEIN, A. et al. 1943. Coffee sterol. Helv. Chim. Acta. 26, 631–641.

WETTSTEIN, A. et al. 1943. Coffee sterol. Helv. Chim. Acta. 26, 788–800.

WETTSTEIN, A. et al. 1943. Coffee sterol. Helv. Chim. Acta. 26, 1197–1218.

WETTSTEIN, A. et al. 1945. Coffee sterol. Helv. Chim. Acta. 28, 1004–1013.

PATENTS[2]

Brown, R.	U.S.	2, 354, 686/44
Johnston, W. R.	U.S.	2, 314, 968/43
	Can.	412, 131/43
Polin, H. S.	U.S.	2, 207, 069/40
	U.S.	2, 277, 252/42
	U.S.	2, 314, 393/43

[2] Also listed above alphabetically

CHAPTER 18

Control of Soluble Coffee
Processing and Product Quality

Product quality control is unfortunately associated with routine laboratory tests and reports. These procedures are, of course, important but apply only to the finished product. If the in-process product is substandard, or production is out of control, the process must then be corrected to prevent changes in product quality. Adjustments are made continually to insure normal and consistent product quality at every step of the processing.

The important working principle in processing instant coffee is to be sure that the final product is of uniform quality. Therefore, all factors affecting the finished product, specifically raw material and processing, must also be held within reproducible limits.

Quality tests on the final product are inadequate because by the time a substandard quality is revealed, tons of the product have been produced. Yet this poor product must be released as it is or be diluted back into the flow of normal production powder. In extreme cases the powder may have to be discarded. In any case, there are losses in product quality and additional costs.

At this time, the foreman (and/or plant superintendent) must trace back to locate the cause of the trouble and correct it. Meanwhile, a considerable amount of "off-standard" instant coffee is being produced. It takes a competent and versatile supervisor to know the normal process. Thus the soluble coffee production supervisor must exercise his position as a focal point. He must gather and receive all pertinent process data with his eyes, nose, ears, tongue, and other senses. Then hemust correlate this data into effective process control through his processing personnel, established procedures, and control instruments, and make the necessary adjustments in equipment, process, and raw materials. The effective plant supervisor, thus controls cup quality, overall processing conditions, and the personnel doing the processing. The unit process operator cannot do this due to the limited scope of his work and responsibility.

When managements limit such overall supervision by sharplpy delineating work areas and responsibilities as well as authority and working knowledge, the overall effect of using taste response in process control is correspondingly impaired.

187

With overall supervisory authority and surveillance, the key organizer through continual probing and feed back (much like a mechanical instrument) can effectively control human relations, the mechanics and cookery of each process step and its relation to the associated steps, under the key influence of repeated tasting while exercising proper processing adjustments. With continual taste monitoring to guide process control, adjustments are usually small and infrequent. Thus processing conditions are stable yet there is an allowance for recognized variations in raw material and human performance.

The object in processing any food is to bring out the best flavor possible with the raw materials used. The primary factor then is the *taste effects* achieved and their *causative factors,* as identified, understood, and subsequently controlled by the supervisor.

Taste control is the key to overall process control. In soluble coffee processing, taste control is closely related to process control because there are so many operating variables.

The process supervisor who does the tasting knows from experience that all in-process conditions are normal, and he needs only confirmation of his personal evaluation from the "cupper" on taste, and the quality control laboratory on properties.

Specifically, if the key supervisor knows the quality of entering and in-process coffee and is assured that processing conditions are normal, he is reasonably sure that taste and laboratory tests will reveal a normal product.

This is a living control over product and plant processing requiring a focal man with broad sensory and technical understanding. Such a man will quickly evaluate a test and/or operating variance and correct it before any or much "off-standard" product is made. This is the real meaning of process and product quality control.

Since other chapters in this book have already covered tasting methods, tasting at process points, physical and chemical properties and their measurement, this chapter will largely concern itself with laboratory functions and factors in production that cause process and product variations.

TASTING COFFEE IN PROCESS

Tasting has already been pointed out as the key factor in processing. Since acceptable taste is the main key to salability of an instant or regular coffee, the control of taste quality of the product assumes many aspects in a coffee plant.

The coffee buyer, often a member of management due to the high responsibility of the position, must have decades of coffee tasting experience. Often he visits the coffee growing countries during harvest to assess crop yields, crop quality, and prices as well as to associate himself with growers and brokers with whom he will deal from time to time. A good coffee buyer knows a great deal about characteristic growth qualities and processing from localized areas.

Some buyers look for the best. Most buyers look for average to less than average quality. In the latter case, a price advantage is obtained, yet the buyer hopes that the ultimate consumer may not detect the poorer cup quality. Some green coffee brokers may work with a roaster specializing in lower priced coffees. Green coffee beans are bought by description from reputable brokers and/or by submitted samples. The coffee may be in the growing country, enroute, or in the consuming country at the time of sale.

Cupping Procedure

The samples are usually roasted lightly in a small batch roaster in quantities of about 200 gm or $1/2$ lb. A regular grind is usually prepared; 10 gm are placed in a 4 oz glass, each sample in duplicate. Often dozens of samples are evaluated at the same time. Behind each pair of 4 oz glasses is a corresponding tray of the green coffee beans with a tray of the roast beans over it. After pouring the pure boiling water into each glass, a period of 5 min is allowed for the grounds to soak. Part of the roast grounds sinks; part remains floating. Then the floating particles are stirred to cause them to settle. Those that still float are removed with a perforated spoon so that cupping can take place without taking particles of the grounds into the mouth. This steeped cup of coffee is rather weak in flavor but adequate for flavor and aroma evaluation. Tasting is done with an air suction of brew into the mouth off the spoon so that aromas are wafted into the back of the mouth and nasal passages. The spraying action also cools the brew. The grounds are usually smelled for flavor revelations. Altogether, at the end of the tasting, the cupper has enough information which may be recorded, to judge whether it is a good or reasonable green coffee purchase. The submitted bean samples are later tasted with samples from the actual shipment.

It is not uncommon for a taster to cup coffees from many parts of the world—Africa, Latin America, East or West Indies, Hawaii, etc. A qualified taster knows the types of coffee characteristic of each growth area, their grades as well as their variances. Such experience takes many years to accumulate, and coffee buyers are usually well paid.

Tasting Laboratory

Surprisingly little investment in laboratory test equipment is required for evaluating coffees. Yet many large coffee brokerage houses and coffee roasters have inadequate tasting facilities. They are often hot in the summer, drafty in the winter, and full of traffic. The atmosphere smells of coffee roasting, stale coffee, green coffee; water vapor raises the humidity; and untidiness raises coffee dust. Tradition binds the taster to his round table. Time-worn customs are slow to change in the cupping room facilities. These distractions, discomforts, and inconveniences cause a reduced sensitivity to tasting. Cupping the samples representing large lots of graded coffee, as offered by green coffee brokers, is a relatively easy task compared to cupping many small lots of vastly differing quality in the coffee-growing country. It is not uncommon for one man to cup 50 coffee samples per day. In the consuming country the imported coffee has usually been well graded and classified as to appearance and taste. In some cases tasting by the roaster's green coffee buyer is only to verify that the proper quality of coffee has been chosen and delivered.

Some of the jargon of the cupper, buyer, or broker is listed in Chapter 15. Terms of off-flavors are common to coffees due to growth, fermentation, and grading. Subjective taste influences are also in play. For example, a coffee roaster, anxious to save money, may compromise on the quality of the coffee bought from time to time.

It is important that the water used is clean and neutral for cupping. A little chlorine or organic matter can alter the taste of coffee markedly. Water alkalinity can greatly reduce acid flavor of a cup of coffee. Some large coffee firms simply use alkaline tap water for cup testing. Water varies in quality through the year. Water may also contribute a prominent taste of its own. Under poor conditions, cupping cannot gain its full objectives. Local water quality must be taken into consideration in marketing coffees. Some coffee tasters dislike using distilled water, but pure water is a good point of taste reference. Distilled water does not flatten the coffee flavor in the cup. This occurs only when the distilled water has not been freshly boiled; it occurs with any water that has not been boiled. Metal contamination also causes off-flavors in cupped coffee. This is discussed further in Chapter 19.

Coffees are always cupped directly after roasting on the same day, if not the same hour. A kettle or urn of boiling water is always on hand for cupping use.

The taster only washes the brew in his mouth, he does not swallow it. Tasters usually do not smoke if they want maximum sensitivity in taste and aroma perception.

Consumer Testing

Consumer evaluation of coffees differs markedly in many ways from the above procedure. The consumer is not educated to recognize desirable coffee aroma and flavor properties; his coffee taste world is small and frequently distorted by the use of stale, weakly brewed, low quality coffees. The consumer uses tap water and frequently does not boil it. He often uses an aluminum pot, heats and reheats the brew, varies the coffee to water ratio, time of brewing, etc. The consumer swallows the coffee with food and adds cream or milk and sugar.

Consumer home taste tests, if run in large enough groups to give a significant statistical preference, are useful. However, there are many variables and conditions in such taste tests. A 55 to 45 preference based on several hundred families will usually correspond to the designation of a markedly better cup of coffee by experts.

Tasting is an evaluation process. Oddly enough, something that tastes acceptable may bring on revulsion if swallowed. One can tolerate tasting many coffees, but sometimes few coffees will pass the test of swallowing.

Cultural and political factors often govern the choice of coffees for consumption. In France and England, at present, one drinks much Robusta coffee and the taster evaluates Robusta coffees. In the coffee growing country, one is more likely to drink coffee from imperfect beans at a dark roast. Commercial coffees are roasted dark in some areas, lighter in others. Chicory may be added. These varying circumstances govern blend choice in purchases, competitive quality, and prices.

Taste Ability

One does not require special abilities to become a coffee taster. If they take an interest and obtain the experience, most people can become quite discriminating in the evaluation of coffee or any other type of flavor. Some coffee tasters are more skilled and sensitive to tastes as a result of experience rather than aptitude although aptitude may play a part. Many of the best coffee tasters in the coffee industry learned tasting by working their way up in a coffee roasting firm from green coffee bag dumper to buyer or even owner. A cupper takes a certain amount of pride in his skill as an expert in evaluating a naturally variable commodity. The scope of taste experience in coffees is very broad, and learning never stops for those who are interested and concerned. However, the best green coffee buyers are occasionally deceived by sharp sellers.

Taste Comparison of Soluble vs Roast Coffees

The function of evaluating the taste of green and roast coffees has long been done by those skilled in recognizing those flavors and values. With the introduction of soluble coffees, many of the tasters enlarged their operation, choosing green coffees for soluble coffees and evaluating the final product. However, preparing soluble coffee is a markedly different process from ordinary roasting just as soluble coffee has never tasted like brewed coffee. Chemically, percolated coffee solubles have practically no oil or brew colloids. Brewed coffee solubles have up to 10 per cent oil in the solubles. Instant coffees have few volatiles which are the heart of real coffee aroma and flavor.

Soluble coffees do not develop stale flavors as compared with roast coffees. Every pound of green coffee beans produces about 80 cups of instant coffee compared to about 40 cups of brewed coffee. Instant coffee has almost twice the carbohydrates of brewed coffee solubles. Instant coffee cups are more acid (pH 4.90) than brewed cups (pH 5.1). Acids form during percolator hydrolysis of instant coffee. Blend differences are more noticeable in brewed than in instant coffees. Instant coffees contain hydrolysis products which characterize their flavor.

The chemical engineer is allowed to design and operate the soluble coffee processing plant. The consumer defines an acceptable cup of instant coffee; the decision as to green coffee quality has partly slipped away from the roaster or green coffee buyer. The source of coffee flavor has a chemical basis. These chemical aromas and tastes can be recognized. The taster should know something about the chemistry and processing of instant coffee in order to alter and control the flavor of his product. The introduction of chemists and chemical engineers into the instant coffee industry is a fact, and these persons have responsibilities in coffee tasting.

Some food processing firms have shifted their taste evaluations to special panels of housewives, but general consumer preferences have been consulted most. The public registers decisions by its buying habits. A "flavor franchise," meaning an established public preference for a branded product, is valuable because consumers do not change from familiar tastes frequently or rapidly. A familiar pleasant taste association is cherished in every culture. The sales growth of new products like dehydrated foods, even canned foods and frozen foods, and especially frozen and dried beverages in the United States in the past 20 yr is a historical departure from established taste and eating habits. Therefore, whoever acquires a "taste franchise" in an instant coffee beverage flavor will not lose it quickly. But the franchise can be transferred from one processor to another or gain an expanded base when competitors duplicate the taste of the leading brand.

Factors in Taste Evaluation of Coffee During Processing

Green Coffee.—This is influenced by (1) botany; (2) growth area and altitude; (3) environmental factors in growth; (4) processing and grading; (5) storage; (6) shipping; (7) blend; (8) contamination; and (9) age.

Development of Roast Coffee Flavor and Color.—This is influenced by: (1) mode of roasting; (2) degree of roast; (3) whether blending is done before or after roasting; (4) whether a water quench is used and how much; (5) time and condition of roast coffee storage; and (6) any deterioration and contamination.

Coffee Extract.—This is influenced by (1) grind; (2) mode of percolation; (3) yield of solubles; (4) extraction time; (5) extraction temperature; (6) final extract concentration; (7) storage time and conditions; (8) degree of tar removal; (9) whether extracts are blended; (10) deterioration or contamination; and (11) mode of drying.

Soluble Coffee Powder.—The physical properties of the powder: (1) must be within standards; (2) must have a taste acceptable to the consumer; (3) must undergo no deterioration or contamination during storage, packaging, and shipment; (4) must be subjected to moistures, storage times, and temperatures that do no harm to the powder's physical or taste quality. Powder may be blended to effect a desired flavor or to dilute an undesirable flavor.

Other Taste Factors.—There must be evaluation or comparison of: (1) competitor qualities; (2) consumer acceptance; (3) modes of preparation; (4) influence of water; (5) utensils; and (6) techniques of tasting and beverage use.

Types of Taste Tests

Blind Tasting between two coffee beverage products, by paired triangles or otherwise, is essential for objective flavor evaluation. Sometimes taste sensitivity to different coffee brands makes distinction so easy that subjective influences will be called upon for preferences and subsequent decisions.

Formal Taste Testing.—Using proper proportions of coffee and water and standardized brew procedures, this testing is necessary, but allowances have to be made for the way instant and roast coffees are actually consumed. For example, a flavor deficiency noted in formal tasting for one coffee may produce a consumer preference for that same coffee when tasted informally by measuring out enough instant coffee to give the best taste. Water quality, paper cups, time of holding hot brew, etc. each influence cup flavor. If superiors insist on cup evaluation late in the day and under trying conditions, taste results will be irregular, if not wrong. A person cannot be forced to taste with discrimination.

Cup testing can be carried out *open,* where the source of the coffee is known, or it can be *partially blind* in that what is being tasted is known but the cups are not specifically identified; or the cupping can be completely *blind.* Circumstances determine which method to use. But in setting up a taste test the objectives must be clear, and taste results should be in writing and not discussed until all tasting has been completed and recorded.

A too common practice is to have six or more cups under evaluation at one time and/or six tasters comparing the same cups. Either circumstance is unsatisfactory for best beverage evaluation. Too many cups are confusing and reduce taste sensitivity; too many tasters allows cups to cool, and the beverage becomes depleted.

Tasting is usually done against a known sample. Reference samples are important, not only for maintaining uniformity of product, but to give a taste standard for common discussion. Aroma and flavor memory, without a reference sample, is often short and distorted. Aroma and flavor are, after all, relative when comparing one coffee with another or, for example, one wine with another. Fatigue or loss in discrimination also sets in with too much tasting.

It is an interesting experience for the skilled taster to train new tasters. It is like a man with eyes leading the blind. After repeated exposures to the fine points of tasting, the trainee progressively recognizes blends, off-flavors, roasts, and other subtle factors.

Sampling

For normal cupping, the laboratory procedure is to take green coffee bean samples (usually from 10 per cent of the bags) with a trier. About 100 gm of beans per coffee bag are sufficient. The accumulated bean samples are mixed (e.g., with a baffled tube). After several passes to mix the beans, the bean sample can be split for storage and the use of smaller quantities. A set of perforated grading screens for pea-berry and normal shaped beans is desirable. Two scales—a scale that can weigh 10 lb and a scale for weighing several grams—are desirable. Instant coffee is usually weighed at 2.0 or 2.2 gm per 5 fl oz of beverage.

Laboratory Supplies

A thermostatically heated urn and/or kettle heaters are needed. There must also be storage space for green, roast, and instant coffee. Roasting should be done in an adjacent room with forced ventilation. Glassware and other laboratory supplies must be kept on hand. A dishwashing machine is desirable to facilitate oil removal from cups and to sterilize them, as well as to save labor. An assortment of brewing equipment such as percolators, espresso machines, vacuum and drip percolators, filters, and hot plates, are needed.

The most important taste properties are freedom from foreign matter or spoilage, and uniformity of product. The sensitivity of the experienced taster to such variations is far greater than that of the lay consumer. This is especially so after the coffee flavor has been altered by staling, water quality, concentration variations, heat treatment, and additions of milk, sugar, and chicory.

Blend vs Process Taste

Figure 272, p. 90, Chapter 15 shows the coffee flavor level change from roast coffee to instant coffee. This situation especially emphasizes the need for different blending and roasting procedures in soluble coffee processing. What the diagram does not show is the degree of coffee flavor carry-through for different soluble coffee plants and processes. For example, a good instant coffee plant and process will show perhaps a 15 per cent retention of roast coffee flavor in the powder. A poor soluble coffee plant and process will show hardly any coffee blend influence but a great deal of process flavor. Therefore, the use of this chart depends largely on the instant coffee plant and process under consideration. The add-back of coffee oil to spray dried powders does not obscure a basically poor flavor resulting from poor blends and processes.

With good flavor retention through the process, better blends show more natural flavor in the instant coffees. Then the instant coffee cup flavor difference between 100 per cent high grown Colombian coffees, 100 per cent low grown mild coffees, 100 per cent Brazilian coffees, and 100 per cent Robustas is easily distinguished. In spite of unclear thinking and statements, there is a significant difference in the flavor quality of soluble coffee products and processes. Soluble coffees and soluble coffee plants are not all the same.

Roast coffee flavor is diminished when soluble coffee is produced, but natural coffee flavor is not completely lost. Furthermore, the hydrolysis volatiles contribute undesirable flavor notes in instant coffees. The more prominent these hydrolysis notes are, the less prominent the natural coffee flavors. On the other hand, some processes are such that most volatile flavors are lost from the original blend. Then low cost, low grade, imperfect, fermented, and Rioy coffees are used with less noticeable downgrading in flavor quality. Neutral green coffees will give neutral flavored instant coffees. If achieving top flavor instant coffees were the only consideration, because of the high loss in coffee flavor in preparing instant coffee, it would be more desirable to use higher flavored green coffees in the blend. But the economics of mass marketing usually discourages this procedure except in the coffee growing countries that have rich flavored beans. Imperfect coffees with basically high grown mild flavor in a good processing plant will carry through appreciable amounts of natural, appealing coffee flavor. Hence, fine soluble coffees

can be made from the heaviest flavored blends. Most of the objectionable flavors that occur in the brew (colloids) do not appear in the percolated soluble coffee and powder. The dream of each coffee producer is
to manufacture a coffee beverage that is better than his raw material.
In this case, it is a reality. Furthermore, some day, even neutral coffee
blends may give good flavored winey instant coffees with *additives* as
well as with more flavor retentive processing.

The choice of green coffee largely governs the flavor of the resulting
roast, extract, and instant coffee.

Green coffees that have the most "body" are well suited for soluble
coffee manufacture. Darker roasts have flavors that are better carried
through the soluble coffee process. Percolation of coffees blended after
roasting and powders blended after spray drying develop broader coffee
flavor and taste appeal.

Due to disproportionate hydrolysis yields of solubles, choice of blends
for soluble coffees is different from choice of blends for roast coffee use.
There is a wide latitude in coffee flavor that is acceptable to the public.
But the instant coffees that have the most and best natural coffee flavor
are those that most often sell best.

Percolator extracts are usually indicative of the flavor to be obtained
from the resulting powder, except that extracts are slightly more aromatic
and acid tasting in the cup.

It is good practice for a production supervisor of a soluble coffee processing plant to taste the roasted coffee brew, the percolator extract, and
the spray dried powder several times per day. This gives a measure of
flavor uniformity and recognition of process variances due to blend, roast,
grind, drying conditions, and other factors. Furthermore, it is up to an
authorized taster to set levels for the reworking of instant coffee, because
of off-flavor, wrong density, or other defects.

PRODUCTION FACTORS INFLUENCING INSTANT COFFEE FLAVOR

Table 94 gives a brief summary of the general rules for processing an
instant coffee high in natural coffee flavor. Because of the very nature
of this subject, all conditions encountered in all plants and countries
cannot be covered. Some phenomena that occur during processing are
deliberately caused by choice of coffee or processing conditions; others
are caused by accident or variations in processing conditions.

The process supervisor must know the coffee blend and degree of roast
at all times through his own visual and taste inspection and from blend
and roast color records. Sometimes, changes in a single coffee lot of
seemingly uniform coffee may cause a change in processing conditions and
results. The supervisor is more or less an overall monitor of materials

TABLE 94

FACTORS CONTRIBUTING TO BETTER FLAVORED INSTANT COFFEES

General Rules For Producing Good Soluble Coffee Extract and Powder
Percolation and Co-current Spray Drying

1. Use a good grade and blend of green coffee beans.
2. Use as dark a roast as is consistent with best flavor development and processing carry-through of flavor for consumer acceptance.
3. Use the shortest possible processing time from green bean to extract and powder.
4. Maintain minimal solubles inventory in the percolators.
5. Extract R & G coffee as uniformly as possible in achieving the desired yield; use uniform processing in general and particularly in roasting.
6. Realize that hydrolyzed solubles contribute no flavor goodness to the final product, unless hydrolyzed solubles are purified and obtained without influencing the extracting of the 20 to 25 per cent coffee flavored atmospheric solubles.
7. Obtain a clear extract of only soluble solids; there should be no particles or noticeable colloids.
8. Extracts should not be unduly exposed to air, or held above 60 F (16 C) for over an hour, nor should powders normally be stored above 100 F (38 C) for more than a day.
9. Extracts must not be heated to the point where they caramelize and develop phenolic burnt flavors.
10. Use as fine a grind as is consistent with avoiding difficulties of excessive percolator pressure drops.
11. Percolator drawoff temperatures of extracts should not exceed 170 F (77 C) and should only attain this temperature at the end of the drawoff.
12. In order to obtain a superior soluble coffee powder by minimal evaporation, the dried extract should be at as high a concentration as possible without damaging the overall quality of percolate normally produced at lower concentrations.
13. Roasted coffee should be ground just before extraction, and coffee should be roasted not more than a few hours before grinding.
14. R & G coffee should not be heated, as against the hot, 250–300 F (121–149 C) percolator column walls for any length of time.
15. Preserve as much fresh percolate aroma as possible in the final consumer product by using low drying temperatures, high extract concentrations, dark roasts, large, dense, and beaded dried particles.
16. Use only stainless steel, glass, or inert materials in contact with the coffee during processing.
17. Use all practices consistent with cleanliness, orderliness, and economy.

and process with the aid of data sheets, taste records, drier and product quality laboratory test results, and conversations with workers. If the reason for a deviation in product flavor, property, or process conditions is not obvious, the supervisor must question the operator, determine the cause of the change and then correct it. He must continually review plant conditions and talk to operators. To ignore any change is to invite further deviations, lessening of product quality and rejection of the final product. Investigation may show, for instance, that atomization pressures are slightly higher and extract temperature is warmer. Why? Perhaps the cooling water for the extract has warmed up due to cooling equipment failure.

Problems are numerous but invariably solvable with a thorough and systematic knowledge of facts. And facts are best drawn out of well trained operating personnel who know what conditions will influence their process step.

An uncontrollable situation such as an electrical power failure may occur. Holding hot coffee in the percolators causes flavor deterioration and difficulty in dislodging the softening grounds. A decision has to be made whether to blow or empty the percolator columns so that coffee grounds do not stick in the columns.

A focal observation point is the spray drier control room. If powder is not continually acceptable in taste and physical properties, then at least one operating factor is out of control. To keep product quality within specifications, the irregular factor must be quickly located and adjusted. In cases where causes are not clear, but product or process variations are apparent, corrective measures can be taken while facts are evaluated and causes are studied. This is where recording instruments and laboratory data are very valuable.

A gradual increase in temperature of feed water to the percolators may reveal higher solubles yields which in turn are causing lighter powder bulk densities of spray dried powder. The monitoring of night shift performance by instruments is often the only reliable reference to process outages and temperature and pressure variances. Examination of strip chart temperature records from the percolator system will reveal immediately any cyclic variation in the past 24 hr. Spray drier temperature and pressure records give the same monitoring advantage. A monitored operation invariably results in a more attentive work crew that can take pride in a uniform process and product.

Uniformity of operation requires good maintenance (repair of leaks, pumps, etc.) handled concurrently to insure a minimum of process variations and interruptions.

When the operating personnel are newly hired, newly coordinated, or simply unfamiliar with their duties, much more "trouble shooting" and corrective action falls to the supervisor. It is far cheaper in the long run to use competent operator help than to allow all the process responsibilities to funnel slowly to the supervisor. Sooner or later coffee losses and/or personal injury will occur with such unbalanced delineation of responsibilities. This means that operators should be well trained in processing and able to take some initiative in process and product control.

Numerous and surprising factors in processing influence the uniformity of the end product. For instance, small factors like darker roasts can cause softening of coffee grounds to the point where serious pressure drops occur in percolation. The same effect can be caused by the addition of a physically soft bean to the blend. Excessive holdup of R & G coffee in a humid atmosphere may cause a stale coffee with associated heaviness in instant coffee flavor. A slippage of rolls on the grinder can cause a coarser grind that may reduce solubles yield. Questions arise such as: are the operator and tester aware of the importance of such changes? Who initiates the spread of operating knowledge? When black floating specks appear in the spray dried powder, does the operator know that the drier may have charred powder on its walls? Or is drying continued until the laboratory tests report rejection of tons of powder? It is up to the unit process operator to correct the variances as they occur. If he does not, then the supervisor of operations must do so before the product reaches the laboratory to become a rework statistic as well as a coffee and quality loss for the day.

Ill-informed, misinformed, or non-informed processing personnel and management can do no better than their information allows them to do. Also, a poorly designed and equipped soluble coffee plant cannot operate beyond its physical limitations, no matter how good its operating crew. These statements are axiomatic, but sometimes overlooked.

PRODUCT QUALITY LABORATORY EQUIPMENT AND FUNCTIONS

The plant supervisor collects his process data sheets and instrument records daily. The plant chemist measures and records the properties of production powder. The plant cupper tastes the resulting powder and passes it if it is acceptable.

Actually the monitoring of the product takes place in three laboratories. First, the powder is monitored by spray drier operating personnel in the spray dryer control room. Here powder bulk density, moisture, solubility, fluidity, appearance, color, and flavor are measured. Also the powder must be free from floating oils, floating specks, sediment, cup rings, foam, and milk curdle. The results of these tests show the drier operator whether an acceptable product is being made. Later the product quality laboratory staff will repeat these tests as an independent confirmation before approving the powder for packaging. The cupper approves the powder for acceptable flavor before and after the packaging. Usually the same cupper who chooses blends of green coffee will approve the taste of the instant coffee. It is desirable to obtain a continuity of operating test and taste results from green to instant coffee so that blend and instant coffee flavor changes can be controlled by the same person with the aid of the chemical and plant knowledge of the processing superintendent.

The spray drier laboratory is, therefore, equipped to measure powder moistures, dissolve powders, heat and store water, examine powder particles under a microscope, vacuum filter the instant coffee after curdle inspection with milk, and to run bulk powder densities.

The product quality laboratory does all these measurements and more. The pH of brew and extracts are measured; extracts may be frozen for future taste reference. Plant water is evaluated and gases are analyzed. Light reflectance of roast coffee and instant coffee powders may also be measured here, and brew light transmission tests may be made. Any and every test of a physical and chemical nature is done in the product quality laboratory. Its supervisor is preferably a chemist. Moistures of green coffee beans and spent coffee grounds are measured here. Screen analyses on R & G coffee, instant powder from the spray drier before and after packaging are made. If inert gas or vacuum packing is used, oxygen content of the can is measured.

Special Tests

These may be required on fuel oils, packaging materials, jars (weights, measurements, and capacities), complaint samples, packaged jars, labels, adhesives, and coffee oil extractions. There may also be analyses of carbohydrate, caffeine, nitrogen, and iron. Sometimes viscosity, surface tension, and refractive indices need to be measured.

Laboratory Equipment

Instruments for measuring relative humidity, fusion temperatures, compressibility, and other physical constants are usually on hand. To support such work a reasonable supply of laboratory glassware and hardware is needed. Standard chemical solutions are needed for water analyses as are pH indicators, burettes, and dilution flasks. Ovens are needed for moisture determinations and for drying materials and apparatus.

After measurements are made, files must be maintained of analytical results, forms, procedures, suppliers catalogs and instructions, reagent supplies, experimental data, etc. Such records are invaluable when historical perspective is desired or references to prior processing conditions are needed.

The laboratory usually prepares the distilled water it uses. Also all laboratory safety equipment is kept here including asbestos and rubber gloves, extinguishers, burn salve, and first-aid kits.

When outside laboratory analyses are made, the plant laboratory should process the work and keep the results on file so as to centralize analytical functions.

A reasonable supply of analytical books, periodicals, society bulletins, and handbooks should be kept here.

The Primary Functions of the Product Quality Laboratory

These can be summarized as follows: (1) to measure, record, and report product properties; (2) to advise production supervisors and management; (3) to perform miscellaneous analytical services; (4) to maintain files of such records; (5) to carry out experiments and report results as required; (6) to prepare weekly summaries of product quality; (7) to advise promptly production of substandard product; (8) to maintain a clean, orderly, and well-equipped laboratory; (9) to work safely.

Frequency and Stage of Testing

In a soluble coffee plant, tests include: (1) *green coffee* trier samplings of 10 per cent of *all* green coffee bags per lot; (2) *all green coffee* for cleaning losses, moistures, bean appearance, grade, bean uniformity, cleanliness, age, color (visual) and cup quality; (3) *roast coffee* for light reflectance, screen analyses, cup quality, bulk density, and uniformity which may be measured several times daily and on request. R & G coffee is analyzed on screens several times per shift; roast losses are taken continually during roasting.

Extract Concentrations.—These are taken every cycle at the percolators and for each tank at the spray drier. A pH and curdling test is desirable once per shift. Extract cup flavor should be measured each day.

Instant Coffee Powder.—Each half hour at the spray drier discharge, moisture, bulk density, and solubility, as well as cup cleanliness and curdling are monitored. Screen analyses for particle size distribution are made as needed at the spray drier and on packaged powder to determine breakage. Moistures of dried and expressed spent coffee grounds moistures may be taken once per shift, on a routine basis. Table 61 (Chapter 12, Vol. I) shows one type product quality data sheet that can be used.

Samples of production powder are kept for reference in reduced samplings up to 1 yr. Equipment for blending without breakage and splitting of powders is needed. The laboratory should be air conditioned to minimize moisture absorption while handling instant coffee powders. Tote bin powder samples (about 180 gm) are sent to the product quality taster and product quality laboratory, and one sample is retained at the spray drier laboratory until the powder is packaged.

FLAVOR CHANGE FROM ROAST TO INSTANT COFFEE

Types of Coffee

The altitude of growth and the resulting physical properties of a coffee influence its processing conditions as well as the carry-through of flavor. For example, a high grown mild coffee with good aroma and body in the cup will make an instant coffee with better flavor than a lower grade green coffee. However, in the processing, the net natural flavor that results in the instant coffee is at a much lower level although it is still discernible. One may note from Fig. 272 that highly flavored coffee is reduced in flavor in the instant coffee product. Flavors that are objectionable in R & G coffees are less so in instant coffee. However, with similar processing conditions the better blend will always make a better flavored instant coffee product than the poorer blend.

Figure 272 also shows that desirable properties in the roasted and brewed coffees are diminished in instant coffees; whereas, objectionable flavor properties such as mustiness, earthiness, and gamey flavors are also reduced.

For example, good neutral flavored Brazilian coffees, not unlike old crop coffees, will give a neutral and acceptable instant coffee nothing more and nothing less. In no case will the Brazilian instant coffee product have a highly desirable flavor. A highly flavorful, high grown, mild roast coffee will give a desirable flavor to the instant coffee that will be more than barely acceptable; in no case should its taste be objectionable. In some cases, an objectionable tasting roast coffee will lose most of its objectionable flavor in processing to give an acceptable tasting instant coffee. In other cases the objectionable taste properties may remain quite prominent in the instant coffee. Each case must be decided on its own merits.

In general, at higher solubles yields, the taste quality of the instant coffee is reduced.

Flavor Carry-Through to Instant Coffee

It is difficult to correlate with certainty which off-flavor of roast coffee will carry through to the instant coffee, and much plant process experience is required in this area. However, there are two taste properties in roast coffee that are highly desirable for carry-through to the instant coffee: (1) "body"; (2) heavy roast.

"Body" may be available either from the fine natural properties of a high grown mild coffee or from the natural properties of coffee dried in the cherry. The trouble with the "body" of the latter type is that these coffees are usually associated with off-flavors, especially fermented flavors. Caution needs to be used in their application.

On the other hand, old crop mild coffees have greater "body," and this carries through to the instant coffee product; whereas, the green "grassy," thin body flavors, although more aromatic, do not carry through as well to the final instant coffee. As a result, new crop coffee gives relatively watery flavored instant coffee.

Blending

Blending of a small amount of high grade mild coffees with good flavor is not very beneficial when outweighed by the major percentage of just acceptable to objectionable coffee flavors. If one mixes equal parts by weight of a good high grown mild flavored coffee with an acceptable tasting neutral coffee that has a noticeable objectionable flavor, the coffee mixture is downgraded in flavor closer to the objectionable tasting coffee than might be expected as an arithmetic mean. This is true in all food products and can be stated as a rule: *mixing a good product with a poor product in equal parts will reduce the mixture closer to the level of the poorer product.*

In addition, there are processing factors that will influence each type of coffee. For example, at a given percolation condition Robustas will give a higher yield of solubles than Brazilian coffees, and the least yield will be obtained from the more dense high-grown mild coffees. Thus, if a blend of such coffees is used, a disproportionate high yield is obtained from the less flavorful coffees. The less flavorful coffees undergo more severe processing than they would alone. Such roasting and extraction results in softening of the percolator particle beds with excessive pressure drop, hence, non-uniform percolation. This is especially true with imperfect coffees. Non-uniform physical properties of the coffee cause uneven roasting and grinding and erratic percolation.

In order to process such imperfect, non-uniform coffees with better control, it is preferable to run them through the cleaning, roasting, grinding, percolation, and spray drying process steps separately. Then the powdered coffees can be blended into the normal production powder stream. This gives the opportunity to run low grade coffees but not to include them in any production blend without strict flavor level control.

Flavor Evaluation

For instant coffee flavor this assumes a different pattern from roast coffee evaluation because: (1) the person evaluating the instant coffee often is not aware of the roast coffee blend used and the flavor changes and contributions of the process; (2) since the soluble coffee beverage tastes so different from roast coffee brew, a new set of taste standards has to be used as a guide.

Taste opinion can be arbitrary but must bear relation to objective facts such as what the consuming public accepts as instant coffee flavor, prices, and open market competition as measured by actual sales growth and profits.

There is a fairly wide range of instant and roast coffee flavor acceptance by the purchasing public since it is known that instant coffee with objectionable flavors and constituted largely of Robusta coffees is being successfully marketed. However, these coffees represent the "bottom of the barrel." They have the poorest flavor and the lowest cost of all. On the other hand, instant coffee products like Yuban which represent the most coffee-like flavors at a premium price are in the desirable instant coffee flavor range.

INSTANT COFFEE FLAVOR

Contributing Factors and Variations

There are two sources of instant coffee flavor: (1) quality of the coffee used in the process; and (2) contributions from the processing methods. Both are often important. In most plants, processing is more important than the coffee used. This is especially true of the less flavorful instant coffees. The processes that protect the flavor of the incoming green coffee and bring it through as naturally as possible give the better quality instant coffees as a rule.

Two important factors in the processing of the instant coffee help bring the flavor through to the final product: *degree of roast* and *degree of hydrolysis*.

Degree of Roast.—The fault with using a dark roast for the whole production is that only burnt flavors carry through. The advantage of using a dark roast on only a portion of the production is that it releases oily matter which helps carry more coffee flavor through the process from both the dark and light roast coffees. This situation is well demonstrated in a case where imperfect coffees are used in a coffee blend, or where a non-uniform type of coffee is roasted as part of the blend. The result is that the beans are not uniformly roasted. In order to get a good average roast, some of the beans will come close to burning or develop a French or Italian roast. This may occur in only a small fraction of the coffee, perhaps only 5 per cent. When this coffee is extracted, enough of the dark roast oily products are carried into the extract to carry through the coffee flavor. Basically, this is an important reason why more coffee flavor is carried through in the coffee-growing country soluble coffee plants. This seems to be demonstrated by the quality of instant coffees particularly from the Nicaraguan and Mexican plants. In soluble coffee plants in the United States, where the beans used are usually of very uniform grade, such a wide variation in degree of roast (with only a small part of the beans becoming burnt) is less likely to occur.

Degree of Hydrolysis.—With little or no dissolution of coffee carbohydrates by hydrolysis (up to about 25 per cent solubles from R & G coffee), the resultant coffee extract from a percolation system, depending on process time, temperatures, etc., tends to taste more like the brew from roast coffee. But as hydrolysis yields of soluble components increase, there is progressive dilution of natural coffee flavors. This is because the hydrolysis products are not coffee-like and tend to be neutral glucosides which have little taste. With a yield of about 33 per cent of soluble components from R & G coffee, there appears a definite acid contribution from hydrolysis reactions accompanied by a furfural-like aroma and flavor. A pronounced sweetness, which might be associated with the increased acetone content, occurs. With a yield of 33 per cent soluble components, the extract has a flavor distinctly different from that with 25 per cent solubles yield. Near 40 per cent solubles yields, a definitely weak flavor becomes evident, distinctly sweet in character due to furfural and acetone, yet sufficiently acidic as compared with brewed coffee. This acidity is, however, different in nature from natural coffee acidity, and tends to be more irritating to the throat surfaces. High solubles yields also produce an after-taste, or coating that sticks to the tongue and mouth surfaces. At high solubles, the newly formed acids may become so concentrated that a puckering sensation is obtained in the extract which is also evident, but to a lesser extent, in the spray dried powder. These lower pH's or greater acidities are often balanced by using Robusta coffees with neutral properties. The net effect is that hydrolysis solubles, whether they are neutral, acidic, or aromatic, equal the weight of solubles from non-hydrolyzed extraction, and the net result is a beverage that is different in chemical composition and in flavor. The prolonged heat and time exposure to effect the higher solubles yields are invariably accompanied by natural coffee flavor losses and alterations.

Upgrading Coffee Flavor (from Roast to Instant Coffee)

It is a common experience when using imperfect and variegated coffees which have a displeasing flavor as brewed coffee that they may make an acceptable tasting instant coffee. The reason is that no brew colloids or oily matter are in the percolator extract. Much of this oily matter is the carrier of the roast coffee brewed flavor. Oily colloids are different from the fatty acids and dark roast coffee products which are soluble in the coffee extract. Thus the objectionable flavors that are associated with the brewed coffee are eliminated when making the instant coffee extract. Hence, there is a true upgrading in the quality of the coffee flavor obtained from the original green coffee.

Flavor Levels Retained and Variations

One factor that contributes to the level of coffee flavor in the final instant coffee product is associated with the amount of tars in the extract at the time of spray drying. If one centrifuges out all the tars from the extract, the resulting powder will give a clean cup appearance but will be noticeably lacking in genuine coffee flavor. It will have a predominant hydrolysis flavor. Similar flavor levels both for the coffee flavor and the hydrolysis flavor are achieved, but this depends on the yield taken, on how the yields are taken, on the amount of tars produced, and on the amount of tars retained at the time of spray drying. For example, within a given process blend, one may manipulate and control the extraction to give the optimum balance between the hydrolysis flavor contribution and the genuine coffee flavor contribution. This is exclusive of the brewed aroma contribution which is usually absent.

Separate Roasting of Green Coffee with Subsequent Blending

The following is a good procedure for best flavor retention and attainment as well as minimum cost:

(1) The separate roasting of green coffees to achieve optimum flavor;

(2) To obtain high hydrolysis yield with the minimum of hydrolysis flavor contribution;

(3) To use a small percentage of dark roast coffee in the blend;

(4) To obtain hydrolysis yield with a minimum of tars so as to retain cup cleanliness;

(5) Off-flavored and non-uniform roast coffees should not be excluded. Where portions of these are used, each must be evaluated in regard to its flavor usefulness as a darker roast portion of the overall blend. The darker roast on this imperfect portion diminishes its off-flavor contribution and augments the roast products which help carry the overall natural coffee flavor into the final instant coffee extract and powder.

CHAPTER 19

Special Aspects of Coffee Processing

DECAFFEINATION

Some persons who enjoy coffee cannot sleep after drinking it in the evening. This nervous tension is attributed to caffeine.

HISTORY

About the turn of the century, a commercial coffee decaffeination process was started in Europe. The Kaffee H.A.G. organization in Bremen, Germany, was the first and most prominent in the development of this process and product. At that time, Ludwig Roselius with Meyer and Wimmer took out numerous patents in the United States and many European countries. The 1908 U.S. patent disclosed substantially the basic idea that was used for decades. Green coffee beans were steamed for 5 hr to 21 per cent moisture, wetted with water, perhaps treated with ammonia or acids; then the beans were solvent extracted with trichlorethylene, chloroform, or benzene, (C_6H_6). The extracted beans were steamed to distill the solvent. Then the beans were dried.

Trichlorethylene and other halides can be detected in solutions by a copper halide flame test (Beilstein), the sensitivity of which is from 10 to 200 ppm, which imparts a green coloration to the gas flame. The trichlorethylene is volatilized into a gas flame, and contact with copper foil or gauze in the flame gives a vivid green color.

The decaffeinated R & G coffee was sold exclusively in that form until after World War II; thereafter, soluble decaffeinated coffees came into prominence both in the United States and Europe.

Punnett (1956 and 1957) reviewed about 100 decaffeination patents in a general way for the period 1908 to 1950. These are listed in the bibliography of this chapter. Lee (1960) covered some of the developments over the past 50 years.

Historically, Kaffee H.A.G. was the world leader in the decaffeination field until World War II. In 1932, General Foods acquired full ownership of its assets, with the trade name Sanka and the Brooklyn, N. Y., plant of German design for decaffeinated roast coffee. In 1946, Sanka was first sold as a *soluble* coffee. Decaffeinated *roast* coffee called Kaffee HAG made by this process was sold before 1946. This was direct contact of chlorinated solvent with pre-steamed and pre-wet green coffee beans. The

Bremen firm of Kaffee H.A.G. is still an important factor in world trade of decaffeinated roast and soluble coffees. It is still directed by the family of Ludwig Roselius.

Today in the United States and Europe about 10 per cent of all soluble coffees sold are decaffeinated. Hence, for the United States where there is a $400,000,000 annual market in soluble coffees, about $40,000,000 to $50,000,000 is in decaffeinated roast and soluble coffees of which General Foods' Sanka leads in sales. About 1955, Nescafé introduced its DeCaf, and Chase & Sanborn its Siesta. About 1960, Tenco produced a decaffeinated instant coffee. Green or instant coffees can be purchased from several firms in Europe, particularly Coffex S.A. of Schaffhausen, Switzerland. Mr. Max Brunner of that firm has several patents with E. Bürgin dated 1934, 1940, and 1941; the first is French, the latter two are American.

Water Extraction of Green Bean

The listed patents on decaffeination show that in 1942–1943 Berry and Walters of General Foods describe a new decaffeination process using a water extract of green coffee beans, U.S. patent 2,309,092. The resulting caffein laden water extract is solvent extracted. This patent recently expired. The process is, no doubt, still used in substantially its patented form. In this process, the aqueous extraction of caffeine from the green coffee beans can also take place in a batch countercurrent system which is not as efficient as a battery of percolators.

The General Foods patent of January 26, 1943 uses eight percolator columns, each holding 1,000 lb of green bean coffee. Extraction is done with a 200 F (93 C) water feed. The water extract removes 98 per cent of the caffeine in 8 hr residence time. Wet beans have about 53 per cent moisture and 0.5 per cent caffeine. The fresh column of green coffee beans undergoes a faster recycling of saturated green coffee solubles water extract to effect better bean wetting. This concentrated solution (from bean wetting) has less than 0.5 per cent caffeine on leaving. Water makeup is required due to such bean wetting. Water is removed from the percolation system by the swollen wet beans which are nearly free of caffeine. As the beans leave they are rinsed with fresh water to free them from solubles

The caffeine extraction rate is slow and is verified by Barch's 1957 patent. It varies with the type and size of beans. Since natural coffee flavor is modified and peak flavor notes are lost in the decaffeinated coffee product as with some instant coffees, there is a strong tendency to use cheaper coffees, e.g., Brazilian and Robusta coffees. The Robusta coffees have twice the caffeine content for by-product value recovery. Caffeine sold for $4 to $5 per lb in 1962. This decaffeination is done through a water phase; the green beans must be wetted. Since the decaffeination process was developed commercially in Germany and then altered in the United States (both coffee-consuming countries), a double drying of the green coffee beans results. Double drying of the green coffee beans has an undesirable influence on the resulting flavor from such green coffee beans. In this regard it would be far better to decaffeinate the green coffee beans in the coffee-growing country after mucilage removal. Barch (1957) states, "Depulped undried coffee beans still retaining parchment may also be employed, caffeine being extracted therefrom at substantially the same rate as from beans without parchment covering." A coffee bean decaffeination plant in the coffee-growing country that processes the beans wet would operate for only a few months each year. But in Colombia, the decaffeination plant might operate continually since harvests occur all year round. Furthermore, the use of small, imperfect beans for decaffeination would make a far better coffee bean product than commercial grades of Brazilian and Robusta coffees as received in coffee-consuming countries. Small green coffee beans would also help to shorten the caffeine extraction time.

Returning to the Berry and Walters 1943 decaffeination patent, the beans that have had their caffeine extracted and have been water rinsed are dried, as in the coffee-growing country. Roasted and ground decaffeinated coffee is vacuum packed or is used for preparing soluble coffee. The two largest decaffeination plants in the United States are the General Foods plants in Hoboken, N. J., and Houston, Tex.; Bremen is probably the largest plant of Kaffee H.A.G. in Germany, but there are other plants in Switzerland, France, and other parts of the world.

Recycling of Green Coffee Solubles in Water Extract.—Decaffeinated water extract, saturated with other green coffee water solubles and halogen solvent, is stripped of solvent, perhaps in a flash evaporator or rotary film vacuum evaporator. Then the green solubles water solution is returned to the countercurrent percolation system.

Caffeine Removal from Green Coffee Solubles Water Extract.—Caffeine is selectively transferred from the aqueous green coffee solubles phase to the trichlorethylene solvent by liquid/liquid countercurrent extraction. In recent years, the General American Transportation Corporation rotating disk contactors (RDC) for liquid/liquid extraction have proved to be more efficient and versatile than packed columns. Figure 293 shows an RDC column. Figures 294 and 295 show, respectively, large and small droplet sizes as governed by rotary disk speed.

This green coffee water extract then rises through a trichlorethylene continuous phase at 190 F (88 C) to take advantage of higher caffeine distribution coefficient in the solvent at elevated temperatures. Columns may be 100 ft tall. Then trichlorethylene leaves at almost 0.1 per cent caffeine with a trichlorethylene to water ratio of about 6 to 8 in an RDC column. Caffeine distribution between the solvents does not go to full equilibrium. Ratios of solvent use to aqueous extract or green beans required to effect 98 per cent caffeine transfer are reported in patents by Adler and Earle (1960), solvent/extract ratio of 6 to 1; Ornfelt (1949),

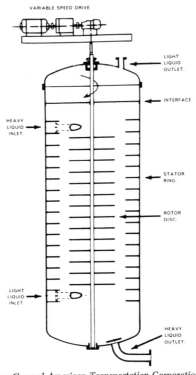

Courtesy General American Transportation Corporation

FIG. 293. LIQUID-LIQUID EXTRACTOR, ROTATING DISK CONTACTOR (RDC)

8 to 1; Durrenmatt (1950), 8 to 1; and Barch (1957), 40 to 1. The first three ratios are for roast coffee extracts; the last is for green beans.

The trichlorethylene solvent contains caffeine and some oils and other green coffee solubles including phenolics. It can be purified in two ways. (1) The solvent may be completely evaporated and the residue redissolved in water with most of the caffeine and water-soluble constituents dissolving; or (2) the trichlorethylene can be concentrated about 10- to 14-fold by evaporating solvent. This gives about 1 per cent caffeine in the trichlorethylene. Some of the chlorinated solvents boil at temperatures much lower than the boiling point of water. Such low boiling points make it easy to strip solvent from the aqueous solutions, but are undesirable because of higher solvent losses. Chlorinated solvents are expensive, and solvent losses must be reduced to a minimum. Also chlorinated solvents are toxic when inhaled in non-ventilated areas.

Return of Caffeine from Solvent to Water.—The 1 per cent caffeine in trichlorethylene may fall through a room temperature water continuous

Courtesy General American Transportation Corporation

FIG. 294.   LARGE DROPLETS IN ROTARY DISK CONTRACTOR UNIT

phas in a packed or rotary disk contactor[1] which results in about a 1 per cent aqueous solution of caffeine in the overflow. Heating to 140 F (60 C) will improve caffeine transfer. A trichlorethylene to water ratio of about 1 to 1 may be used. The caffeine distribution between the solvents does not go to full equilibrium.

---

[1] Manufactured by General American Transportation Company.

Caffeine Recovery.—The 1 per cent caffeine in water can be stripped with live steam and heated with an auxiliary steam coil. This step drives off solvent and evaporates water. The caffeine can be concentrated to 25 to 30 per cent. Subsequent cooling of this concentrated aqueous caffeine solution in a chilled wall tube or tank that is slowly but continually scraped free of caffeine crystals gives the product, see Bender (1949) U.S. patent.

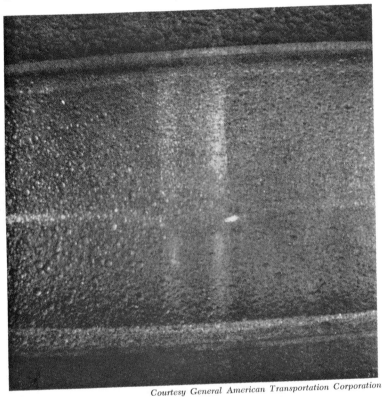

Courtesy General American Transportation Corporation

Fig. 295.   Small Droplets in RDC Unit

Caffeine has a high temperature coefficient of solubility in water. This property is advantageously used to crystallize out pure caffeine. Merck Index (1960) gives the following solubilities: 2.2 per cent caffeine at room temperature, 15 per cent caffeine at 176 F (80 C), and 40 per cent caffeine at 212 F (100 C). Thus a concentrated aqueous solution of caffeine at 212 F (100 C) is cooled slowly with agitation to crystallize out pure caffeine. The crystals may be filtered or centrifuged. Carbon purification of the caffeine solution may be necessary. A second crystallization gives United States Pharmacopeia grade caffeine useful for pharmaceuticals or in the cola soft beverages.

Caffeine Solubilities and Solvent Distributions.—A point to keep in mind is that hot water is an excellent solvent for caffeine. Few other solvents at room temperature have better solubility for caffeine than water. Two that do are methylene chloride and chloroform. The transferability of caffeine from one solvent to another must be obtained from caffeine equilibrium concentration distributions between two contacting immiscible solvents at various temperatures. For example, at 77 F (25 C), 1.00 per cent caffeine in water is in equilibrium with about 0.75 per cent caffeine in methylene chloride. The temperature influence in caffeine distribution is considerable. For example, at 158 F (70 C), 1.00 per cent caffeine in water is in equilibrium with 0.35 per cent caffeine in trichlorethylene; but at 77 F (25 C), 1.00 per cent caffeine in water is in equilibrium with 0.20 per cent caffeine in trichlorethylene.

Even though the caffeine is at a lower concentration in the two water-contacting solvents mentioned, by using larger ratios of solvent to water countercurrently, the caffeine content of the water phase can be exhausted.

As a measure of the selective solubility of caffeine in the chlorinated and other solvents, solubilities are listed in Table 95.

TABLE 95

SOLUBILITY OF CAFFEINE IN VARIOUS SOLVENTS

		Temperature	
	Per Cent	C	F
Trichlorethylene	1.5	29	84
	3.0	67	153
	3.6	85	185
Methylene chloride	9.0	33	91
Chloroform	15.0	25	77
Dichlorethylene	1.8	25	77
Benzene (C_6H_6)	1.0	25	77
	4.8	100	212
Acetone	2.0	25	77
Ethanol	1.5	25	77
	4.8	60	140
Ethylacetate	Sol.		
Water	2.2	25	77
	13.3	80	176
	40.0	100	212

Advantages of Water Extraction.—The Berry and Walters patent (1943) states that the advantages of not having the solvent contact the beans are: (1) a continuous operation is possible; (2) a better flavored end product because solvent does not directly contact green coffee beans (disputable); (3) solvent traces are difficult to remove from the beans, probably due to oils in the bean which retain the solvent preferentially; (4) long holdup time of green coffee beans in aqueous condition from 40 to 48 hr; (5) waxes are carried over in solvent from beans; (6) more rapid extraction of caffeine into 200 F (93 C) water than into solvent; (7) lower decaffeination process costs. The Berry and Walters process (1943), due to its attainment of high concentrations of caffeine in the aqueous phase, uses less solvent to transfer caffeine out of the water phase, making the process practical. High extraction temperatures are desirable to increase caffeine extraction rates from green beans and in the water-solvent system. A corresponding reduction in process time is obtained, with an improved coffee flavor. Barch's patent of 1957 claims that the presence of the chlorinated solvent inhibits the deteriorative changes in the wet green coffee. However, since the General Foods patent is symbolic of the increased and successful sales of regular and instant Sanka, its patent claims deserve full consideration.

Decaffeination of Roast Coffee Extract

Although there is no indication yet that soluble coffees have been commercially prepared from decaffeinated roast coffee extracts, in the past few years several such patents have appeared and no doubt will be the basis for such commercial operations if flavor and cost advantages are proven an actuality. Decaffeination of roast coffee extracts have been patented by Whitaker and Metzger in 1915, Ornfelt in 1949, Durrenmatt starting in 1942, Nutting in 1957, and Adler and Earle in 1960.

The Nutting and Adler and Earle patents for decaffeinating roast coffee extracts are similar. The exception is that Nutting (1957) steam distills the coffee aroma volatiles from the R & G coffee before water extraction of the R & G coffee, while Adler and Earle (1960) strip the coffee aroma volatiles from the extract. The Nutting recovery of volatiles seems more feasible, but both systems probably would make a fair flavored end product, depending on the protection the volatiles are given between recovery and drying in the extract.

In all patents cited, considerable concern is voiced regarding emulsification of solvent and extract (whether from green or roast coffee). The mechanics of emulsification must be understood and eliminated to have a successful process. Decaffeination of roast coffee extracts has the advantage of reduced plant investment, and this is an important factor.

Caffeine Analyses and Chemistry

Punnett (1942) reported on analyses of caffeine and theobromine, both of which are found in chocolate. A cup of tea has about 60 to 80 mg caffeine. A cup of coffee has 60 to 100 mg caffeine. Cola beverages (6 oz) have about 30 mg caffeine. A milk chocolate bar (1 oz or 30 gm) has 60 to 80 mg caffeine and 300 to 400 mg theobromine. Methylation of theobromine forms caffeine. This is done commercially by the Monsanto Chemical Company from the theobromine in cocoa. Chemical compounds related to caffeine and theobromine are called xanthates, purine and uric acid. The formulas are given below.

```
      N=C—H                            H—N—C=O
      |   |    H                       |   |    H
  H—C   C—N /                      O=C   C—N /
     ||  ||    \C—H                   |   ||    \C=O
     N—C—N /                      H—N—C—N /
                                                \H
       Purine                          Uric Acid
```

```
   H—N—C=O
   |   |    H
  O=C   C—N /
   |   ||    \C—H
   H—N—C—N /
  Xanthine (dioxypurine)
```

```
   H—N—C=O                          H₃C—N—C=O
   |   |    CH₃                      |   |    CH₃
  O=C   C—N /                      O=C   C—N /
   |   ||    \C—H                   |   ||    /C—H
  H₃C—N—C—N /                     H₃C—N—C—N
  Theobromine (dimethyl xanthine)   Caffeine (trimethyl xanthine)
```

THE BREWING OF COFFEE

Brewing coffee was pretty much left to the preference and ignorance of the consumer until the Pan-American Coffee Bureau (coffee growers of the Western Hemisphere) and the National Coffee Association (United States coffee roasters) formed the Coffee Brewing Institute (C.B.I.) in 1952. The objectives of the C.B.I. are to encourage improvements in the preparation of coffee beverages.

The outstanding facts that led to the establishment of this C.B.I. scientific project were: (1) common practices in brewing coffee were poor; (2) the average taste of a cup of coffee was not nearly as good as it might be, given the available blends and roasts. This was true both in the home and in large scale brewing of coffee. One of the main causes of this situation was that, for reasons of economy during and after World War II, and then often merely as a matter of habit, the usual coffee brew was about 60 cups per pound of roast coffee. This brew was weak in flavor and also unnecessarily high in very harsh and undesirable flavor notes. Merely using a higher ratio of roast coffee to water was not enough. The roast coffee flavor might still be spoiled by poor brewing techniques.

By 1957, some of the C.B.I. sub-contracted research work on coffee chemistry and brew preparation became available to members and those interested in the subject in the coffee industry. The work was largely developed under Dr. Earl E. Lockhart, the C.B.I. Scientific Director. Dr. Lockhart had formerly been with the teaching staff of the food technology department of the Massachusetts Institute of Technology (M.I.T.). It was at M.I.T. in 1954 that numerous card indexes were prepared of published articles on coffee since 1925. The nature of the C.B.I. support is such that it does not recommend coffee blends. Not recommending blends may be politic, but it certainly limits a complete presentation or judgment of coffee flavor values and even brewing. For example, some modes of brew preparation may be more suitable for Brazilian than for Colombian coffees.

Brewing, an unorganized and personal matter, still allows a wide area for useful research, consumer education, and publication. In 1961, the C.B.I. took an important step forward by establishing a brewing school in its offices in New York City so as to train sales and other interested personnel of coffee roaster members in the recommended ways of brewing coffee. Proper brewing of a good cup of coffee, regardless of blend and roast, requires specific education and a knowledge of principles, and procedures. One main impetus came from the fact that in the United States much roast coffee was being brewed at the rate of 60 cups per pound. Brewing 40 to 50 cups per pound of roast coffee would give the consumer a better flavored beverage.

The growers and roasters of coffee stood to gain sales (1) if the consumers used more coffee per cup, and (2) if they drank better brewed coffee. In this way, both producers' and consumers' interests would be served. The C.B.I. has been progressively successful in attaining these goals.

Before examining current brewing practices, it is worthwhile to look at the origin of coffee beverages and coffee use as historically presented by Ukers (1935). Coffee beans were not originally made into a beverage; coffee beans were a food. Coffee beans contain protein, carbohydrates, and oils. The coffee cherry was candied. The bean was used as a medicine. Coffee was first drunk as an ingredient of a wine. African warriors crushed the green beans with fat and made food ration balls, about 900 A.D. A fermented drink was made from the pulp. Although green coffee beans were extracted about 1000 A.D., roasting of the beans did not take place until about 1400 A.D. The water soluble extract of roast coffee did not evolve until about 1300 or 1400 A.D. At first, roasting was done in earthenware trays and later in metal trays. The roast beans were fragmented by mortar and pestle; *cooked* in boiling water and then consumed as grounds and a strong water extract. This is still the custom in the Middle East. Variations of boiling, adding cinnamon, cloves, or other spices developed untold variations of coffee flavors. These beverage preparation procedures predominated through the 17th century when the beginnings of the boiling and serving pot came into use. Orientals are reported to be the first to pour boiling water on the roast coffee grounds in the cup. About 1625 in Cairo, the use of sugar in coffee was introduced to reduce bitterness. When much sugar, often brown sugar, is added to the strong brew, a syrupy cup results.

Brew Preparation

Boiling the beverage continued well into the 18th century, and it was usually served black in English coffee houses. About 1660 in Holland and 1685 in France, milk was first used in coffee. By 1760 boiling coffee was generally recognized as producing an objectionable tasting beverage, and steeping with or without a bag to separate the grounds was first used in France. In France, the drip method of coffee preparation was initiated about 1800, and was actually percolation (central tube lift of boiling beverage) as we know it today. Originally iron or tin, and then porcelain brewers were used. During the 19th century, many improved brewing devices were evolved, especially the vacuum and drip methods as widely used today. Although many of these devices were known in the early 1800's, they were not widely or commercially manufactured until after 1900. Automated brewing equipment was neither commercially important nor fully developed until after World War II.

Coffee was largely for the wealthy, or, in any case, a luxury beverage through the 18th century. Being exotic, it was accepted as prepared for almost a century. As coffee's commercial importance grew in the 19th century, more attention was given to its natural flavor, quality, origin, and modes of preparation. Not until after World War I was there any significant scientific work done on coffee chemistry and beverage preparation; and only after World War II has this work been reinforced by the Coffee Brewing Institute and brewing equipment fabricators and users.

In colonial America coffee grounds were *boiled* in tin coated copper pots and drunk with sugars and spices, sometimes with milk. In New Orleans, due to the French influence, the coffee was generally brewed by percolating the coffee grounds and allowing the water to drip slowly through. New Orleans and the southern part of the United States still produces, on the average, a relatively good and strong cup of coffee. In Europe's Scandinavian countries and in parts of the United States where Scandinavians settled, egg was often used in the hot brew to clarify it and reduce bitterness. Since 1900 until today, the three most common methods of brewing coffee at home are the vacuum, percolator, and drip systems. Figure 296 shows the home brewing equipment. For large scale coffee beverage preparation, as in institutions or restaurants, the muslin bag full of coffee grounds flushed with hot water or drained-off coffee brew has been common. Since 1946, the vacuum 10 cup brewer and more recently the automatic coffee grounds extraction system have been more widely used.

Brew Taste.—Brewing can be considered a personal taste adventure. The majority of people brew coffee to make an acceptable to pleasant brew for others. Not everyone's taste preferences can be pleased, nor to the same degree. But the majority of persons served can be given an acceptable cup of coffee.

There are some generally accepted rules about the proper way to brew a good cup of coffee. It is the lack of good quality coffee taste experience and the numerous variables in brew preparation and coffee use that con-

FIG. 296.   HOME COFFEE BREWERS: VACUUM, DRIP,
AND PERCOLATOR

fuse the consumer. This gives restaurateurs or roasters an opportunity to claim that their coffee is "best" or "good."

Influences on Brew Quality

It is worthwhile to examine why a really good tasting cup of coffee is hard to find.

Roast Coffee Quality.—Competition in the United States fixes large volume sale prices. Most coffee blends must be bought to fit within this price structure. If the consumer boils his coffee brew, uses sugar and cream or milk, has poor quality water and poor brewing procedures, he might just as well buy the cheapest roast coffee. This could be a Robusta blend in a paper bag exposed to air. For the person who has some knowledge and appreciation of the better brewed coffee flavors, a premium priced roast coffee of good reputation is in order. The number of consumers buying average priced coffee far exceeds the consumers buying premium priced coffee; hence, the roast coffee market functions for the broader market. The large middle fraction coffee consumer is not so fussy about coffee flavor that he (usually the housewife) will pay a premium price. Yet he does not want to be stuck with the "bottom of the barrel" quality. So in the United States he buys the large regional or national brand of roast coffee (one usually on sale) often at a reduced price. This brand of roast coffee is blended to suit the average competitive price. Roast coffees in the United States are of fair cup quality. Probably 75 per cent of the bag and/or vacuum can brands purchased would make an acceptable to pleasing cup of coffee if brewed properly. Since almost half of United States' imports are Brazilian coffees, the average cup is bound to be only fair tasting, depending on how much and what quality mild coffees are blended with Brazilian coffees. Only a small percentage of name brand roast coffees use Robustas in their blends, but Robustas are used in some roast coffees. In France, Robustas are about 95 per cent of coffee imports, and the discussion of coffee blends within any such political boundary must take these factors into consideration.

Watering and Staling.—Most coffee in the home in the United States is brewed too weak. For example, 60 cups per pound of roast coffee are not uncommon. This watering ratio reduces markedly the possibility of a good tasting cup of coffee in most homes, regardless of the quality of the roast coffee. Furthermore, staling of an opened 1 lb can of R & G coffee invariably downgrades cup flavor in more than half of the cups of coffee prepared. So with water dilution and staling, perhaps one can get one good tasting cup of coffee in four, probably fewer. But these are only two of the many coffee flavor deteriorating factors in brewing.

Water Quality.—In the United States, drinking water quality, as good as it is relative to the public water supplies of the rest of the world, is often poor for brewing coffee. Chlorination, organic content, hardness, softness, alkalinity, brackishness, yearly quality variations, off-odors and tastes downgrade the water quality to varying degrees and hence downgrade the resulting brewed coffee flavor. Water quality influences are important in developing a clean coffee flavor and will be discussed in detail in the following sections. The net result is that with all brewing conditions perfect except for water, at least half the coffee brewed in the United States will be downgraded by the water quality. The basis of this statement is Fig. 297, a water hardness map of the United States. Hardness in natural waters in limestone areas is usually associated with comparable alkalinity. In some areas good brew quality is impossible due to the water quality.

Home Percolation of Coffee.—This is the boiling action of the coffee brew which raises the brew up a central tube to flow over and through a shallow bed of coffee grounds. It is a common method of brewing coffee.

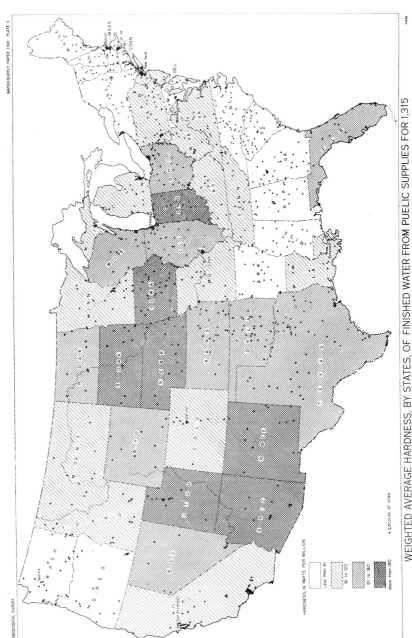

WEIGHTED AVERAGE HARDNESS, BY STATES, OF FINISHED WATER FROM PUBLIC SUPPLIES FOR 1,315 OF THE LARGER CITIES IN THE UNITED STATES, 1952

Courtesy U. S. Geologic Survey

With percolation time exceeding 10 min, most of the natural coffee aromas and flavors have been depleted and altered. The continual exposure of roast coffee grounds and diluted hot brew to air drives off aromatic volatiles, which one can easily smell, and oxidizes brew flavor solubles. The resulting brew is often heavy tasting, caramelized, non-aromatic, and oily. Vigorous percolation is a daily ritual in many homes and is, no doubt, suited to low grade stale coffees. Automatic percolators are widely used. If percolation is limited to 5 to 10 min, the flavor damage done is not as serious; that is, the coffee beverage is still acceptable in flavor. However, considerably more natural coffee flavor will be retained in the cup if the roast coffee has been drip or vacuum brewed (extracted) in 1 to 3 min with much less exposure to oxygen.

Taking into consideration available coffee blends, water quality, water to coffee ratios used, and modes of extraction, it is probable that only a small fraction of the coffee brewed has good quality natural coffee flavor.

Materials of Construction.—The lower priced percolators are made of aluminum which dissolves in acid coffee brew. Aluminum coffee pots corrode. Aluminum also reacts with fatty acids. Even though coffee brew contact time is short and aluminum contamination small, there may be a small deterioration of coffee flavor. Aluminum is not inert under brewing conditions and is now considered inferior to stainless steel. The materials of construction of coffee brewing equipment deserve special attention. When copper and copper alloys, as well as iron or carbon steel, are in contact with coffee brew they cause flavor deterioration. In general, glass, stainless steel, glazed ceramics, tin, nickel or chromium plate are inert to coffee brew acids. The disadvantage of metal plating is that when the film is broken, the protective surfaces are lost.

Cleanliness.—The design of the brewing equipment so that it can be easily and thoroughly cleaned is as important as the materials of construction. It should be possible to inspect and wipe all surfaces of a brewing vessel. Alkali cleaners recommended for such use normally do a good job of removing coffee oils, tars, and films. Inspection is desirable after cleaning to be really sure. A sanitary brewer will have shiny smooth and curved surfaces; there should be no crevices for deposits to build up. A "dirty" brewer is a factor contributing to brew flavor alteration and, usually, degradation.

Commercial Urn Brewing.—Several coffee flavor downgrading practices are common here. Muslin bags may not be kept clean; urns may not be cleaned every time they are used; extraction may not be uniform; brew may be held for hours; the brewer may be used at only half capacity which means inefficiency; concentrated coffee extract in the lower part of the urn will be poured through the sack of grounds losing solubles and extracting bitter flavors. Solubles may not be mixed uniformly in the urn reservoir. The residue of the urn brew will be added to a fresh batch of brew, thus downgrading all the freshly prepared coffee brew. In other words, the urn brew preparation is susceptible to poor brew management. As this has been recognized, automatic, small, fast batch brewers have been growing in use.

Restaurant Coffee Brewing.—This has advantages and disadvantages over modes of home brewing. In some cases, vacuum methods are used both in the home and the small restaurant. Restaurants often contract to buy their roast coffee from coffee roasters and/or suppliers in exchange for the loan of brewing equipment. Under such an arrangement, the restaurant owner often does not have much freedom to choose his coffee quality and price. The profits to this coffee roaster must cover his investment in outstanding loaned equipment. The blends supplied are therefore frequently high in Brazilian and sometimes even Robusta coffees. The restaurateur may pay 5¢ per lb more for comparable quality coffee. If he uses 40 lb per day for 365 days, he has paid out $730, which would amortize most of his investment in brewing equipment. Many restaurants would be better off in buying name brand roast coffee and their own brewing equipment, on a bank loan if necessary. This discussion shows how coffee blends and brewing equipment are controlled in some restaurants. It is therefore not uncommon to have an excellent meal and service at a restaurant with a fair to good reputation, and then an unpalatable cup of coffee.

To obtain a clean flavored, fresh cup of brewed coffee at the right concentration and temperature containing most of the natural coffee aroma and flavor is not simple. This is amply demonstrated by the coffee served in private homes and in many public restaurants. Part of the attainment of such a goal is taste, brew, and coffee education for both consumer and server. Attaining better brewed coffee flavor involves the use of better brewing equipment procedures, water quality, and coffee blends.

Five Essentials of Good Coffee Flavor

To control the five essentials for preparing a cup of really good coffee takes many talents and skills. One must know the quality of the coffee used; a brand name is not necessarily any assurance of coffee quality. One must also know something about keeping coffee fresh and be able to evaluate the packaging. One must determine whether the water quality is influencing the cup flavor. For the taste desired, economy must be secondary and the right water-to-coffee ratio must be used. The brewing method must be fast, thorough, yet not exhaustive. The serving must be prompt. In a fine coffee shop, the green beans are chosen, roasted on the day of use, ground just before extraction, brewed in minutes if not seconds, and served promptly in suitable cups.

(1) **Coffee Quality.**—Admittedly, experience can tell a person what a good tasting coffee is. However, to be absolutely sure of the basis of choice, the coffee type by variety (Arabica or Robusta) and origin (mild or Brazilian) must be known. Then the geographical (political) source; altitude of growth; quality of processing of green coffee beans (fermentation, drying, cleaning, grading, storage); age, purity (freedom from foreign matter); bean size; and moisture ought to be known. Usually most of this is not possible, so the taste and aroma must become the final basis of judgment.

Assuming that a good quality green coffee is used, aroma and flavor are not developed until roasting. The degree of roast, uniformity of roast, size of roaster, the fuel for heat, the time of roasting, use of batch or continuous roaster, the heating temperatures, and the mode of cooling may influence the aroma and flavor of the final roast coffee.

Depending on the brewing equipment used, the grind or fineness of final coffee particles before extraction has a great deal to do with the subsequent rate of staling, aroma loss, and flavor of brewed coffee. Further whipping in chaff, beating out oil and driving off volatiles with incorporation of air (oxygen) or even adding water, can lose a great deal of flavor during the grinding operation.

(2) **Package.**—Reports have been cited here and elsewhere that coffee can be held fresh indefinitely in a vacuum can, vacuum bag, inert gas filled container, etc. In every case, some oxygen is left in the container, and this oxygen goes on to react with the key aroma and flavor factors in the coffee. Hence, some staling goes on within every package. Considerable staling occurs after the package is opened and the major portion of coffee from every package is stale long before it is brewed. To put it another way, the best vacuum packed coffee is never as good in flavor as the day it was placed in the can. In fact, the process of drawing a vacuum about the coffee particles draws flavor away. The storage of coffee before it enters the can exposes it to staling. Hence the coffee house that roasts and grinds its coffee just before use has a real flavor advantage over the commercial vacuum pack. Some evaluations state that ground coffee stays fresh up to three or more weeks. According to any coffee taster, this is absurd. The ground coffee may be acceptable to a less critical and/or a less informed consumer who uses milk and sugar and possibly not the best brewing and serving methods. Hence the freshness of the roast coffee volatile flavors and their abundance are important factors from the moment of grinding until brewing, and package protection can play a vital part in this time interval.

(3) **Water Quality and Water-to-Coffee Ratio.**—Since water constitutes 99 per cent of the coffee beverage, its impurities and quality can markedly downgrade coffee brew flavor. Water may be hard, alkaline, brackish, have organic matter, chlorine, odors, gases, and metal impurities. It is an error to make weak coffee because this type of extraction brings out the undesirable flavors. An axiom in brewing is, in case of doubt, make the cup stronger. A frequent error is not measuring water nor coffee at all, so that control is lost entirely in this variable.

(4) **Brewing Method.**—Numerous methods have been cited; some of the most popular home and commercial methods destroy the aromatic properties of the best coffees. These include boiling, preparation of large batches that cannot be rapidly served, urn extraction, mixing an old batch with a fresh batch, and percolation which intimately mixes coffee extract brew with air and spent coffee grounds. Essential to good brewing technique are speed, a reasonable extraction yield, and solubles concentration. Most brewing methods take five or more minutes. Channelling of rinse drip, percolate or wash does not uniformly extract the coffee solubles. Fine grinds are seldom used. In fact, fine grind is difficult to get in many United States retail stores. Some of the newer pressurized extraction methods through granular coffee beds, not slurries, give fast uniform extraction. Some methods such as urn, drip, and percolation cannot give uniform flow through the granular bed.

(5) **Serving Method.**—If all the foregoing essentials of preparation have been perfect, it is not uncommon to find the brew boiling or near boiling for many minutes on a pot heater. Admittedly, adding sugar and milk or cream covers up the bitterness of the coffee. But if really good coffee is desired, it is best enjoyed black. Cleanliness of utensils is, of course, essential for brewing and serving but is frequently neglected. Adding a held-over pot to a freshly brewed pot is common "economical" practice. The espresso method which brews one cup at a time offers some very desirable features.

Rise in Instant Coffee Use

The fact that there are so many variables in preparing and serving a cup of good coffee has been responsible for a wide latitude in acceptable flavors for coffee. Further, the fact that brewing coffee gives variable results has increased the consumption of instant coffees.

Instant coffees also vary in flavor quality, so this discussion will be limited to the best flavored instant coffees currently available on the market. Instant coffees eliminate all brew processing and equipment. There is no cleaning of equipment. If the cup flavor concentration is weak, more powder is added; if flavor is too strong, more water is added. There is no wasted coffee brew in the pot and no grounds to be disposed of. There are neither filters nor accessories. A pot of boiling water or a decanter are the only preparation tools required. Instant coffee is ideal for 1 or 2 cup servings. Dissolved in a decanter, instant coffees retain more and better flavor than when made in individual cups. Some of the shortcomings mentioned earlier in brewing and brewed coffees have been eliminated by the use of instantly soluble coffees and not always at a sacrifice in coffee flavor value. Instant coffees, cup for cup, are about half the price of regular coffee. Instant coffee has even more advantage when brewing time, brewing equipment, unused coffee brew, grounds disposal, pot cleaning, and staling of roast coffee are considered. Good instant coffees are better flavored and more uniform in cup flavor than poor brewed coffees, even at this stage of development of the instant coffee industry. With about 18 per cent of roastings going into soluble coffees, at least 30 per cent of the cups of coffee consumed in the United States are instant coffee. The success of soluble coffees is in no small part due to the existence of poor quality and stale roast coffees. The best instant coffees are uniform and acceptable, sometimes enjoyable. Thus the growing acceptance and sales of instant coffees are a natural evolution and upgrading of available coffee beverage. Restaurants, military, and other institutions are now using more instant coffee. Although an average roast coffee brew may be superior in flavor to an average instant coffee brew, the better flavored instant coffees are to be preferred over the poorer flavored roast coffee brews.

Factors in Brew Preparation

One must have all beverage preparation factors under control in order to prepare a good tasting cup of brewed coffee: coffee and water, brewing equipment, and finally, the mode of serving and consuming. It is not always possible to control all preparation factors. In some cases one preparation factor may be restrictive or controlling, e.g., the quality of R & G coffee. The roast coffee quality may be dictated by price, not by consumer preference.

The brewing equipment manufacturer may not be directly concerned with the quality of roast coffee used, water quality available nor how long the coffee brew is held before it is consumed. The brewing machine should be designed for low price, utility, elimination of labor, and reproducibility of efficiently extracted full flavored coffee brew. Commercial coffee brewing equipment as used for large volume service in large feeding areas, is sometimes similar to mechanisms designed for use in vending machines. The most highly developed restaurant brewing equipment is completely automatic. With a coin and dispensing mechanism the brewer might be a vending machine.

Some of the shortcomings of the urn brewing of coffee have already been mentioned. The shortcomings of brewing with many manual steps are self-evident from higher labor costs as well as from variable brew flavor results.

Time Factor.—The most important point regarding the processing of coffee, whether it is roasted coffee, instant coffee powder, or brewed coffee beverage, is that processing must be done quickly. Coffee aroma and flavor are very delicate and transient phenomena. Elusiveness is part of their attractiveness. They can be captured only momentarily (unless one stands downwind of the roaster or grinder) at the consumer level. The aroma and flavor are fragile and fleeting. Thus the R & G coffee must be fresh and of good flavor. The water must be of good quality. The apparatus must brew with speed and reproducibility. The brew must be delivered and consumed promptly. Any gap in this timing sequence destroys the end result and the pleasure and satisfaction the brew ought to bring. Reducing the brewing process to a set of mechanically reproducible steps, automatically carried out without human interruption until the brewed beverage is dispensed, attains the desired goal. This has already been achieved to varying degrees in commercial brewing units which control times, temperatures, and proportions accurately.

Grind.—Niven and Shaw (1957) show that with 185 F (85 C) water, the rate of solubles extraction with fine, drip, and regular grinds is relatively low after 5 min of slurrying, at which time about 20, 18, and 16 per cent solubles have been respectively extracted. Niven's work forms the basis for the C.B.I. recommendation that suitable brewing times for each grind are respectively 1 to 3 min for fine grind, 4 to 6 min for drip grind, and 6 to 8 min for regular grind.

Solubles Yield and Concentration.—Further, the C.B.I. states that an 18 to 22 per cent solubles extraction is desirable for idealized brew cup flavor at a 1.15 to 1.35 per cent solubles concentration in the cup, with outside limits of 1.0 to 1.5 per cent solubles concentration. In practice solubles yields of closer to 18 per cent are more common.

Measurement of soluble solids content of coffee extract is, of course, an indication of solubles extraction efficiency. However, solubles concentration and yield must be considered within the whole structure of coffee brew flavor. This includes volatile aromatics and the basic quality of the roast coffee being extracted. The amount of colloids in the brew reflects blend, roast, and grind; colloids contribute mouth texture to the coffee beverage. Thus aroma and colloid quality and quantity influence coffee brew acceptability.

The C.B.I. has of necessity evolved the solubles concentration chart for coffee brews (see Lockhart 1957B). This shows: (1) if a watered coffee brew has been made, it is measured objectively; and (2) if a roast coffee extraction in an urn is inefficient, the low solubles yield and concentration will be seen.

The solubles yield is associated with a coffee brew solubles concentration. The two conditions of coffee solubles concentration and solubles yield must be satisfied so that they fall within the idealized cup flavor area, see Fig 298. Low solubles yields do not give a wholesome flavored

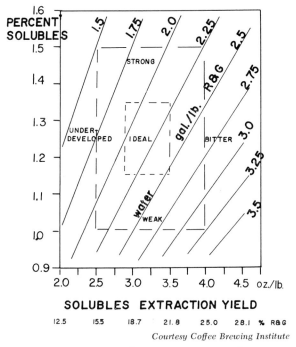

Courtesy Coffee Brewing Institute

Fig. 298. Coffee Brew Concentration of Solubles vs Yield on Parameters of Water/Coffee Ratio

cup of coffee even in the ideal solubles concentration range. High solubles yields do not give a wholesome coffee brew flavor either, even if the brew solubles concentration is in the acceptable range.

Brew Specific Gravity.—Variances for Brazilian and mild coffees on a specific gravity (C.B.I.) chart for brew are not likely to be as great as for Robusta coffees which give higher solubles yields and concentrations and a very different coffee brew flavor. A 1.5 per cent brew has a specific gravity at 80 F (27 C) of only about 1.006, and the C.B.I. has obtained special hydrometers for this use. Flavor boundary conditions in Fig. 298 are not sharp because of individual taste preferences, influences of blend, roast and grind, and time and mode of extraction as well as pH and titratable acidity. However, the solubles yield and concentration target, as fixed, is an improvement over no target at all. Thus the Coffee Brewing Institute has given the current user of coffee urns a measuring tool for their brew extraction process.

Water to Roast Coffee Ratio.—In the English weights and measures system, the water to coffee ratio of about 2.00 to 2.25 gal of water per pound of roast coffee is recommended for the best brew flavor. This corresponds in the metric system to a water to coffee ratio of 16.7 to 18.8 liters per kilogram.

Cup Sizes.—A secondary problem enters here in that the number of cups of brewed coffee per unit weight of R & G coffee is loosely spoken of, e.g., 40 cups per pound roast coffee, or 88 cups per kilogram roast coffee. Figure 298 on coffee solubles concentration and yield fixes the volume of brew solution drawn off, hence the number of cups. However, there are various cup sizes and cup fills. Cups per unit weight of roast coffee can therefore vary accordingly.

The most common cup size in the United States home is 8 fl oz (240 ml) and would be filled with brew to 6 fl oz (180 ml). But smaller cups are 7 and 6 fl oz, holding 4.5 to 5.5 fl oz of brew. Restaurants usually have the smaller cup sizes. Demitasse cups when full may hold only 3 fl oz (90 ml) or 4 fl oz (120 ml) and actually hold 1.5 to 3 fl oz of coffee.

Water Absorption.—Roast coffee grounds hold twice their dry weight of water, plus whatever water does not drain off completely from the interstices. Therefore, each pound of original R & G coffee holds about 10 per cent solubles after extraction and about 760 gm absorbed water plus interstitial undrained water. For convenience, the drained coffee brew can be taken as 90 per cent of the original water added to the roast coffee grounds. For example, 2 gal (7,570 ml) water and 1 lb (454 gm) of grounds will yield close to 1.8 gal or 6,810 ml drained brew. If the R & G coffee was flushed so that few solubles remain in the spent grounds, (10 per cent of total solubles yields) then the 91 gm of solubles (20 per cent yield on R & G coffee) are dissolved in the 6,810 ml water. This is a 1.30 per cent solubles solution. If 4.5 fl oz (135 ml) cup portions are used, this is equivalent to 50 cups; if a 5 oz cup portion is used, this is equivalent to 45 cups, and so forth.

Urn vs Automatic Brewer.—Urns are an obsolete way of coffee brew preparation under service circumstances where about 500 cups of coffee per hour (or 10 cups per minute) can be prepared from an automatic brewer. These can be prepared in brew batches of 60 cups; other units can prepare 12 cup portions in 3 min and 1 cup in 10 sec.

The advantage of the automatic coffee brewing units is that the human element is removed from the operation and the resulting batches are small —12 cups or less. Yet if heavy demand occurs, either the 60 cups per 6 min or the 12 cups per 3 min would handle the corresponding demands. The larger unit is for the higher demand rates, and the smaller unit may be used by the same caterer during low demand periods.

It hardly seems justifiable today to use an urn with an initial coffee brew reserve of 5 gal or more; this would be more than an hour's coffee supply, serving at about 3 cups per minute. The hold time for finished brew should be such that the longest a brew is held is less than 1 hr, preferably only a few minutes. Appropriate brew makers are readily available today. The restaurant that uses large brew batch preparations (aside from other shortcomings in urn use, which are many) will find his competitors able to deliver fresher coffee. To be able to deliver a fresher cup of brewed coffee is consistent with the transient nature of coffee aroma and flavor. Figure 299 shows a section through a coffee urn system. In Fig. 299 the urn has a gas burner with vents for combustion gases, but electric heating is also very common. The outer water jacket is usually

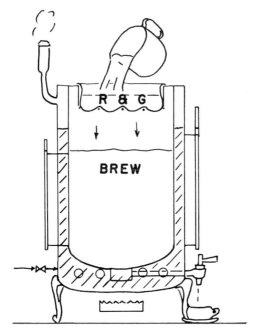

Fig. 299. Section Turough Coffee Urn

not insulated, but it should be. There are sight glasses for the inner brew reservoir and for the outer water jacket. Excessive pressure on the jacket is avoided through a safety valve. Water from the jacket is used to flush through the R & G coffee. Make-up water goes to the jacket. Figure 300 shows a pair of urns in one water jacket. Figure 301 shows a water distributor used over R & G coffee on a perforated plate. Figure 302 shows the grid and muslin bag. Urns of 2 or 3 gal size are most consistent with a fresh coffee brew concept with complete consumption in less than 1 hr.

Courtesy Western Urn Manufacturing Company

FIG. 300. PAIR OF COFFEE URNS IN ONE WATER JACKET

The brew equipment buyer may be influenced by the lower initial cost and higher labor operating costs with urns compared to possibly higher initial cost with less continuing labor costs with automatic brewing equipment. Maintaining freshness of coffee brew flavor at any time means a minimum hold time for brew. This is an objective consistent with retaining the most coffee flavor, while satisfying the rate of consumer demand as it arises. The small batch, fast brewer is well suited to this objective.

During periods when the rate of coffee use is only a few cups per hour, an instant coffee, espresso, or one cup drip brewer is best. For 12 to 200 cups per hour, the small batch fast brewer is best. Home use drip and percolator coffee brewers for 40 cups per batch are sold, both in aluminum and stainless steel, but their usefulness is mostly related to the speed of coffee consumption.

Brewing Principles

There are several ways to prepare coffee brew in principle.

The *urn method* allows boiling water to pass slowly through the roast coffee grounds by gravity percolation (often with channelling of flow). The *espresso brewing machine* achieves the same pressure extraction effect except that the roast grounds are finer and better confined; chan-

FIG. 301. WATER DISTRIBUTOR OVER COFFEE GROUNDS RESTING ON PERFORATED PLATE

Courtesy Western Urn Manufacturing Company

FIG. 302. URN SUPPORT GRID FOR MUSLIN BAG

neling does not occur for the most part. Figure 303 shows an application of the espresso principle in an Italian home coffee brewing machine. Figure 304 shows a section of an espresso machine, and Fig. 305 shows espresso machines in a retail store in Bremen, Germany. Espresso extraction takes only 1 or 2 sec. Water volume is usually fixed by a volumetric piston displacement. The water heating reservoir is under 5 psig steam pressure. The volumetric water measure by piston is more usual for commercial espresso machines while the steam pressure from a confined volume of water is more common to smaller, less expensive home use models.

Espresso Machine.—In principle, this machine performs good extraction for the following reasons: (1) coffee is ground just before use; (2) the coffee used is volumetrically measured as is the amount of extraction water; (3) the water in the reservoir comes to a full boil to expel any dissolved gases before extraction begins (see oxygen solubility in Fig. 306); (4) the extraction time is almost instantaneous.

The amount of espresso extraction water used is much less than in United States brews. United States methods use a water to R & G ratio of 20 to 1 and attain a 1.25 per cent solubles content in the extract. The espresso method uses 6 to 8 to 1 water to R & G coffee ratio, and yields concentrations in the extract of from 3 to 5 per cent solubles. Its extraction solubles yield may even be higher than with United States methods.

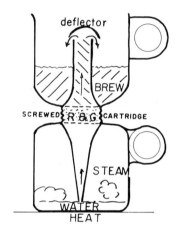

FIG. 303. ITALIAN HOME BREWER,
UPWARD PRESSURE EXTRACTION

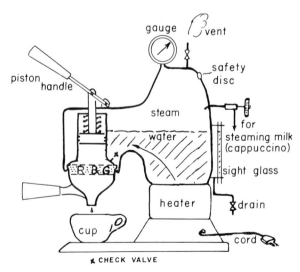

FIG. 304. SECTION THROUGH ESPRESSO MACHINE

But, due to the potentially higher solubles and oil yields available from pulverized coffee, the rapid extraction is not exhaustive. Hence, the resulting brew does not have the bitter taste that occurs when exhaustive, long time, diluted solubles extraction is done in the United States type of brewers.

Courtesy Probat-Werke

FIG. 305. ESPRESSO MACHINES IN COFFEE SHOP

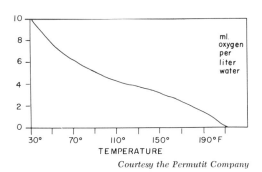

Courtesy the Permutit Company

FIG. 306. OXYGEN SOLUBILITY IN WATER VS TEMPERATURE

Of course, espresso coffee is quite a different beverage from the lower solubles and flavor content of United States brewed coffee. Espresso is drunk with sugar and perhaps a twist of lemon, hot milk, or liquor. The harm of exhaustive extraction is easily demonstrated by allowing perhaps 50 per cent more hot water than normal through an espresso machine process. The resulting coffee flavor will be bitter and unpalatable. This phenomenon shows that extraction must not be exhaustive. It is a common procedure in some European countries and in Latin America to make the original coffee brew very strong, but not to take a high and complete solubles yield from the fine grounds. Thereafter, boiling water is added to suit personal taste.

This is one way to make a good coffee brew, but it is not customary in the United States or in many other places. Espresso machines are usually used to extract Italian (almost burnt) roasts, but the extraction machine works just as well with a French roast.

Airline Brewer and Espresso Machines.—This principle has been used in the coffee brewing machine designed especially for vending coffee and for the jet air liners (see Fig. 307) in the past few years. These coffee

Courtesy REF Manufacturing Corporation and
Coffee & Tea Industries Magazine

Fig. 307.   Airline Hostess Drawing Coffee

brewers make an excellent cup of brewed coffee and operate as follows: a 3.2 oz (91 gm) polyethylene packet of fine grind roast coffee is emptied into a plastic cup of about 8 fl oz (240 ml) in volume. This has a screen of about 100 mesh in the bottom. See brewer section and Fig. 308, p. 235. The filled tube cap is screwed on and is then set inside a stainless steel tube which is twist-set and tightened into an upper gasket, see Fig. 309 for assembly. The R & G coffee is then ready for extraction. A receiving flask (later used for pouring cups) is the bottom stainless steel bowl of a vacuum type brewer. This is set in a spring clamp which simultaneously sets an actuating micro-switch to release an interlock so that coffee brewing can begin. A button is pushed which opens a valve from the hot water supply and actuates a metering pump. In 3 min, when the metered volume of about 1,350 ml (or ten 5.5 fl oz cups) of hot water has passed through, coffee brew is produced, and the system shuts itself off. A panel light shows that the extraction is complete and the coffee brew can be served. Extract at 18 per cent solubles yield is 1.26 per cent solubles

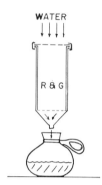

FIG. 308. SECTION THROUGH WATER PRESSURIZED EXTRACTOR

Courtesy REF Manufacturing Corporation and
Coffee & Tea Industries Magazine

FIG. 309. PARTS OF AIRLINE BREWER

concentration (2 gal per pound), and with good roast coffee makes a delicious cup of coffee. All processing factors are effectively controlled.

Comparison of Extraction Systems.—Espresso type extraction is the positive displacement of water through the granular coffee bed. It is efficient, rapid, and results in a good flavored coffee brew which has some resemblance to the commercial percolation of soluble coffee. The major differences are in the ratio of water to R & G coffee, the geometry of the R & G coffee bed, concentration, yield, and time. The *espresso machine* has an R & G coffee chamber that is about 1 cm high and 5 cm in diameter; this will hold about 20 ml fine grind dark coffee or about 8 gm. The volume of water that passes through is less than 2 fl oz (60 ml), giving about a 3 to 4 per cent solubles concentration and 25 per cent solubles yield. Note that the inlet water to R & G coffee espresso ratios are by volume 3 to 1; by weight, 8 to 1 and effluent temperatures are low.

There is an *Italian household type extractor* that looks like a Silex bowl over bowl, but operates on a positive displacement principle. The cartridge volume of R & G coffee lies between the bowls. When water boils, it is forced up through the chamber of ground coffee, and the extract is deflected down into the top bowl, see Fig. 303.

Espresso coffee is collected in the drinking demitasse cup and is brought directly to the consumer. There is no reheat of brew to be concerned about. It is prepared cup by cup, not by the gallon. The espresso brew method is technically sound. However, poor quality coffee or water and over-extraction can make a poor tasting cup. In other words, the espresso machine is only one part of the brew process. Even though it does a good job, all the sequential brewing factors have to be correct to obtain a good cup of coffee.

In the *airline cartridge* of R & G coffee (about 5 cm diameter and 10 cm high), the 200 ml volume holds 96 gm R & G coffee. The inlet water to R & G coffee ratios are by volume 7.5 to 1; by weight, 15 to 1.

In the *commercial percolator* for soluble coffee manufacture, there is a series of columns, and there are hydrolysis yields which differ from the foregoing. But due to the high extract solubles concentrations achieved, the water to R & G coffee ratio is only about 3.5 by weight.

In every case the extraction conditions are controlled.

Vending Machine Brewers.—Having evolved the variable factors in the brewing of coffee, it requires only a nominal modification to install the same extraction mechanism in a coin-operated vending machine. Three general types of extractors have been developed.

The Vendo Company of Kansas City, Missouri, has used (1956 to date) a system of puncturing with several slotted tapered points a standard $1/4$ lb can of vacuum packed coffee. The hot water enters from one side, and the brew leaves from the same side. The machine holds 54 $^1/_4$-lb cans of regular grind roast coffee, averaging 16 cups per can, or 64 cups per pound. The vacuum sealed can protects the roast coffee until brewed. A time mechanism may purge the batch to drain if it is held too long.

The Automatic Canteen Company of America also makes a coffee brewing vending machine that makes 10 cups of coffee per batch; hot chocolate and soup are also dispensed. The volume of coffee is measured and washed free of solubles with pressurized water. If the brew is held too long, the old batch of brew is dumped.

Rudd-Melikian has since 1958 made 1 cup at a time by packaging the roast coffee in 1-cup portions in a filter fabric tape. This eliminated the poor weighing mechanisms used in vending equipment of the loose ground coffee type. Also the tape gives limited protection from oxygen and staling by a Pliofilm liner until the coffee is used. This avoids piling the ground coffee in an unclean hopper. Rudd-Melikian pioneered the single-cup tape principle, see Figs. 312 and 313, page 250.

The International Bally Coffee Vending Company has a novel arrangement wherein 1 cup is brewed at a time. A compartment holds 7 lb R & G coffee. One cup of hot water is placed in a reservoir; then about 8 gm of R & G coffee are added. A top chamber cover with built-in filter closes. Upward piston motion of the bottom of the chamber displaces the brew into the cup. The chamber then opens, and water flushes the grounds out for the next cup. This system is not unlike an espresso operation except that the coffee grounds do not get the full water washing action.

Another machine called Perk-O-Fresh used a radial design of 40 cartridges of R & G coffee each dispensing a 16 cup batch of brew.

Still another type of brewing vending machine makes 1 cup at a time and operates so that the volumetric measure of coffee grounds falls into a stainless steel funnel. Six ounces of hot water flush the R & G particles about, and the brew slowly filters through a fine stainless steel screen into the cup. By having two such funneled cups, one over the other, two rinses are effected; one of a single rinsed coffee, and a second of fresh R & G coffee. The wet coffee grounds will stale rapidly.

Restaurant Slurry Brewer.—The single rinsed R & G coffee slurry type extractor which filters out the brew has been used in the numerous 8 to 12 cup restaurant brewers. This slurrying of coffee grounds followed by drainage of brew differs from the columnar displacement of extract with water sometimes called pressure brew coffee making. The use of a paper filter takes out most of the colloidal matter as well as fine grind particles. Such paper filters are used as a means of disposing of the spent coffee grounds which is neater than washing out the funnel chamber and refilling the metal cartridge with fresh R & G coffee. Paper absorbs stale coffee and other odors, and therefore must be carefully handled.

Positive water displacement type extractors are the most efficient because finer grinds can be used, action is positive, and timing is accurate. Also the extraction is countercurrent. The slurry type extractors have solubles in batch equilibrium. Figure 310 shows the inside of a restaurant pressure brewer.

Brewing Equipment Standardization

The Coffee Brewing Institute observes that there has been little attempt in the past to standardize equipment design in terms relating to the quality of coffee beverage prepared. This is also true in soluble coffee plants, and,

Courtesy Western Urn Manufacturing Company

FIG. 310.   RESTAURANT WATER PRESSURIZED EXTRACTOR

no doubt, for other types of food processors. In addition, there has been a general lack of suitable instructional material emphasizing proper use of brewing equipment to attain product flavor quality and equipment performance. This is no doubt due to the fact that the brewing equipment manufacturers are not experienced concerning coffee quality or do not really have an ideal brew flavor in mind when the brewing machine is designed and built. The user of the equipment, however, must strive for a good quality brew.

The advantages of improved brewing equipment and procedures as well as coffee quality and water quality, are increased coffee beverage consumption and increased consumer satisfaction. For example, the improved quality of pressurized brew on some of the jet airliners showed immediate passenger response by increasing consumption more than 50 per cent. The use of 2 vs 3 gal of water per pound of R & G coffee on the airlines brew equipment reveals marked preference for the stronger brew, which is in agreement with other surveys.

WATER PROPERTIES THAT INFLUENCE COFFEE BEVERAGE FLAVOR

Water represents about 99 per cent of the coffee beverage whether it is brewed or instant coffee. Yet it was not until about 1955 that the Coffee Brewing Institute supported the initial research for gaining understanding of the effects of water composition on coffee flavor. Since then four reports have been issued. These were based on three groups of experiments covering mineral and ion threshold concentrations as they directly and indirectly influence final coffee brew flavor. No work to date has been published on the effect of water properties on instant coffee flavor.

Mineral Ion Taste Thresholds

Thresholds were found by Lockhart, Tucker, and Merritt (1955) to vary with taster, with associated cation or anion and whether ion is in water or coffee brew. The following ranges of ion concentrations are near taste threshold:

(1) Calcium ion about 125 ppm in water, 300 ppm in coffee brew
(2) Magnesium ion about 100 ppm in water, 200 ppm in brew
(3) Potassium ion about 300 ppm in water, 400 ppm in brew
(4) Sodium ion about 100 ppm in water, 250 ppm in brew
(5) Ferric ion about 4 ppm in water and brew, although others report less
(6) Phosphate ion about 100 ppm in water
(7) Chlorides about 200 ppm in water, 400 ppm in brew
(8) Carbonates about 50 ppm in water, 100 ppm in brew
(9) Bicarbonates about 500 ppm in water, 1,000 ppm in brew

The United States Public Health
Drinking Water Standards (1960)

These standards call for clear, colorless, odorless, and tasteless water, free of bacteria and with less than: 0.2 ppm copper, 0.3 ppm iron, 250 ppm sulfates, 100 ppm magnesium, 250 ppm chlorides, 1,000 ppm total solids, and with no caustic akalinity, more than 10 ppm alkalinity yet less than 50 ppm sodium and potassium carbonate alkalinity. It should be noted that 0.3 ppm copper sulfate will kill many types of fish.

It is beyond the scope of this text to go into water analyses and the meaning of various ion contents and water properties. The references list Betz (1957), Permutit (1949), and Hoover and Riehl (1962) as well as Powell (1954), Lange (1961), Nordell (1961), and Ellis *et al.* (1948). The U.S. Department of Interior water supply papers (1955) are useful in giving the water hardness distribution for 1,300 major United States cities, and Fig. 297 shows this geographically. These reports contain water analyses and many other details. For example, the water hardness maps can serve as alkalinity maps for many parts of the United States since water hardness and alkalinity are almost the same in limestone areas of the Midwest of this country. In areas of the West and Southwest this relation usually does not hold because hardness is a non-carbonate type. Analyses are provided for the waters of the Great Lakes and major rivers.

Iron and Copper.—Lockhart, Tucker, and Merritt (1955) point out that when comparing brewed coffee samples containing cream and one brew has 1 ppm iron, there is a greenish cast which becomes more prominent and more evident without a control cup above 4 ppm. The iron is believed to react with phenolic compounds in coffee brew. The reaction of iron and phenols is so sensitive that it is used as a qualitative and quantitative test. Iron may enter soft (non-alkaline) water from rusting pipe after the water leaves the treating plant. Copper ion in such aggressive water areas also dissolves in water and is evident from green sink stains. Such copper content in the water may produce some coffee brew flavor deterioration at concentration levels comparable to iron. However, the color changes in the brew are not so evident.

Local water supplies may have exceptionally high contents of certain ions. Sea water intrusion into potable water supplies will result in high chlorides, for example, 400 ppm chlorides in Galveston, Texas water. Sarasota, Florida water has about 800 ppm sulfates. Some deep well waters in arid regions, parts of Michigan and elsewhere are very brackish and have over 1,000 ppm and sometimes several thousand ppm of solids.

Sodium Bicarbonate and Time of Drip.—Gardner (1958) reports the results of brewing tests with various formulated and actual city waters in the time required for water to drip through roast coffee grounds. The test results showed that when bicarbonates were 300 ppm or higher, drip-through time was longer. For example, with deionized water as a 6-min control, a 300 ppm $NaHCO_3$ solution took almost 9 min to drip through, and the 400 ppm $NaHCO_3$ solution took 10 min to drip through. Similar results were obtained with natural waters having bicarbonate alkalinity. Further, removing water hardness with substitution of sodium ion for calcium or magnesium ions increased the drip-through time 50 per cent. The series of tests showed that alkalinity of carbonate and bicarbonate anions regardless of cation (Na, K, or Li) and other alkalinities increased drip-through time. This data has direct bearing for drip brew devices and percolators. Segall (1962) studied this matter thoroughly for vending brewing devices and excessive pressure buildup was found with a definite change in the character, composition, and taste of the brew. This appears to be less significant in commercial percolator extractors. In any case Gardner's (1955) 6 to 9 min drip-throughs were found to give a less flavorful coffee brew. A coffee flavor deterioration also occurs due to the water alkalinity neutralizing part of the coffee acids. The change in pH is sufficient to affect rates of extractability but would more directly affect the brew pH, brew titratable acidity, and brew flavor.

Coffee Acid Neutralization by Alkaline Waters.—This has always been a serious problem with soft beverage acids, Sivetz (1949). The loss in acidity and corresponding soft beverage or coffee flavor is costly. The coffee buyer argues about $^1/_4$¢ per lb of green coffee. Then the coffee user, even with 100 ppm alkalinity water, goes about neutralizing roughly one-third of coffee acidity and corresponding coffee flavor. Such a coffee acid neutralization raises the pH from about 5.1 to 5.4, and the cup taste is insipid and flat. Figure 311 shows the neutralization effect of waters of various alkalinity on hydrolysate coffee solubles, instant coffee solubles

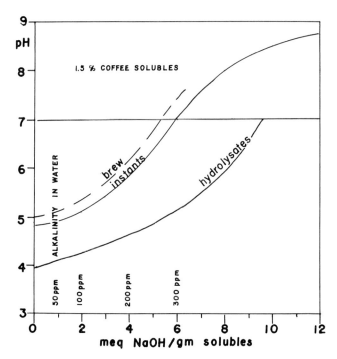

FIG. 311. ALKALINE WATER TITER VS pH
OF COFFEE SOLUTIONS

and brew coffee solubles. Not only are one-third of the coffee acids neutralized at 100 ppm alkalinity, but the cup taste becomes flavorless. This is not a quality loss of 33 per cent on the coffee purchase price, but a 100 per cent loss. What good is the fraction of 1¢ per lb more paid on green coffee quality when the water used in coffee brewing process spoils the brew flavor? No one brewing or using instant coffee with water having 100 ppm or higher alkalinity can make a good tasting cup of coffee without neutralizing the alkalinity. Some flavor advantage can be gained by using 33 per cent more coffee, a higher coffee to water ratio, i.e., more acid. But this is an expensive way to neutralize the water alkalinity.

Liberation of CO_2.—The introduction of bicarbonate alkalinity into R & G or instant coffee acids still results in an acid solution, and all the CO_2 gas is released. Water having 300 ppm alkalinity, for example, will liberate 44 mg CO_2 which is 22 ml CO_2 gas for 150 ml water and 10 gm (20 ml) R & G coffee. Even at 100 ppm alkalinity 7 ml tiny CO_2 gas bubbles per 10 gm of R & G coffee properly distributed in particle cells may retard water flow and wetting. Ten grams of R & G coffee with 1 per cent CO_2 (100 mg CO_2) would give up about 50 ml CO_2 gas into the extraction process.

Neutralizing Alkaline Waters.—Alkaline waters raise brew pH (or reduce the final solution acidity) and give a darker brew color (less light transmission).

In Chapter 8, it was stated that coffee roasters tend to use lighter roasts in the Midwest limestone areas of the United States where alkaline water is prevalent. The higher coffee acidity at lighter roasts neutralizes water alkalinity leaving more coffee acidity for flavor.

Table 71 in Chapter 15 shows the reported volatile and non-volatile acids in R & G coffee. Ten grams of R & G coffee have about 3.5 meq of acids per gram; 80 per cent are non-volatile acids depending on the roast and blend. The NaOH titer to completely neutralize brew or home type R & G coffee extract is only about 0.5 meq acid per gram of cup solubles. More of the coffee acidity stays within the unneutralized grounds during such a short extraction time with limited water rinse. Adding a pinch of citric acid or other suitable food acid such as ascorbic (Vitamin C) into the boiling water just prior to extraction reduces water alkalinity but it is still not a cheap neutralization method.

The rise in brew pH from distilled to 200 ppm alkaline water may be as follows with cups of coffee from commercial percolator extract—4.80 vs 5.00 pH; for instant coffee powder from the same percolation extract —4.90 vs 5.20 pH. Distilled water is best for tasting controls, but the quality of the waters used by the consumers must be evaluated.

COFFEE ACIDS ACCOUNTABILITY

Mabrouk and Deatherage (1956) have reported the non-volatile acids of roast coffee. Clements and Deatherage (1957) have reported the volatile acids of roast coffee. These are listed and totaled in Table 71, Chapter 15, showing 0.345 meq acidity per gram roast coffee on exhaustive extraction; 80 per cent of the acidity is non-volatile.

Reference to Miner (1934) shows that the brew acidity is chiefly determined by the blend and the degree of roast. For example, NaOH titer from light to dark roast varied from 1.0 down to 0.5 meq per gm solubles assuming that a 16 per cent solubles yield from R & G coffee was obtained. A 0.2 meq per gm solubles adjustment is made for Chicago water which has about 110 ppm alkalinity.

For roast and ground coffee these acidities would correspond to about 0.16 to 0.08 meq acidity per gram or about half the exhaustive extraction yield of acids.

Miner (1934) also shows that titratable acidity is related to acidity recognized by taste and taste comments on acidy coffees, relative to aromatic, neutral, and rough coffees. Between high grown Colombian mild and Brazilian coffees there is about 0.1 meq acidity difference per gram R & G coffee. The higher grown mild coffees are more acid. This 0.1 meq per gm of R & G coffee is about 20 per cent of total coffee acid.

There is no published data on Robusta coffee acid titer, but brewed coffee from mild and Robusta coffees may be respectively at pH 5.1 and 5.5; the difference in titer may be 100 per cent as judged from Fig. 311, coffee solubles NaOH titer vs pH.

Note that 100 ppm alkalinity in the water used to prepare instant coffee will neutralize about one-third of the coffee acidity, 200 ppm alkalinity will neutralize two-thirds of the coffee acidity flavor, and 300 ppm alkaline water will neutralize all coffee acidity.

Altogether the green coffee blends, degree of roast, extraction yield, and water alkalinity markedly influence the final cup pH and titratable acidity.

The acids in coffee are weak organic acids. Fig. 311 shows this in coffee solubles titer vs pH. There is no sharp change from acidity to alkalinity. The NaOH titer curve crosses the pH 7.0 line gradually. Further, if every carboxylic acid group were neutralized with NaOH, the resulting pH would be 8.0 or higher. This is because we have a weak acid and a strong base compound. Further, many of the organic acids are only slightly dissociated and acid hydrogen ions evolve only as neutralization takes place. It is this dissociation that causes pH buffering. This means that only slight changes in pH are accompanied by large changes in titratable acidity. As far as taste is concerned, pH changes of 0.1 are noticeable.

Thus, even though there are 0.345 meq acid per gram of light roast coffee on exhaustive water extraction, normal brewing is not exhaustive extraction. When titrating with NaOH to neutrality, pH 7.0, not all the organic acids react fully.

Hydrolysis and Natural Acids

For instant coffees whose beans are roasted darker, the atmospheric or brew level solubles yield (about 20 per cent) gives titratable acidities of 0.5 meq per gm solubles or 0.1 meq per gm R & G coffee. However, hydrolysis of coffee solubles in pressure percolation forms acids. In Fig. 311 the NaOH titer of hydrolysate coffee solubles vs pH shows 0.8 meq acidity per gram solubles.

Assume: 1 gm R & G coffee yields 0.15 gm hydrolysates and 0.25 gm free solubles, 0.40 gm is the total. The acidic contribution of: (a) hydrolysates is 0.8 meq per gm × 0.15 = 0.120 meq, and (b) free solubles is 0.5 meq per gm × 0.25 = 0.125 meq; 0.245 meq per 0.40 gm solubles, is the total or 0.613 meq per gm R & G coffee for the instant coffee compared with 0.1 meq per gm R & G coffee for brewed coffee mentioned above. In other words, the instant coffee solubles are more acid than brewed coffee solubles from the same source. This is confirmed by tasting.

Consider the following four sources and types of acidities in coffee solubles: extractable (1) non-volatile, (2) volatile; and hydrolyzable, (3) non-volatile, (4) volatile. These are depicted in the following three equations in milliequivalents per gram solubles.

	1		2		3		4		Total
Brew	0.4	+	0.1	+	0	+	0	=	0.50
Extract	0.4	+	0.1	+	0.2	+	0.05	=	0.75
Powder	0.4	+	nil	+	0.2	+	nil	=	0.60

Distilled Water.—Using distilled water is no assurance that the water has no odor or taste. Not infrequently organic volatiles come over in the distillation process, depending on original water quality, oxidation of the organics prior to distillation, and degree of entrainment. This is one reason why distilled water is sometimes observed to have a taste and odor.

Temporary Hardness.—Boiling water that is hard due to bicarbonate salts of calcium and magnesium will drive off CO_2 and precipitate insoluble carbonates. This is called temporary water hardness. Boiling to remove temporary hardness reduces total hardness and alkalinity which otherwise may noticeably harm coffee flavor.

Chlorine.—Most municipally treated and chlorinated waters, especially when organic matter is high, will leave chlorine residues (at several tenths up to 1.0 ppm) to destroy bacteria. A 0.3 ppm chlorine level in the coffee brew is clearly damaging to coffee flavor. Since brewed coffee contains around 1 per cent solubles, this content of chlorine in the water is 30 ppm chlorine in coffee solubles. Chlorine's chemical equivalent weight relative to coffee solubles is about 0.5 equivalent per million (epm). The coffee solubles from the R & G coffee may have 1.0 to 2.0 epm. The net effect is a chlorinated coffee taste. This taste is unmistakable, undesirable, and disagreeable. At other times chlorinated waters from natural or industrial areas carry *phenols* that have an objectionable flavor (especially when hot) and do great harm to natural coffee flavor. Chlorine is easily detected in water by taste and smell. Chlorine can readily be measured with an ortho-tolidine reagent and color comparator tube. Residue chlorine is entirely removed by passing water slowly over an activated carbon bed. One basic water supply problem is the seasonal variation in organic matter content in natural waters in some areas. This is accompanied by excessive chlorination by municipalities during spring periods of water runoff. The original organic matter content and the high chlorine dosage give an odor and taste to the water that cannot be hidden without complete water treatment. A demonstration of what less than 1 ppm chlorine can do to coffee flavor can be made by diluting standardized solutions of chlorine water and brewing coffee.

Organic Matter.—Organically contaminated water can usually be identified quickly by mustiness or off-odor, yellow color and the reduction of applied chlorine. Waters in warm climates that are rich in vegetation, or areas where runoff of water is high have periods of high organic content, as, for example, in Rio de Janeiro, Brazil, or Houston, Texas.

Instant coffees undergo more flavor change from impure waters than brewed coffees. Brewed coffees have greater flavor buffering capacity due to the greater mass of grounds. It is unlikely that such water quality situations will be resolved completely or in the foreseeable future. Water treatment being a municipal function and drawing public taxes does not progress much faster than its citizens allow. Often water treatment is not practiced until water quality becomes intolerably poor. Enlightened, progressive communities willing to pay for good water are rare. In certain geographical areas, where mountain water comes from melted snows to constitute a water reserve, there is a clean water supply.

Water quality in commercial soluble coffee percolation is less important because only two parts by weight of water leave the percolation system with one part by weight solubles. For brews this ratio is 100 to 1. In plant percolation the feed water travels through 60 to 100 ft of coffee grounds which act as adsorbents. Use of an acid water to feed the percolation system may accelerate hydrolysis rates at lower temperatures and will avoid scale on the feed water heaters.

Oxygen Solubility.—Figure 306 shows the solubility of oxygen in water from freezing to boiling temperatures. Cold water can dissolve 10 ml of oxygen per liter (about 14 ppm or 0.9 epm of oxygen). The solubility falls off with rising temperature. The data shown from the Permutit Handbook (1949) is at equilibrium. Raising water temperature does not drive off the oxygen and gases instantly; it takes time. That is why water must come to and be kept at a rolling boil before brew extraction. It must be recalled that 0.3 ppm chlorine is equivalent to 30 ppm or 0.5 epm in solubles, which is half the 1.0 epm of oxygen in cold water. Oxygen and chlorine are strong oxidizing agents.

The oxygen is removed by bringing water to a boil in a plant water system feeding the boiler so as to remove CO_2 and O_2, both of which are corrosive to carbon steel in the presence of water. The deaerator can also be used for removing gases entering the percolator feed water system.

Oxygen in air is in contact with percolated coffee extract at 45 F (7 C) in storage tanks. Oxygen is somewhat less soluble in extract than in pure water, but oxygen still may be at 10 ppm. On a coffee solubles basis this is about 0.6 epm, whereas the oxidizables in the coffee extract are about 1.0 epm. It is for this reason that inert gas purging of fruit juices during cold storage is practiced so as to reduce the oxygen and oxidizing conditions that deteriorate flavor. Excluding oxygen is also good practice for coffee extract flavor protection.

Hydrogen Sulfide Gas.—When H_2S is present in water supplies it is readily noticed by its rotten egg odor at 0.05 ppm in water and 0.10 ppm in coffee brew. Hydrogen sulfide gas occurs occasionally in some well waters, and its presence is sufficiently objectionable and corrosive to make it necessary to remove H_2S before the water is used for food preparation or other uses.

COFFEE BEVERAGE VENDING MACHINES

There were no coffee beverage vending machines during and prior to World War II. Melikian and Rudd, ex-servicemen, built their first coffee vending machine in a Philadelphia garage in 1946 and made their first sales to a local football audience. Both men were engineers, and their early machines were designed to use coffee extract. R & G coffee brewed through tapes was not commercially made by Melikian and Rudd until 1958. Their business grew in two ways: manufacture of frozen coffee extract and the use of extract in coffee vending machines. Kwik-Kafe at Hatboro, Pa., made the percolated coffee extracts which were kept frozen until placed in the vending machine. Their sales grew from a beginning in 1946 to about 45,000 vending machines and 2,000,000 cups of coffee per day with a nationwide franchise system by 1960. But the reported total daily cups of vended coffee in the United States in 1960 was about 10,000,000. Other vending machine manufacturers developed their own coffee brewing machines. The Vendo Company of Kansas City did not enter this market until 1956 with a 16-cup brew from a punctured $1/4$ lb can of R & G coffee. Vendo Company is one of the largest vending machine manufacturers in the United States. Automatic Canteen, another large vending machine manufacturer and caterer, entered the coffee brewing market also in the 1950's. Other coffee vending machine firms in the United States include Bally-Seeburg, Rock-Ola, Hava-Java, Perk-O-Fresh, and a dozen others.

Vended Coffee Sales

In 1961, the vending industry for all merchandise had total sales of about $2,500,000,000 which would qualify it as big business. Coffee represents about 6 to 8 per cent of these annual sales or about $150,000,-000. At a price of 10¢ per cup, this is 1.5 billion cups of coffee per year. Some sales estimates for cups of coffee run over 2 billion cups per year. In 1961, there were about 140,000 coffee vending machines in use averaging about 60 cups of coffee per work day per machine. At this time, the rate of coffee beverage sales from vending machines has grown faster than for any other vended product. The development of a $150,000,000 sales volume plus the production of the machines in 15 years is indeed a rapid growth.

Vended Coffee: One-Half Per Cent of Total United States Coffee Use

The volume of sales of vended coffee must be placed in proper perspective in the United States green and roast coffee sales picture. One-half per cent would amount to two billion cups of coffee. Calculated as instant coffee at 2 gm per cup, this is 9,000,000 lb of instant coffee or about 5 per cent of United States coffee solubles consumption. In 1961, 60 per cent of soluble coffees were actually vended as powder and 40 per cent as extract. The United States vended use of soluble coffees in 1961 was 6,000,000 lb solubles. The coffee extract use has been losing ground to R & G coffee which in 1961 represented about one-third of the vended coffee sales. Thus two-thirds of a billion cups of brewed coffee (from R & G) at 10 gm per cup requires about 100,000 bags of green coffee. This is only about $^1/_2$ per cent of United States imports of green coffee.

Cost of Coffee in Cup.—The coffee vending market is still a fast growing market, and its sales growth in the next decade is expected to double, possibly triple, present sales. The dollar volume of the vended cup of coffee is about 10 to 15 times the value of the roast coffee used. Hence, the retail dollar volume of vended sales is large. For example, a 2-gm cup portion of instant coffee has a value (at $1.50 per lb) of two-thirds of a cent. For ten grams of R & G coffee (at $0.60 per lb) the value is about 1.3¢ per cup. Both examples are higher in coffee dosage than is actually used and higher in coffee cost than actually paid in general. The advantages and disadvantages of using soluble coffee powders against coffee extracts or coffee brews are not yet clearly settled in this sales area because many complex factors are involved.

Extracts.—Coffee extract flavor can easily deteriorate in a few days. In many of the coffee extract vending machines, extract holding temperatures are too high. They should be about 35 F (2 C). The extract is exposed to air and storage for days, if not weeks. This is why coffee extracts have lost favor. Extracts under these storage conditions give a poorly flavored cup.

R & G Coffee.—As this is subject to staling, it also has a storage and flavor preservation problem not easily solved.

Instant Coffee Powders.—These may be lacking in flavor appeal, depending on the quality used, but their flavor does not deteriorate under proper storage. In current practice bulk powder flavor deterioration has been noticed in a few days. This is mostly due to moisture pick-up. On a single cup of powder or R & G coffee brew there is no waste as there is in batch brew preparation of R & G coffee.

Factors in Flavor Quality of Vended Coffee

Inasmuch as the merchandise vending machine business is a specialized field and coffee is but a small part of this dynamic business, only the highlights of vended coffee beverage operations will be covered.

King (1962) and others have noted that the flavor quality of vended coffee beverage is too often poor in quality. In addition to the conditions of coffee brewing that make for a low probability of a good flavored cup of coffee, other factors in vended coffee also affect this probability.

Instant Coffee Powders currently represent 40 per cent of vended cups of coffee. Soluble coffee processors make what is called a "special" coffee for vending machines. This means that the vending machine manufacturers have adopted the use of a heavier powder bulk density, that is, 33 instead of 22 gm per 100 cu cm. It so happens that these bulk densities are usually achieved by particle breakage which downgrades the flavor of the instant coffee. It also reduces instant solubility and makes for poor powder fluidity. Another special property of vended instant coffee is that it has to be low priced. Low price is usually achieved in two ways. The lowest priced coffees such as Robustas or other types with off-flavor that may have heavy body are used. Usually a very dark roast is used, a French or perhaps Italian roast. Heavy body coffees at a dark roast do increase cup strength taste but not flavor quality. This has been aptly described as thinking only in terms of acceptability of the cup of coffee. The net effect is that instead of using at least 2 gm of instant coffee per cup (as recommended for home use) which gives about 227 five-oz cups per pound of instant coffee, instant coffee powders are used in quantities of 1.4 to 1.9 gm per cup. This yields respectively 324 and 239 cups per pound with the emphasis on the 324 cups per pound of instant coffee. This economical policy on the instant coffee product is said to be due to the following reasons: (1) location management wants a high commission; (2) vending management wants a high return; (3) the coffee buyer is pressured to make a good showing by paying a low price; and (4) it is assumed that the consumer is not very critical and will accept a low standard of quality and strength.

The instant coffee powder may be packaged in an 8 oz ($^1/_2$ lb or 227 gm) laminated moisture-proof paper bag. This portion is used for filling the vending machine powder reservoir.

The R & G Coffees used in beverage vending machines also have "special" properties and prices. Coffee beverage vending machines operate on several different principles, hence roast coffee grounds fluidity, grind size, and several other coffee properties might have to be specified. Figure 312 shows the Rudd-Melikian tape with ground roast coffee chamber. Figure 313 shows the Rudd-Melikian tape being prepared. Figure 314 shows the inside of the tape used for 1-cup coffee brew vending machine.

Low cost R & G coffee blends are as common in tapes as in other fields. Cups of coffee are brewed 45 to 65 cups per pound of R & G coffee (7 to 10 gm in one tape portion). There may be some cup strength at the 65 cup per pound level, but not much flavor.

Machine Costs for Vending Coffee Beverage

These cost about $1,200 to $1,500. On an average year's sales, the machine can be amortized with maintenance in about 3 to 4 yr; in a good location the machine can be amortized in less than 2 yr. At 60 cups of coffee per day per machine and 250 days per year, this is a $1,500 gross. Raw materials are a small fraction of the sales cost unit. There are

Courtesy of Rudd-Melikian, Inc.

FIG. 312.　TAPE OF ROAST AND GROUND COFFEE UNITS

Courtesy of Coffee & Tea Industries Magazine

FIG. 313.　TAPE OF ROAST AND GROUND COFFEE UNITS BEING PREPARED

vending operations in which an individual owns about 10 to 25 vending machines; he maintains and services the machines and the income constitutes his whole livelihood.

One-Cup Machine

In principle, the 1-cup coffee brew or vending machine gives the least coffee brew deterioration since there is no holding of a batch. Staling of ground coffee in brew vending machines is a problem. For this reason

Courtesy of Rudd-Melikian, Inc.

FIG. 314.   VENDING MACHINE FOR ONE CUP TAPE BREW

and because they are basically lower in cost than R & G brews instant coffee powders hold their sales well. From a sanitation and health viewpoint, and there are public health codes that have to be met, the powdered instant coffee with powdered cream and sugar is the best arrangement but may not give the best flavored cup of coffee. Brewed coffee can be good when fresh, but that depends on the probability of delivering a fresh brew into the vending machine.

One of the factors influencing cup quality in vending machines is that many machines have a captive market in plants, shops, offices, amusement or other transient areas. Where local managements, as in company plants, insist on cup flavor quality and there is repeat machine use, day after day, quality will be offered. It takes incentive and pressure to maintain consistent high quality.

Water Quality

Another factor that makes it difficult to vend a good flavored cup of coffee is water quality. Some machines have no water treatment equipment. Machines simply draw city water. If there is water alkalinity, chlorine, organic matter, or a noticeable odor and taste, each will downgrade the coffee flavor. The vending machine is not capable of dealing with wide variations in water qualities. However, filters can remove insoluble particles. Resins can remove brackishness, alkalinity, hardness, H_2S, and chlorine. Carbon also removes chlorine. A fraction of a ppm chlorine will ruin the coffee flavor. Few vending machines have ion exchanger resins in the water supply line. Further, *cold* beverages can taste satisfactory with a water heavy in some organic matter, but the malodorous substances become prominent and objectionable in the hot beverage.

Most coffee vending machines do not boil water, but the machine is designed to hold 208 to 210 F (98 to 99 C) water which largely obviates a flat taste.

Water heating systems in vending machines usually are constructed of stainless steel. Metal contamination from iron or copper causes serious flavor loss and change as has been stated.

Dispensing of liquid coffee extract, liquid cream, and liquid sugar is mechanically simple. However, it has associated bacterial growth, sediment, and cleaning problems. The resultant flavor loss has caused liquid systems to lose their share of the total vending market. Patents have been issued to Reich (1957) for eliminating precipitated gels from frozen coffee extracts. Also Lee (1959) has a patent for adding a desiccant to instant coffee powder to retard its caking when it absorbs moisture from the air.

For quality flavor in vending coffee, the vending machine operator must be persuaded to use good quality coffee whether it is liquid extract, instant powder, or ground roast coffee. Another major technical problem is to control feed water quality which is so bad in some areas that good coffee cannot be made without water treatment. Until complete purification of water for a vending machine is developed, a "quality vending operation" could use a 5-gal bottled water container similar to an office cooler. A 20-gal water reservoir could be built in the vending machine and water could be transferred into the reservoir from the portable tank at each servicing. Twenty gallons is equivalent to 500 cups of coffee, which is about the vending capacity of most machines. Water storage eliminates plumbing in the vending machine installation.

In the matter of driving out all the dissolved gases from the hot water, the vending machine could be operated like an espresso machine, which keeps the water supply at about 5 psig above atmospheric pressure with intermittent gas venting. A safety disk or valve would have to be used.

Every coffee flavor quality suggestion, of course, means additional but not prohibitive cost. Also, the machine that makes a really good cup of coffee will draw more customers.

Instant Coffee Envelopes

Another system of providing coffee beverage is the sale or give-away of 1 cup portions of instant coffee powder in laminated moisture-tight envelopes at motels, offices, shops, etc. With these, powdered cream in envelopes, powdered sugar in envelopes, and a source of near boiling 210 F (99 C) water, cup, and mixing stick must be available.

Cups.—Before the advent of hot coffee beverage vending machines in 1946, wax coated or paper cups were used for cold beverages. However, wax or paper cups cannot be used with hot coffee. The wax melts and heat penetrates, making these cups impractical. Non-wax type coatings were developed. About 1957 foam plastic insulated cups came into use. These cups protect the hand contact surface from the hot cup contents. A critical problem in using plastic or paper cups is to prevent the odor or flavor of the cup material from affecting the coffee aroma and flavor. It is a common observation that coffee, beer, and other beverages do not taste "right" in some paper cups, but cups are rapidly being improved.

COFFEE FLAVOR ADDITIVES, SUBSTITUTES, AND SYNTHETICS

Additives to foods, especially for flavor change, are as old as time. With laws on the labeling of packages and jars, additives vary from commonplace substances such as sugar and salt to pyroligneous acid and artificial flavors.

Purpose of Additives

The National Academy of Science (1956) lists twelve groups of intentional additives used in processed foods; (1) preservatives; (2) antioxidants; (3) sequestrants; (4) surfactants; (5) stabilizers and thickeners; (6) bleaching agents; (7) maturing agents; (8) buffer acids and alkalies; (9) food colors; (10) non-nutritive sweeteners; (11) nutrient supplements; (12) flavoring agents, and miscellaneous. In regard to coffee flavoring agents there are aromatic chemicals, essential oils, and others, that have been used for decades or longer, especially in candy and imitation fruit flavors. Merory (1960) also lists chemicals used in imitation flavors that are related to coffee flavor such as butter, rum, butterscotch, caramel, imitation maple syrup, and others. Specifically, the traditional items that have been identified and confirmed in coffee aroma and flavors are the following:

Acids.—Formic, acetic, propionic, butyric, valeric, pyruvic, and oleic; *aldehydes*- acet-, propyl, n- and iso-, butyr-, valer-, furfur-, all appear in natural fruits. But propyl- and valeraldehydes are not much mentioned in prepared flavor compositions. Acetoin or acetylmethylcarbinol has been used for a long time in butter flavor as has diacetyl. Ketones are used in some imitation flavors, but acetone and methylethyl ketone are not specifically noted. Imitation coffee flavor constituents appear to run more toward *esters*, possibly due to the instability of aldehydes and ketones. Instability is, of course, the very nature of coffee aroma and flavor. Ethyl acetate and ethyl formate have been used for a long time in many types of beverages, candy, ice cream, and baked goods. The latter is associated with rum flavor. Furfuryl mercaptan has been used in imitation coffee flavor, but it is really not representative of coffee.

Pyroligneous acid is used for smoke flavor. Dimethyl sulfide is used in imitation garlic flavor; this compound is a key natural flavor note in high grade coffees. Oddly enough, dimethyl sulfide also appears in Merory's imitation raspberry flavor.

Imitation Flavors.—These are the stock in trade of flavor compounders. It is difficult to find much published information in this field. Much of what has been published is outdated by current "know-how" evolved from modern analytical instruments like gas, column, and paper chromatography, infra-red patterns, and mass spectroscopy.

The U.S. Food and Drug Administration has been more liberal in allowing food additives that have been used for decades, especially at low levels, such as a few parts per million. Hall (1959) and the National Research Council Food Protection Committee (1956) highlight this aspect. The Chemical Week (1958) nicely summarizes the extent and character of the flavor-making business in the United States, which is about $200,000,000 per year. Although almost every one of these flavor houses offers an imitation coffee flavor for sale, none of these offerings ever is acceptable to men who know coffee aroma and flavor. Most of the flavor makers will confidentially agree with this conclusion. This is so because coffee is made up of numerous unstable and volatile constituents.

The ratio of investment cost to gain for resolving the components of coffee aroma and flavor is estimated to be too high relative to other investments that flavor makers can make. This is partly a rationalization because with a good chemical and working background in coffee aroma and flavor chemistry plus modern analytical instruments and skills, results from coffee analysis come much faster and at less cost than is realized by those who work at coffee without the requisite background.

United States Food and Drug Law

With the change in the United States Food and Drug Law in 1958 and as amended in 1960, it is necessary to keep abreast of current progress in approved additives. This can be done through references in food magazines, especially from the continuously revised Food and Flavor Additives Directory by the Hazelton Laboratory of Falls Church, Virginia, as well as the Food Law Institute in New York City, the *Federal Register*, and the *Food Drug Cosmetic Law Journal*.

From time to time articles are published in journals like the *Perfumery and Essential Oil Record (London)*, *American Perfumer and Aromatics* and others that mention flavor additives. Publication of advances in flavor composition is slow even though considerable expansion of flavor chemistry knowledge has occurred in the last decade with the application of chromatography techniques. Jacobs (1947) and Merory (1960) contribute two books which, praiseworthy as they are, only scratch the surface of a vast field.

Flavor Additives and Imitation Flavors

These have been used widely (and to some extent almost exclusively) in the candy and soft beverage fields for decades. Imitation fruit flavors are cheaper and have a chemical stability formulated into them that the natural flavor products sometimes do not have. Successful imitation of natural flavors is variable, but some imitation flavors are very good representations of their natural counterparts. In such cases, certain flavors have become firmly and relatively permanently established in the flavor trade. In some cases a single chemical compound may dominate the flavor property; for example, vanillin from lignin for the vanilla bean extract; for licorice flavor, anethole, the major chemical portion of anise; caffeine bitterness, methylation of theobromine; for sugar sweetness there are saccharin and cyclamate; for butter, margarine (representing 50 per cent of the market) has color and flavor additives although the fats are easy to distinguish; for cocoa butter, reasonable substitutes have been developed; benzaldehyde is classically cherry or almond flavor, depending on concentration; butyric and caproic acids have long been recognized as constituents of fermented cheeses and dairy products and are used in salad dressing mixtures; monosodium-glutamate is a distinct chemical protein and with similar compounds has evolved in the past decade into a significant flavor additive. See National Research Council (1956) for many more discrete chemical substances used for flavoring.

The purpose of the foregoing discussion of flavor additives of discreet chemical composition is to show that additives are commonplace in the food industry and that as chemical identities and compositions are evolved, the use of flavor additives also grows. There is no reason why many additives cannot be used to fortify instant coffee aroma and flavor in the foreseeable future. It has always been the dream of coffee men to upgrade and control green coffee quality, and indeed we stand at the threshold of such an application.

Instant coffee flavor is a departure from natural coffee flavor due to differences in brew composition. Flavor additives can help make instant coffee taste more like natural coffee. Appealing additives can restore some of the imbalance coffee flavor undergoes in preparing instant coffee. Introduction of discrete chemical compositions promises to exercise an element of control over the coffee aroma and flavor not yet attained.

Technological Progress

This is the increasing control of man over his environment as exemplified by synthetics: fibers; rubber and plastics; detergents for soap; dyes; pigments; paints; metals; gems such as diamonds, rubies, emeralds; medicinals; vitamins; insecticides; etc. Instant foods are in some cases a distinct flavor departure from their original nature. This modification of natural flavors has been intensified since 1950. The net result has been to widen the convenience, number, and appeal of foods and flavor available to the consumer. If an acceptable tasting, reasonably priced food can be produced in a process plant, it makes little sense for each housewife to devote a disproportionate number of hours to such preparations. Unfortunately, the quality of mass processed convenience foods is sometimes inferior and it costs more than natural food prepared at home. But flavor quality progress is continually being made and is gaining customer acceptance and purchasing power.

Time for New Flavor Acceptance

The transition from the use of a natural flavor to a synthetic flavor does not usually occur overnight. There must be a process of acceptance and transition. This may take decades. Change in the properties of a food, especially a basic food flavor and appearance, cannot be accepted promptly.

After flavor additives, which only superficially fortify or perhaps only subtly change food aroma, flavor, and appearance, there are substitutes.

Substitute Flavors

These imitate the natural flavors but usually do not exactly produce the original flavor. Coffee substitutes and additives have a long and continuing history. Chicory is an outstanding example, as are other cereal grains, caramelized carbohydrates, fruit sugars (figs, raisins, etc.). Some are beverage extenders used in time of coffee shortage, while others are appealing and economical enough to perpetuate their use.

A Synthetic Coffee Flavor

This is an exact reproduction of the natural flavor. Since natural coffee flavor varies substantially, there is some latitude allowable in its flavor composition. The fact that it is complex in number and variety of constituents extends the time needed to discover its composition and chemistry. The coffee composition problem is solvable when systematically studied and developed. The most difficult part is to ascertain the properties of the coffee composition, its volatility, and its instability in air. But this, too, is solvable with today's instruments and skills. The money and motivation to do this work completely has been lacking to date, but this may be changed in the future. Figure 266, Chapter 14 shows the evolution to date of soluble coffee use and the possible development of flavor additives as well as partially or wholly synthesized instant coffee flavors. The end result is dependent on natural coffee costs as well as the rate of application of disciplined research to this area.

Original Soluble Coffee Manufacture

This was instituted by non-roast coffee firms such as G. Washington, Gail Borden, Nestlé, and others. The soluble coffee manufacture is now strongly participated in by non-roast coffee firms like Sol-Cafe, Coffee-Instants, Bordens, Schroeder, United Instants, Brooke-Bond, and Lipton Tea; and a whole new, fast-growing group of soluble coffee plants in coffee-growing countries.

Economic Factors for Flavor Fortifiers

The instant coffee market has over $400,000,000 annual sales, and the world market for roast coffee is several billion dollars per year at the retail level. The expenditure of several millions of dollars (or perhaps only a fraction of this) to develop imitation or even flavor fortified or upgraded coffee beverage would not be out of proportion to the market advantage possible. There are, of course, few firms that are inclined to venture into such a development project or are capable of it. It is not because the end result is unattainable or not worthwhile.

The encouragement for such a product and its flavor development may actually come from surprising places. The subsistence level of the low paid, ill-housed, poorly fed, diseased labor pool in the coffee growing countries may, in today's overpopulated world, force political alterations that may change today's coffee surpluses into tomorrow's coffee shortages with associated higher coffee prices.

It is interesting to note that many of the men and women who pick coffee and have a relatively reasonable income for only a few months of the year cannot even afford to buy coffee in many cases. The use of soluble coffees in the coffee growing countries is a significant sales item because it offers a uniform product of acceptable quality and at a lower price than the locally roasted (burnt), adulterated (beans and corn) stale roast coffees. The coffee industry is still fluid, and new firms or new managements rise to prominence every 5 to 10 years. The opportunities for profitable action are still present.

It is likely that coffee flavor additives and substitutes may yet enjoy their first sales in countries that are economically impoverished. Here the desire for a better standard of living will have to be at first made possible by lower priced alternates. For example, in South Africa a chicory-carbohydrate instant coffee is very popular, and in some countries control of flavor additives is practically non-existent. The circumstances are thus ripe for commercial coffee flavor developments to be pioneered.

Coffee Flavor Additives and Fortifiers

It is most likely that development of coffee flavor additives and fortifiers will come through instant coffees. Current methods including coffee oil add-back to spray dried instant coffee and the addition of freeze-dried coffee brew still do not make a wholly balanced coffee flavor.

In the 1920's imitation and synthetic coffee flavor types were investigated. Now, from time to time, news is made by someone compounding a substitute coffee beverage. Such announcements are often exaggerated, partly because of the fear among the coffee growers and coffee roasters who can see their stable businesses threatened. The National Coffee Association of United States roasters supported at the cost of tens of thousands of dollars a study by Lee (1960) on the probability of synthetic coffee. Lockhart (1959E) stated that synthetic coffee was "improbable in the foreseeable future." The original basis for this alarm was the reported coffee aroma and flavor analyses by Sivetz and Zlatkis

(1960). During the same period, Rhoades (1958 and 1960) published two papers on his analyses of coffee aroma, sponsored by the Coffee Brewing Institute. Also similar confirming analyses on coffee aroma were reported by the Quartermaster Corps at Natick, Mass. The original report and projection for the development of synthetic coffee was made by the Stanford Research Institute. It was a study and report to the committee on foreign relations of the United States Senate of September 1959. Synthetic coffee was viewed as a political problem that could result from technological advances displacing agricultural crops of some nations. The suggestion that coffee beverage could be substituted or synthesized has often been made. But the formal presentation of the idea to the United States Senate committee caused considerable consternation in coffee quarters. Basically the realization of such a suggestion is a question of circumstances. The technological tools are generally admitted to be at hand. Batey (1960) and Lee (1962), revived the theme of synthetic coffee.

The chemical components in high purity can be procured from such firms as Distillation Products, Aldrich Chemicals, K & K Laboratories, and others. The use of labeled isotopes of coffee flavor constituents can help trace their loss and change.

COFFEE FLAVORED BEVERAGES

Coffee with Chicory

In Europe and especially in France, Southern Germany, Belgium, Holland, and Switzerland coffee with chicory is the common beverage much as it is in and about New Orleans. Romans recorded their use of chicory root for themselves and their animals. During the Napoleonic blockade when coffee, cocoa, and tea were procured only with great difficulty, the use of roast chicory rose and was retained long after roast wheat, grain, other cereals, peas, and acorns were no longer used. Chicory, roasted and ground, was used to extend coffee when coffee was hard to get and when coffee was too expensive alone. The use of chicory has always flourished during wars, and its use rose in the United States during World War II. Chicory solubles add "body," depth of color, and a spicy tang to coffee. The chicory "body" contribution is also used for soup seasonings, and it blends well with meat and vegetables. Chicory also is used in cookies and cakes by chefs in Europe. A brew of 100 per cent chicory is bittersweet and not very unlike unsweetened cooking chocolate. It is claimed that the use of chicory in coffee reduces the rate of coffee deterioration when the brew is held hot.

Production.—In 1943 during the war, about 40,000,000 lb of chicory (raw root) or 20,000,000 lb roast and ground chicory were grown and used in the United States. Current annual use in the United States is less than 15,000,000 lb, while European use is about 90,000,000 lb.

At a 2 to 1 weight ratio of roast coffee to roast chicory, 30,000,000 lb of coffee, i.e., 200,000 bags of green coffee (about 1 per cent of all coffee imports into the United States) are used with chicory.

Cost.—Currently, practically no chicory is grown in the United States for commercial use. A small amount of chicory is roasted and ground from dry root from Yugoslavia. By far, the greatest quantity of chicory is imported in roast and ground form (in moisture-proof bags) from France, Belgium, and the Netherlands. Chicory is roasted separately from coffee. European growers receive about $10 per ton raw chicory roots, whereas the United States farmer would have to obtain $25 per ton. Hence, there is no chicory production in the United States.

R & G chicory varies in price. During 1943, it was at a high of $0.17 per lb, and currently (1962) is about $0.11 per lb. This is about one-fifth the price of roast coffee.

Blend.—Roast chicory is blended in the United States with roast coffee in varying proportions to suit taste; in the North about 15 per cent; Mid-Atlantic states about 25 per cent; South 25 to 45 per cent, with a 35 per cent average.

In Europe several brands of instant chicory-coffee mixtures are sold. In Switzerland, the brand Nectar is about 75 per cent coffee solubles and 25 per cent chicory solubles; Nescore by Nestlé, and Incaroma by Thomi and Franck have 27 per cent coffee solubles, 23 per cent chicory solubles, and 50 per cent carbohydrates. Other mixtures by other brands are 50 per cent soluble coffee with 50 per cent chicory with fruit and/or cereal solubles. The fruit solubles are often raisin or date extracts; the cereal solubles are often roast wheat extracts.

In Europe some soluble coffees are still sold with 50 per cent carbohydrates. Also beverages are made from roast wheat grains and bran with molasses. This is similar to Postum but is more common in Europe. In recent years, General Foods has sold Postum in the United States with *"imitation* coffee flavor." Such cereal beverages cost much less than soluble coffees; coffee and chicory with or without carbohydrates are also cheaper than 100 per cent coffee solubles. Nestlé sells a coffee-chicory-carbohydrate product called "Rickory" in England. Lyons in England as well as in other European countries sells its brand, "Quoffy," which is half coffee solubles and half carbohydrates.

A Swiss chain store, Usego, brand Service-2, is 65 per cent coffee solubles and 35 per cent chicory. Even soluble coffee and chocolate mixtures are sold in Europe. It is common in Switzerland to buy chicory extract which is added to brewed coffee, but the instantly soluble powders are gaining in popularity. Roast and ground chicory is also sold; it is mixed with roast and ground coffee at the time of brewing. Chicory solubles in coffee have a clean peppery taste at 50 per cent levels with coffee solubles, and make a very dark brew. Chicory-coffee mixtures are more often consumed with milk than black. In cases where restaurant brews are served with chicory at 10 to 15 per cent of coffee levels, the consumer can judge for himself whether he likes to drink the brew black. After one acquires a taste for brews from chicory and coffee mixtures, these can be consumed black with pleasure.

Yield Per Acre.—Chicory used to be grown in the Saginaw Valley of Michigan. Root yields vary from 4 to 13 tons per acre with a 7 ton per acre average. Chicory root (*Cichorium intybus*) is a plant related to the dandelion, resembling the parsnip and sugar beet, but slightly smaller. Its culture and harvesting are very similar to those of the sugar beet, and chicory used to compete with sugar beet on adjacent fields. Chicory seeds are planted with special drills in mid-May. The chicory plant is resistant to disease, insects, drought, and excessive moisture. The roots develop best in the cool weather during harvest time in September. A beet lifter pulls the roots which allows the dirt to be brushed off, and the green leaves are cut off. The forced second growth of the leaves is known as French endive and is used for salads.

Processing.—The harvested chicory roots are promptly delivered to a washing and drying plant. Sliced root is dried with hot air in a kiln to remove 80 per cent of its original 50 per cent moisture; this takes about 8 hr. The dried root can be stored in a silo indefinitely without deterioration until roasting, grinding, and packaging for shipment are required. Roaster machines, not very different in appearance and principle from coffee roasters, are used to roast the chicory root slices. The heating must be slower than for coffee because the slices are larger and a uniform roast color through the root slice is desired. The ground chicory is screened for particle sizes to suit its ultimate use. Some chicory is made into stick or tablet form; one tablet may be used per 6 cups of coffee. Powered chicory is packed in 6.75-oz (200 gm) moisture-proof packages for home use and in bulk for bakeries that use it to flavor dark rye or pumpernickel bread. Coffee roasters blend chicory with their coffee to suit themselves and their trade.

Composition.—Roast chicory has the following composition: about 3.5 per cent moisture, 4.7 per cent ash, 3.6 per cent petroleum ether extract, 7.3 per cent protein ($N \times 6.25$), 7.9 per cent crude fiber (8.6 per cent reducing sugars as invert, 0.4 per cent sucrose), and 73 per cent total carbohydrates by difference, to give a 100 per cent total. Hot water will extract 69 per cent solubles, hence solubles yield from chicory is about twice that from roast coffee with hydrolysis.

Extraction and Drying.—The normal procedure is to extract the chicory separately because chicory is a much softer particle than coffee. However, some firms percolate roast coffee-chicory mixtures. The resulting solubles in the extract, if percolated, are at least 40 per cent in concentration. The pure chicory solubles solution is syrupy. It can be stored cold and may be mixed with coffee extract as it is produced. Carbohydrate solution can also be added if used. Spray drying the coffee-chicory-carbohydrate solution mixture is not very different from spray drying soluble coffee extract except that the powder has a lower temperature fusion point and melts more readily on the spray drier walls.

Starchy Character of Chicory.—As with Jerusalem artichoke, this is inulin which is broken down by hydrolysis to levulose. The root is a mixture of pentose, levulose, and dextrose. Taraxarcine is the bitter tasting principle like dandelion. Roasting causes caramelization and some of the similar complex pyrolysis changes that occur in coffee sugars and carbohydrates.

Storage.—As long as roast chicory is kept dry, it is stable. Otherwise, if exposed to the atmosphere it will absorb moisture and ferment or gain off-flavors. The E. B. Muller Company and H. Franck Company handling chicory have offices in Port Huron, Mich.[1]

CREME DE CAFE

There are sweet alcoholic liqueurs prepared from coffee extracts that enjoy some popularity as after-dinner drinks (but not after a cup of brewed coffee). Tia Maria from Jamaica and Kahlua from Mexico are two popular brands.

Although liqueur preparations are held secret, the preparation of an after-dinner drink is simple. It can be made from instant coffee powder, although more flavorful and more natural coffee flavors are retained when the crème de cafe is prepared from fresh coffee extract. Soluble coffee production plant extracts can be used. Better flavored liqueurs are obtained when no hydrolysis flavored products are present in the coffee extract such as occurs during percolation start up.

---

[1] We are indebted to Mr. H. G. McMorran, President of E. B. Muller Company, for information about chicory.

The formula for the liqueur can be varied in sweetness by the amount of sugar in the formula; also sugar purity in regard to molasses content will influence overall flavor. Sweetness is strictly a personal taste preference that may be made to suit a sweet or dry taste. Most liqueurs are at least 40 proof or 20 per cent alcohol by volume. Liqueur is defined as a spirituous liquor flavored with aromatic substances. Pure alcohol can be used (95 per cent ethanol) in this liqueur preparation, and it has the advantage that more water can be used with the coffee solubles or sugar solubles. Where 80 or 100 proof alcohol is used to make the liqueur, very high concentrations of coffee extract solubles and sugar solubles are necessary.

Formulations

Example: The water content of the finished liqueur must be low to effect best coffee flavor stability. The water present is actually tied up with the ethanol and sugar. Hence, water cannot easily react with the coffee flavor constituents. In dilute water solution coffee extract flavor will deteriorate in hours or less at room temperature; whereas in water bound solutions, the delicate coffee flavors will keep at room temperatures for many months without marked change.

I.—Mix thoroughly coffee extract fortified with instant coffee powder to 67 per cent solubles (100 gm coffee solubles and 50 gm water) and simple syrup of 85 per cent sucrose (300 gm sucrose and 50 gm water). Add 80 proof vodka (flavorless alcohol) 200 gm ethanol and 300 gm water. Stir. The resulting combination is 15 per cent coffee extract, 35 per cent simple syrup, and 50 per cent vodka. By composition the final mixture is 10 per cent coffee solubles, 20 per cent ethanol, 30 per cent sugar, and 40 per cent water. The water to alcohol ratio is 2 to 1 or about 67 proof. This liqueur is good tasting, but does not afford as good room temperature stability as formula II below.

II.—Mix 33 per cent coffee solubles (300 gm) with 67 per cent sucrose solution (300 gm). Add 400 gm 95 per cent ethanol. A much more stable flavored liqueur results. Its composition is 10 per cent coffee solubles, 20 per cent sucrose, almost 40 per cent ethanol, and 30 per cent water. This, too, is a good tasting liqueur. It has less sugar solubles and water but more alcohol; it is about 80 proof.

CARBONATED COFFEE FLAVORED SOFT BEVERAGE

This has a moderate sales volume in Mexico, Puerto Rico, Brazil, and other warm countries in Latin America and is sold occasionally in the United States. It makes a satisfying cold coffee flavored soft beverage.

Suggested Formula

Mix 700 gm of a 72 per cent simple syrup (500 gm sugar with 200 gm water) with 300 gm of a 27 per cent concentration coffee solubles extract (80 gm coffee solubles and 220 gm water). This gives 50 per cent sugar, 42 per cent water, and 8 per cent coffee solubles.

Each 2 fl oz (60 ml) syrup is diluted with carbonated water 6 to 1 to give 12 fl oz (360 ml) carbonated beverage. The sugar concentration is thus diluted from 50 to 8.3 per cent, and the coffee solubles are diluted from 8 to 1.35 per cent in the final carbonated soft beverage.

The coffee flavored simple syrup is held and used at 40 F (4 C) or less in the syrup (bottle) filling machine. The bottle temperatures should be less than room temperature, preferably 60 F (16 C) or lower to minimize foaming. The carbonated water should also be at 40 F (4 C) or lower. A proper effervescence is obtained with a 3.0 to 3.5 volume of carbon dioxide.

Tartness.—Commercial percolated coffee extract with hydrolysis solubles contributes a tart taste as well as a fresh coffee flavor and aroma. For additional tartness some stock (50 per cent) citric acid solution can be added to the coffee syrup.

With carbonation and tartness blended with the sugar sweetness, an over-all pleasant flavored cold soft drink with a creamy texture is obtained.

Freshness.—The freshness of the coffee flavor does not keep as well as in the crème de cafe liqueur. However, an acceptable coffee flavor is retained if the bottled beverage is consumed in a few weeks after preparation. The bottled beverage should not be exposed to prolonged sunlight and warmth and should be uncapped only when at 40 F (4 C) or less. To protect the coffee syrup and beverage from oxidation, ascorbic acid or an equivalent reducing agent may be added to react preferentially with any oxygen thereby protecting the natural coffee flavor.

Taste.—The balance between sweetness, tartness, carbonation, and coffee flavor can be varied to suit the user from the above formula. The quality of the coffee solubles, and sugar will bear on the overall beverage flavor.

The Cost of the Final Beverage.—This is influenced mostly by the coffee solubles quality and quantity as composed in the syrup used. For example, with the cost of coffee solubles liberally taken at 0.5¢ per gm, a 2 fl oz (60 gm) syrup "throw"[1] having 8 per cent coffee solubles costs 2.4¢, and the 50 per cent sugar solubles (at 6¢ per lb) is about 0.4¢. For a 12-oz final volume soft beverage the coffee and sugar cost is 2.8¢. Actually the 6 oz bottle of this beverage with the same quantity of syrup is better

---

[1] The syrup used for one bottle or portion.

because it is fully satisfying. For the bottler, a coffee quantity that only suggests coffee flavor is usually sufficient.

Even though coffee solubles are controlling in syrup costs, it is notable that the soft beverage even at 16 per cent coffee solubles in the syrup makes a satisfactory-tasting soft beverage.

DOMESTIC USE OF COFFEE

Although our primary concern is with the processing and bulk use of coffee, whether it is roast or soluble coffee, there are numerous uses for both as flavoring substances in many food preparations. For example:

Variations of Coffee Flavored Beverage

These include iced, carbonated, liqueur, and foreign methods of preparing the beverage such as with whipped cream, lemon peel, cinnamon, cloves, chocolate, flavoring for milk or milk beverages, etc. Variations in coffee beverages may be both in coffee and additives strength. Some additives are molasses, sugar, chicory, other roast cereal grain extracts, fig or raisin extracts, as well as decaffeinated coffees or alcoholic beverages.

Coffee Flavorings

These are used in ice cream, soda fountain drinks, candy, and cakes. There are many household and commercial bakery items that refer to coffee in their names. For example, coffee cake, coffee brioche (roll), and other cakes and pastries. These are usually consumed while drinking coffee beverage, but in themselves contain no coffee flavor. Coffee flavored icings on cakes are used occasionally. Often this is instant coffee powder mixed in with butter (or shortening) and powdered sugar. There are some cake recipes in which coffee flavor is used directly.

Compatability.—Since coffee beverage is normally taken with a dessert, it is usually unsatisfactory to have a strong coffee flavored dessert (that is, coffee flavored ice cream, cake, icing, candy, or liqueur). Certainly the coffee flavored dessert is not compatible with a tea beverage. Coffee flavored desserts are compatible with milk.

Beverage

In general, it may be said that a higher rate of consumption of coffee can be achieved simply by preparing a stronger flavored brew of coffee such as one encounters in demitasse after dinner coffee or Vienna coffee with whipped cream.

Brewing Notes

Although this text is not concerned with the individual taste preferences of the consumer and the many ways of preparing coffee beverage, the following comments are listed as being pertinent to the preparation of good tasting coffee beverage from roast and ground coffee:

(1) *The coarser the coffee grind* the less efficient is the water extraction and the yield of coffee flavor and solubles.

(2) Any brewing method that involves *holding the hot coffee beverage* will contribute to its deterioration in flavor. Household percolation is a poor method of preparing flavorful coffee beverage. In fact, household coffee percolation drives off the coffee aroma by steam distillation and leaves a strong tasting solubles residue.

(3) The drip or vacuum type (Silex) of coffee preparation is superior because the contact *time* between the water and the coffee is short. Steeping roast coffee grounds for a few minutes in water that has just boiled followed by separating (decanting or cloth filtration) the coffee grounds promptly from the beverage make a fine tasting beverage provided no additional heating is done. The use of espresso demitasse which is prepared by allowing pressurized water to pass through a finely ground coffee offers a fine tasting beverage.

(4) *Cleanliness of the equipment, purity of the water, the grind and freshness of the roast coffee* as well as the *quality of the coffee,* the *weight ratio* of coffee to water, and the *time of contact* will bear on the flavor of the coffee beverage prepared. The Coffee Brewing Institute Standard is to prepare 40 to 45-five fl oz (150 ml) cups of brew per pound of roast coffee. In Latin America 30 cups per pound are common with a darker roast, finer grind, heavier blend, and different modes of brew preparation.

National Brews

Turkish coffee is prepared differently from other types of coffee brew. The coffee grounds are pulverized, and enough is added to boiling water to give an extremely strong cup. Much sugar is added. The custom is to drink the syrupy beverage with the fine grind residue. This manner of use is, of course, a local Middle East custom. There are many ways to prepare coffee beverage. Some have traditional origins but there are many other reasons for the preparation methods used today. For example, Italian, French, and Turkish coffees are usually roasted extremely dark. The reason is that the coffee is often of poor quality. The dark roast obscures and diminishes these undesirable flavors. Greece, Turkey, and Italy are economically poor countries, and the importation of good quality coffee is a luxury which the average consumer cannot enjoy. Therefore, the consumption of these dark roast coffees is customary. In the case of France, and to some extent, England and Portugal, where their former or current colonies are prime producers of Robusta coffees, it is the custom to use the colonial coffees. Since Robusta coffees have such a characteristic (and not very pleasant) flavor, a dark roast may obscure and diminish some of this flavor in some types. Therefore, in these countries one finds a relatively foreign flavored cup of coffee. The people there have become accustomed to this taste.

Additives

Because the coffees imported into European countries are relatively expensive, it is the custom to mix roast coffee with chicory or other cereal grains to economize on the cost of the coffee beverage. In fact, in extreme cases, a beverage of molasses, wheat grain and bran or chaff can be roasted and extracted to make a caramelized flavored beverage in place of coffee. This is widely used in Europe; and in the United States such a product is sold under the trade name of Postum.

Cafe au Lait

In general, when serving coffee at home or at hotels outside the United States, it is common (especially at breakfast) to pour strong coffee and an equal volume of hot milk. Or the strong coffee can be diluted with hot water to the desired strength.

Robustas

Due to the widespread use after World War II of Robusta coffees in roast coffees to reduce retail selling price, the resulting poor taste quality of coffee beverages has been an inducement to the consumer to use soluble coffee.

U.S. Government Specifications for Roast and Instant Coffees

The Federal specification for roast coffee is HHH-C-571a, Amendment 3 of Feb. 13, 1958 and deviation of Nov. 9, 1961; for instant coffee it is HHH-C-575 of May 24, 1956 with deviation of Sept. 17, 1961. The Quartermaster Food and Container Institute for the Armed Forces oversees such specifications, evaluations of samples, and bids submitted. They are located in Natick, Mass. Roast coffee blends are specified as being Santos 4's 70 per cent by weight and MAM's (Colombians—Medellin, Armenias, or Manizales) 30 per cent by weight. This specification is incidently better than average restaurant or home user can procure. The *instant coffee specifications* state caffeine and carbohydrate levels which must not be exceeded; however, nothing is specified about blend or solubles yield. This specification is really not well drawn because if blend and yield were specified, the large purchases of the government would assure the best product from the best process plants since cost between bidders would be very close. As it stands, high Robusta blends and mediocre processing typify the instant coffees purchased by the government.

BIBLIOGRAPHY

Decaffeination

ANON. 1962. Caffeine Bulletin. Monsanto Chemical Company, St. Louis, Mo.

ANON. 1962. Caffeine. Tech. Bull. No. 18, Charles Pfizer and Company, New York.

ANON. 1960. Merck Index. Merck and Company, Rahway, N.J.

ANON. 1960. Rev. every 5 years. Official Methods of Analysis. Association of Official Agricultural Chemists (A.O.A.C.), Washington, D.C.

ANON. 1962. The story of General Foods decaffeinated coffee. 1932–1948. Food Technology Library, Univ. of Calif., Davis, Calif.

BRUINS, A., and WESTER, D. H. 1914. Caffeine. Pharm. Weekblad *51*, 1443–1446.

BRUINS, A., and WESTER, D. H. 1915. The solubility of some substances in tri- and dichlorethylene. Chem. Zentralblatt 86, I, 248.

BRUNNER, M. 1962. Sale of caffeine-free coffee. Tea and Coffee Trade J. *122*, No. 2, 27.

LEE, S. 1960. Fiftieth anniversary of decaffeinated coffee. Tea and Coffee Trade J. *118*, No. 1, 26, 114–115, 118.

MARVEL, C. S., DIETZ, F. C., and COPLEY, M. J. 1940. Hydrogen bonds involving the C–H link. X. The solubility of donor solutes in halogenated hydrocarbons. J. Am. Chem. Soc. *62*, 2273–2275.

McGOVERN, E. W. 1943. Chlorohydrocarbon solvents. Ind. Eng. Chem. *35*, 1230–1239.

MOORES, R. G., and CAMPBELL, H. A. 1948. Determination of Theobromine and caffeine in cacao materials. Anal. Chem. *20*, No. 1, 40–47.

PUNNETT, P. W. 1956. Decaffeination coffee patents. Tea and Coffee Trade J. *111*, No. 6, Part I, 16, 84; *also* 1957. *112*, No. 1, Part II, 15, 55; *also* 1957. 112, No. 2, Part III, 20.

PUNNETT, P. W. 1942. Facts about caffein and theobromine in foods. Food Inds. *14*, No. 3, 52.

TODD, D. B. 1962. Chart helps choose the best extractor. Chem. Eng. *69*, No. 7, 156.

Coffee Brewing

Coffee Brewing Institute (C.B.I.). 1952–1963. 120 Wall Street, New York.

Technical C.B.I. Publications

ANON. 1948. Coffee grinds. Simplified practice recommendation R231-48. U.S. Department of Commerce, Washington, D.C. C.B.I. publication No. 118.

CAMPBELL, C. L., DAWES, R. K., DEOLALKAR, S., and MERRITT, M. C. 1958. Effect of certain chemicals in water on the flavor of brewed coffee. Food Research *23*, 575–579. C.B.I. publication No. 38.

CLEMENTS, R. L., and DEATHERAGE, F. E. 1957. A chromatographic study of some of the compounds in roasted coffee. (Chemical study of coffee flavor.) Food Research *22*, No. 2, 222–232. C.B.I. publication No. 26.

GARDNER, D. G. 1958. Effect of certain ion combinations commonly found in potable water on rate of filtration through roasted and ground coffee. (Water composition and coffee brewing.) Food Research *23*, No. 1, 76–84. C.B.I. publication No. 31.

GOLDSMITH, G. A., MILLER, O. N., UNGLAUB, W. G., and KERCHEVAL, K. 1959. Human studies of biologic availability of niacin in coffee. Proc. Soc. Exp. Biol. Med. *102*, No. 3, 579–580. C.B.I. publication No. 50.

LENTNER, C. L., and DEATHERAGE, F. E. 1959. Organic acids in coffee in relation to the degree of roast. Food Research *24*, No. 5, 483–492. C.B.I. publication No. 45.

LENTNER, C. L., and DEATHERAGE, F. E. 1958. Phenolic acids in coffee. Chem. & Ind., 1331–1332. C.B.I. publication No. 36.

LITTLE, A. C. 1960. Collaborative study of the measurement of color of ground coffee. C.B.I. publication No. 51.

LITTLE, A. C., and MACKINNEY, G. 1956. On the color of coffee. Food Technol. 10, 503–506. C.B.I. publication No. 17 (1957).

LITTLE, A. C., CHICHESTER, C. O., and MACKINNEY, G. 1958. On the color of coffee. II. Food Technol. 12, 505–507. C.B.I. publication No. 37.

LITTLE, A. C., CHICHESTER, C. O., and MACKINNEY, G. 1959. On the color of coffee. III. Effect of roasting conditions on flavor development for a given color. Role of initial moisture level on roasting characteristics of green coffee beans. Food Technol. 13, 684–688. C.B.I. publication No. 48.

LOCKHART, E. E. 1958. Analysis of coffee grinds. C.B.I. publication No. 32.

LOCKHART, E. E. 1959A. Characteristics of coffee relating to beverage quality. C.B.I. publication No. 40.

LOCKHART, E. E. 1957A. Chemistry of Coffee. From "Chemistry of Natural Food Flavors," a symposium sponsored by the National Academy of Sciences, National Research Council for the Quartermaster Food and Container Institute for the Armed Forces and the Pioneering Research Division, Quartermaster Research and Engineering Center, May, 174–191. C.B.I. publication No. 25.

LOCKHART, E. E. 1959B. Coffee grinds. II. Classification and analysis. Food Research 24, No. 1, 91–96. C.B.I. publication No. 39.

LOCKHART, E. E. 1961. Grind analysis and quality control. C.B.I. publication No. 55.

LOCKHART, E. E. 1960. Roasted coffee. Color measurement and classification. Food Technol. 14, No. 11, 597. C.B.I. publication No. 53.

LOCKHART, E. E. 1959C. The coffee hydrometer. Coffee and Tea Inds. 82, No. 6, 50–51, 68, 70; also 1959. Tea and Coffee Trade J. 117, No. 2. C.B.I. publication No. 43.

LOCKHART, E. E. 1957B. The soluble solids in beverage coffee as an index to cup quality. (Coffee solubles and beverage acceptance.) Tea and Coffee Trade J. 113, No. 1, 12–13, 45–46, 48. C.B.I. publication No. 27.

LOCKHART, E. E. 1959D. The strength of coffee. Coffee and Tea Inds. 82, No. 9. C.B.I. publication No. 44.

LOCKHART, E. E. 1961. Water, coffee, and beverage preparation. C.B.I. publication No. 56.

LOCKART, E. E., and BLOOMHART, F. B. 1956. A survey of world literature on coffee (1953). C.B.I. publication No. 7.

LOCKHART, E. E., and BLOOMHART, F. B. 1956. A survey of world literature on coffee (1954). C.B.I. publication No. 13.

LOCKHART E. E., and BLOOMHART, F. B. 1957. A survey of world literature on coffee (1955). C.B.I. publication No. 23.

LOCKHART, E. E., CAWLEY, B. A., MERRITT, M. C., and TUCKER, C. L. 1957. Storage properties of vacuum packed coffee. Food Technol. 11, 586–588. C.B.I. publication No. 30 (1958).

LOCKHART, E. E., TUCKER, C. L., and MERRITT, M. C. 1955. The effect of water impurities on the flavor of brewed coffee. Food Research 20, 598–605. C.B.I. publication No. 6 (1956).

MABROUK, A. F., and DEATHERAGE, F. E. 1956. Organic acids in brewed coffee. Food Technol. 10, No. 4, 194–197. C.B.I. publication No. 12.

MERRITT, M. C., and PROCTOR, B. E. 1959A. Effect of temperature during the roasting cycle on selected components of different types of whole bean coffee. Food Research 24, 672–680. C.B.I. publication No. 46.

MERRITT, M. C., and PROCTOR, B. E. 1959B. Extraction rates for selected components in coffee brew. Food Research 24, 735–743. C.B.I. publication No. 47.

NIVEN, W. W., and SHAW, B. C. 1957. Critical conditions for quantity coffee brewing. Coffee and Tea Inds. *80*, No. 4, 44, 75–76, 78; *also* Tea and Coffee Trade J. *112*, No. 4, 28, 30, 32, 34–35. C.B.I. publication No. 19.

O'MEARA, J. B., TRUBY, F. K., and SHAW, T. W. 1957. Free radicals in roasted coffee. Food Research *22*, No. 1, 96–101. C.B.I. publication No. 18.

RHOADES, J. W. 1960. Coffee volatiles. Analysis of the volatile constituents of coffee. Agri. and Food Chem. *8*, No. 2, 136. C.B.I. publication No. 52.

RHOADES, J. W. 1958. Sampling method for analysis of coffee volatiles by gas chromatography. (Coffee aroma analysis by gas chromatography.) Food Research *23*, No. 3, 254–261. C.B.I. publication No. 34.

SEGALL, S., and PROCTOR, B. E. 1959. The influence of high temperature holding upon the components of coffee brew. Food Technol. *13*, No. 5, 266–270. C.B.I. publication No. 41 (1960).

SEGALL, S., and PROCTOR, B. E. 1959. The influence of high temperature holding upon the components of coffee brew. II. Volatile reducing substances. Food Technol. *13*, No. 7, 383–384. C.B.I. publication No. 42.

SEGALL, S., and PROCTOR, B. E. 1959. The influence of high temperature holding upon the components of coffee brew. III. Hydrogen sulfide, sulfur dioxide, and sulfhydryl compounds (mercaptans). Food Technol. *13*, No. 12, 679–683. C.B.I. publication No. 49 (1960).

TEPLY, L. J. 1958. Nutritional study of instant coffee powder. Food Technol. *12*, 485–486. C.B.I. publication No. 35.

TEPLY, L. J., and PRIER, R. F. 1957. Nutritional evaluation of coffee including niacin bioassay. J. Agri. Food Chem. 5, No. 5, 375–377. C.B.I. publication No. 24.

General C.B.I. Publications

About Good Coffee. National restaurant association collaboration. C.B.I. publication No. 21.

Coffee brewing control chart. C.B.I. publication No. 15.

Coffee for a crowd. What to do and how to brew in quantity. C.B.I. publication No. 16.

Equipment evaluation. A program for the evaluation of coffee making equipment. C.B.I. publication No. 126 (1963).

How you can make good coffee every time. C.B.I. publication No. 1.

Publications, materials, and services list. 1963. C.B.I. publication No. 29.

Survey of beverage coffee. Preferences of consumers patronizing public eating places. C.B.I. publication No. 5 (1956).

The coffee brewing institute. 1953–1963. C.B.I. publication No. 8.

There is no substitute for good coffee. Here's what you need to make it. C.B.I. publication No. 14.

ANON. 1962. Coffee brewing (eleven articles). Tea and Coffee Trade J. *118*, No. 1, 46; No. 1, 56; No. 1, 64; No. 2, 18; No. 3, 17; No. 3, 18; No. 4, 45; No. 5, 46; *119*, No. 1, 26; No. 2, 20; No. 4, 18.

ANON. 1962. New Brewing Equipment. World Coffee and Tea *3*, No. 1, 13–24.

ANON. 1959. Revolution in airline coffee. Coffee and Tea Inds. *82*, No. 9, 9, 11, 42.

ANON. 1962. School for brewing. Coffee and Tea Inds. *85*, No. 1, 12–13.

DRIVER, J. 1958. Which kind of coffee for good flavor and aroma? Consumers Research Bull., *41*, No. 8, 13–14, Washington, N.J.

LEE, S. 1959. Egg coffee. Tea and Coffee Trade J. *117*, No. 3, 21, 50, 52–54.

PAPASHVILY, H. 1962. Handbook of coffee. Holiday *31*, No. 2, 117–120.

PUNNETT, P. W. 1962. Brewing in vacuum type coffee maker. Tea and Coffee Trade J. *123*, No. 1, 22, 24.

PUNNETT, P. W. 1959. How fast does brewed coffee deteriorate? Tea and Coffee Trade J. *117*, No. 2, 22, 43–44.

PUNNETT, P. W. 1960. The importance of temperature in brewing. Tea and Coffee Trade J. *118*, No. 4, 45, 67–68; *also* No. 5, 47, 49.

UKERS, W. H. 1922 and 1935. All About Coffee. Tea and Coffee Trade J., 79 Wall Street, New York.
UKERS, W. H. 1948. Romance of Coffee. Tea and Coffee Trade J., 79 Wall Street, New York.

Water

ANON. 1957. Handbook of Water Conditioning. 5th Edition. Betz Laboratories, Philadelphia.
ANON. 1956. Manual on Industrial Waters. American Society for Testing Materials, Philadelphia.
ANON. 1954. U.S. Public Water Supplies. Papers 1299 and 1300. U.S. Department of the Interior, Washington, D.C.
ANON. 1949. Water Conditioning Handbook. Permutit Company, 50 West 44 Street, New York.
CAMPBELL, C. L., DAWES, R. K., DEOLALKAR, S., and MERRITT, M. C. 1958. Effect of certain chemicals in water on the flavor of brewed coffee. Food Research 23, 575–579. Also C.B.I. publication No. 38.
CLEMENTS, R. L., and DEATHERAGE, F. E. 1957. A chromatographic study of some of the compounds in roasted coffee. (Chemical study of coffee flavor.) Food Research 22, No. 2, 222–232. Also C.B.I. publication No. 26.
ELLIS, M. M., WESTFALL, B. A., and ELLIS, M. D. 1948. Determination of water quality. Research report No. 9, U.S. Fish and Wildlife Service, Washington, D.C.
GARDNER, D. G. 1958. Effect of certain ion combinations commonly found in potable water on rate of filtration through roasted and ground coffee. (Water composition and coffee brewing.) Food Research 23, No. 1, 76–84. Also C.B.I. publication No. 31.
HOOVER, C. P., and RIEHL, M. L. 1962. Water supply and treatment. 9th Edition. Bull. 211. National Lime Assoc., 925 15th Street, N.W., Washington, D.C.
LANGE, N. A. 1961. Handbook of Chemistry. 9th Edition. Handbook Publishers, Sandusky, Ohio.
MABROUK, A. F., and DEATHERAGE, F. E. 1956. Organic acids in brewed coffee. Food Technol. 10, No. 4, 194–197. Also C.B.I. publication No. 12.
MINER, C. S. 1934. Acidity of roasted coffee. Nat'l Fed. of Coffee Growers of Colombia, May 25, 120 Wall Street, New York.
NORDELL, E. 1961. Water Treatment. 2nd Edition. Reinhold Publishing Corporation, New York.
POWELL, S, T. 1954. Water Conditioning for Industry. McGraw-Hill Book Company, New York.
PUNNETT, P. W. 1962. Analytical approach to better coffee brewing. Tea and Coffee Trade J. 122, No. 5, 32–34.
PUNNETT, P. W. 1962. Chemical compounds in brew water. Tea and Coffee Trade J. 122, No. 4, 12–13.
PUNNETT, P. W. 1961. Effect of water content on coffee flavor. Tea and Coffee Trade J. 120, No. 4, 13, 46.
PUNNETT, P. W. 1956. Feathering and discoloration of coffee. Tea and Coffee Trade J. 110, No. 6, 18, 68.
PUNNETT, P. W. 1960. How minerals affect coffee brewing. Tea and Coffee Trade J. 119, No. 4, 18, 52–53.
PUNNETT, P. W. 1959. Minerals in water often affect coffee. Tea and Coffee Trade J. 116, No. 4, 48.
PUNNETT, P. W. 1958. Removal of iron from water for coffee. Tea and Coffee Trade J. 115, No. 2, 20.
PUNNETT, P. W. 1959. The effect of chloride on brewed coffee. Tea and Coffee Trade J. 116, No. 5, 34.
PUNNETT, P. W. 1959. Water minerals that affect coffee flavor. Tea and Coffee Trade J. 116, No. 3, 30.

PUNNETT, P. W. 1958. What can be done about iron in water. Tea and Coffee Trade J. *114*, No. 6, 24.
SIVETZ, M. 1949. Acids play important roles in flavor. Food Inds. *21*, No. 10, 74–75.
SIVETZ, M. 1950. Hard water costs the bottler plenty. Food Inds. *22*, 58–60, 171–172.
U.S. DEPARTMENT OF AGRICULTURE. 1955. Water. Handbook of Agriculture. Superintendent of Documents, Washington, D.C.
VAUGHAN, J. W. 1962. Water quality in brewing coffee. Tea and Coffee Trade J., *123*, No. 2, 20, 50–53.

Coffee Vending

ANON. 1959. Coffee in a tape brewed automatically. Machine Design *31*, No. 20, 15.
ANON. 1962. Coffee machine shipments rose in 1961. Tea and Coffee Trade J. *123*, No. 1, 57.
ANON. 1961. Controlled until the last drop: machine for making coffee automatically from instant coffee. Prod. Eng. *32*, No. 7, 16–17.
ANON. 1961. Picking the right plastic for the right part: drink dispensers. Modern Plastics *38*, No. 5, 168.
ANON. 1960. Pressurized coffee extract. Tea and Coffee Trade J. *118*, No. 3, 51–52.
ANON. 1960. Vend coffee booms. World Coffee and Tea *1*, No. 1, 51–52.
ANON. 1956. Vending machines. Business Week Dec. 15, 68, McGraw-Hill Publishing Company, New York.
ANON. 1960. Vending machines. Business Week Nov. 12, 59, 62–63. McGraw-Hill Publishing Company, New York.
ANON. 1962. Vending U.S.A. World Coffee and Tea *3*, No. 2, 69.
ATTERBOM, P. A. 1962. Coffee beverage vending in Europe. Coffee and Tea Inds. *85*, No. 9, 36–38.
GIGGARD, E. D. 1960. Pressure dispensed liquid coffee concentrate. Paper 135. Institute of Food Technologists meeting. Continental Can Company, 1350 West 76 Street, Chicago.
GOTTSCHALL, P. B., and GIGGARD, E. D. 1958. Pressure dispensed food packaging. Food Technol. *12*, No. 1, 8–14.
GREENBAUM, F. R. 1956. Manufacturing coffee and tea for automatic merchandising. Coffee and Tea Inds. *79*, No. 9, 63, 65.
KING, J. E. 1962A. Changing profile of coffee vending. Tea and Coffee Trade J. *122*, No. 1, 34–35, 73–74.
KING, J. E. 1962B. King coffee futurama (vending coffee). Coffee and Tea Inds. *85*, No. 5, 53.
MELIKIAN, K. C. 1960. How roasters can cash in on the roasting bonanza. World Coffee and Tea *1*, No. 3, 39–40.
MELIKIAN, K. C. 1960. Let's vend 6,000,000 more cups per day. Coffee and Tea Inds. *83*, No. 1, 81, 142.
MELIKIAN, K. C. 1960. Record coffee sales in 1960. Coffee and Tea Inds. *83*, No. 7, 7, 9.
See also vending machine manufacturers' pamphlets and instruction manuals.

Chicory

RATHER, H. C. 1934. Chicory culture and use. Bull. 127. Michigan State College Extension, East Lansing, Mich.
STOUFFER, L. 1943. Production processing and uses of chicory. Food Inds. *15*, No. 10.

Coffee Flavor Additives, Substitutes, and Synthetics

ANON. 1954. Coffee essence-Moka 889. Food Trade Review *24*, No. 3, 16.

ANON. 1961. FEMA (Flavoring Extract Manufacturers' Association) expert panel judges flavoring substances GRAS. Food Eng. *33*, No. 4, 93.

ANON. 1960. Food additives—tracer migration and toxicity. Chem. Eng. News *38*, No. 34, Aug. 22, 38.

ANON. 1961. Food additives, what they are, how they are used. Manufacturing Chemists Assoc., Washington, D.C.

ANON. 1959. Food and Drug Administration (F.D.A.) lists safe food additives. Chem. Eng. News *37*, Nov. 30, 32.

ANON. 1960. Food and Drug Administration (F.D.A.) names 182 safe additives. Food Eng. *32*, No. 1, 81–82.

ANON. 1960. How to proceed under food additives amendment. Manufacturing Chemists Assoc., Washington, D.C.

ANON. 1962. Isotopes Specialties Catalog. No. 587. Box 688, Burbank, Calif.

ANON. 1944. Proposed standard for coffee essences. Analyst *69*, No. 10, 308, Cambridge, England.

ANON. 1958. Requirements of the U.S. Food, Drug, and Cosmetic Act. Food and Drug Administration publication No. 2, U.S. Department of Health, Education, and Welfare, Washington, D.C.

ANON. 1962. Research Chemicals Catalog. Aldrich Chemical Company, Milwaukee, Wis.

ANON. 1954. Synthetic coffee flavor. Food Eng. *26*, No. 6, 165.

ANON. 1958. Taste makers ready for law makers' tests. Chemical Week *83*, No. 15, Oct. 11, 123, 126.

ANON. 1959. What's in that morning coffee aroma? Chem. Eng. News *37*, April 20, 51.

BATEY, R. W. 1960. Will coffee of the 60's be synthetic? Tea and Coffee Trade J. *118*, No. 2, 16, 34.

EASTMAN KODAK COMPANY. 1962. Organic Chemicals Catalog. 44th Edition. Distillation Products, Rochester, N.Y.

HALL, R. L. 1959. Flavoring agents as food additives. Food Technol. *13*, No. 7.

JACOBS, M. 1947. Synthetic Food Adjuncts. D. Van Nostrand Company, Princeton, N.J.

KATZ, A. 1956. Newly developed flavoring aromatics. Am. Perfumer Aromat. *67*, No. 3, 66.

LEE, S. 1959. Egg coffee. Tea and Coffee Trade J. *117*, No. 3, 21–22, 48, 50, 52–53.

LEE S. 1962. Flavor and aroma of African robusta coffee. Tea and Coffee Trade J. *112*, No. 3, 30, 32, 34–36.

LEE, S. 1960. Report on "the quest for synthetic coffee." Tea and Coffee Trade J. *119*, Nos. 4 and 5, 22, 24–25.

LEINEN, N. 1959. The food law Institute's big mission! Food Processing *20*, No. 9, 31, 33, 45.

LOCKHART, E. E. 1959E. Synthetic coffee improbable in foreseeable future. Tea and Coffee Trade J. *117*, No. 5.

MERORY, J. 1960. Food Flavorings. AVI Publishing Company, Westport, Conn.

MERRITT, M. C. 1957. Fresh cabbage volatiles composition; analyses by mass spectrometry. U.S. Army Q.M. Corps Research and Eng. Center, Natick, Mass.

NATIONAL RESEARCH COUNCIL. 1959. Principles and processes for the evaluation of the safety of food additives. National Academy of Sciences, Washington, D.C.

NATIONAL RESEARCH COUNCIL. 1956. Use of chemical additives in food processing. Publication No. 398, National Academy of Sciences, Washington, D.C.

OSER, B. L. 1959. Food additives—new law causes many problems. Chem. Eng. News *37*, Feb. 15, 108–116.

PEPPERCORN, L. 1960. Fear of U.S. synthetic coffee grips Brazil. Tea and Coffee Trade J. *118*, No. 1, 126.

RHOADES, J. W. 1960. Analysis of volatile constituents of coffee. Agri. and Food Chem. 8, No. 2, 136. *Also* C.B.I. publication No. 52.

RHOADES, J. W. 1958. Sampling method for analysis of coffee volatiles by gas chromatography. Food Research 23, No. 254–261. *Also* C.B.I. publication No. 34.

TIBBLES, W. 1912. Foods: Their Origin, Composition, and Manufacturing. Pages 792–805. Bailliere, Tindall and Cox, Heniretta Street, Covent Garden, London.

ZLATKIS, A., and SIVETZ, M. 1960. Analysis of coffee volatiles by gas chromatography. Food Research 25, 395–398.

Chronological List of Coffee Decaffeination Patents

Number and Date	Inventors	Title or Description
Br 6,375 3/16/06	Meyer, J. F.	Treat green coffee with dry steam; extract with NH_3, H_2SO_4, or HCl to remove caffeine and furfurol; extract with benzene; decaffeinate; add-back.
Fr 364,389 3/19/06	Meyer, J. F.	Same as Br 6,375/06 above.
Ger 237,810 10/19/06	Utescher, E.	Extraction with aqueous ammonia.
Ger 227,380 8/4/07	Utescher, E.	Extraction of green coffee with acetic or sulfurous acid.
Ger 219,405 12/1/07	Utescher, E.	Fixing caffeine and extraction in a weak electric current.
Ger 243,539 1/28/08	Wimmer, K. H.	Decaffeinate green coffee with dilute alcohol; extract aqueous extract with organic solvents.
Br 2,035 1/29/08	Wimmer, K. H.	Swell green coffee with hot water or steam; extract with benzene or chloroform.
897,763 9/1/08	Meyer, J. F., Roselius, L., & Wimmer, K. H.	Extract green coffee with water; remove extract under vacuum; decaffeinate extract; reuse decaffeinated extract.
Fr 396,930 11/24/08	Seisser, L.	Decaffeinate green coffee with ethyl acetate at 68 C in centrifuge.
936,392 10/12/09	Wimmer, K. H.	Steam green coffee; extract with solvent; steam again to remove solvent.
950,357 2/22/09	Trillich, H.	Moisten green coffee; pass electric current to dissociate caffeine and tannic acid; extract caffeine.
Ger 276,014 10/29/09	Klein, L.	Extract raw or roasted coffee with sodalime solution under pressure.
Br 1,328 1/18/10	Hubner, R.	Soak green coffee in water at 15 C; partially germinate; extract with water at 50 to 60 C.
947,577 1/25/10	Hubner, R.	Same as Br 1,328/10 above.
Br 5,827 3/7/10	Lifebelt Coffee Company	Treat whole green coffee with steam under pressure; extract with benzene.
953,073, 4 3/29,/10	Trillich, H.	Extract green coffee with acetic acid, then acetic ether under pressure.
9539643 3/24,/10	Seisser, L.	Extract whole green coffee with volatile solvent using centrifuge for circulation of solvent.
96 944 7/19/10	Trillich, H.	Extract with 10 per cent alkali; decaffeinate aqueous extract with heavy organic solvent.
Br 24,793 10/25/10	Klein, L.	Soak and steam green coffee; extract with hot aqueous lime-soda solution.
Br 8,815 4/8/11	Klein, L.	Sealed drum with special valves for caffeine-free coffee.
1,000,692 8/15/11	Roselius, L.	Electrolysis of green coffee in a conducting solution; extraction with a selective solvent.
1,009,610 11/21/11	Wimmer, K. H.	Extract green coffee with hot water at 70 to 120 C; decaffeinate aqueous extract; impregnate beans with decaffeinated extract.
897,840 9/1/08 reissue 13,261, 2, 3 6/27/11	Meyer, J. F. Roselius, L., & Wimmer, K. H.	Treat green coffee with gaseous dry steam, then acids; extract with volatile solvent; treat with dry steam.
1,015,271 1/16/12	Geisler, L. W.	Extract green coffee with boiling water; decaffeinate extract; then soak coffee in decaffeinated solution.

Number and Date	Inventors	Title or Description
1,016,293, 4 2/6/12	Rosewater, N.	Extract whole green coffee with hot water; chill extract to precipitate caffeine; soak coffee in decaffeinated extract.
1,039,961 10/1/12	Klein, L.	Extract green coffee with aqueous alkali; then treat with CO_2 under pressure.
1,041,160 10/15/12	DePury, H.	Cause ligneous cells of green coffee to burst; extract, then roast.
1,073,929 9/23/13	Rosewater, N.	Apply dry heat to whole green coffee, agitate, decorticate, extract caffeine, restore constituents other than caffeine.
1,123,827 1/5/15	Whitaker, M. C., & Metzger, F. J.	Steam distillation of R & G coffee, then aqueous extraction; combine distillate and extract to recover caffeine.
1,216,671 2/20/17	Eden, F. R.	Aqueous extraction of caffeine from green coffee; partial drying; moist roast.
Br 144,998 3/19/20	Lombaers, H. C. E.	Dry steaming; solvent extraction; steaming to remove solvent.
1,400,992 12/20/21	Rosewater, N.	Subliming alkaloids from green coffee.
1,414,096 4/25/22	Roselius, H.	Steam green coffee; extract with benzene.
Br 206,145 10/24/22	Lombaers, H. C. E.	Soak green coffee to 20 per cent moisture; extract with solvent boiling point 36 to 45 C.
Ger 515,604 10/23/23	Kaffee, H. A. G.	Extract green coffee with dichlormethane.
Ger 538,439 10/23/23	Kaffee, H. A. G.	Same as Br 206,145/22 above.
1,502,222 7/22/24	Wimmer, K. H.	Extract green coffee with halogen hydrocarbons boiling below 45 C.
Br 247,039 4/22/25	Kundig, F.	Extract green coffee with organic solvents, alcohols, esters, ketones.
1,629,512 5/24/27	Walliseller, F. K.	Extract whole green coffee with caffeine solvents at 15 atmosphere pressure.
1,640,648 8/30/27	Gross, H.	Soak green coffee in alkaline solutions; pass inert gas through; separate caffeine; recycle gas.
Sw 128,984 11/8/27	Kundig, F.	Caffeine. Heat steeped green coffee under pressure; extract with solvent; remove solvent by current of air and steam.
Fr 665,682 9/22/28	Gassner, C. O.	Remove caffeine or theine from coffee or tea with aqueous solutions of salts in extractive substances.
Br 314,059 6/4/29	Klappreth, W.	Decaffeinate aqueous extract of green coffee; reuse extract.
Br 314,308 6/22/28	Neustadt, G., & Neustadt, I.	Extracted and decaffeinated green coffee is enriched by decaffeinated extract from a larger quantity of beans.
Br 339,543 1/31/30	Paffgen, W.	Decaffeinate coffee extract by charcoal.
Fr 694,602 4/28/30	Farben, I. G.	Extract caffeine from green coffee by liquid ammonia.
Belg 373,515 10/31/30	Laitat, G.	Treat green coffee at 60 to 90 C with solution of free alkali.
Ger 562,863 4/11/31	Closmann, E. A.	Extract green coffee with hot water; decaffeinate; reuse extract.
Br 362,313 4/22/31	Levelt, W. H.	Steam green coffee to disrupt cells; extract with solvent; steam. Apparatus described.
Fr 733,915 3/19/32	Koro Kaffee Cie.	Treat green coffee with higher alcohols or ketones to swell; dry at 100 C: extract caffeine, use pressure.
Fr 739,527 7/6/32	Scheele, E.	Extract caffeine from green coffee by emulsion of water and organic solvent.
Br 397,323 10/15/32	Massatsch, C.	Decaffeinate coffee extract by passing it through solvent; filter.
Fr 743,900 4/7/33	Massatsch, C.	Same as Br 397,323/32 above.
Br 404,228 7/19/33	Gilbert, P.	Treat green coffee with H_2O_2 to swell beans and destroy tannates; extract with dichlormethane.
Belg 399,292 11/30/33	Cafesa	Treat green coffee with steam under pressure; remove caffeine with organic solvent.
Sw 166,486 4/2/34	Brunner, M.	Caffeine-free coffee by extraction with aqueous emulsion of paraffin oil.
Sw 167,162 4/16/34	Brunner, M.	Extract green coffee with cis-dichloroethylene to remove caffeine.

Number and Date	Inventors	Title or Description
1,957,358 5/1/34	Scheele, E.	Extract with emulsion of organic solvent and water.
Ger 597,001 5/18/34	Brumund, D.	Extract green coffee with water and organic solvent.
Fr 764,456 8/22/34	Grethe, T.	Extract with mixture of acetic ether and water; steam and dry.
1,964,814 7/3/34	Gilbert, P.	Treat green coffee with H_2O_2; extract with dichlormethane.
Br 442,230 7/27/34	Helmke, W. A. C.	Apparatus for continuous extraction of green coffee, inclined cylinder.
Fr 768,452 8/7/34	Brunner, M.	Extract with sym. cis-dichlormethane in autoclave.
Fr 771,526 10/10/34	Rennotte, J. F.	Alkaloids from green coffee. Extract with H_2CO_3.
1,977,416 10/16/34	Wilder, H. K.	Moisten green coffee; extract with volatile solvent; steam at 170 F.
Fr 775,227 12/21/34	Produits Silgelac	Coffee extract passed over bed of silica gel pellets.
Br 439,617 8/30/35	Helmke, W. A. C., Tyberghein, E. C. E. & Backer, P. J.	Extract green coffee with ethylene-chloride; treat with steam and air.
2,007,405 7/9/35	Meijer, F. M.	Steam green coffee; extract with organic solvent; dry steam.
Ger 598,379 7/9/35	Ruppert, F.	Extract green coffee with trichlorethylene; coffee oils added back to extract to conserve aroma.
2,016,634 10/8/35	Grethe, T.	Extract green coffee with acetic ester and water; steam and dry.
2,023,333 12/3/35	McLang, J.	Extract green coffee with $\alpha\alpha$ and $\alpha\beta$ dichlorethane.
2,036,345 4/7/36	Merkel, H.	More digestible infusion at pH 6.4 to 6.9; add noninjurious alkaline substance.
2,045,854 6/30/36	Hoffman, W. F.	Immerse green coffee beans in liquid conducting medium; electrolyze with direct current; neutralize acid.
Ger 632,208 12/5/36	Kallman, A.	Use of egg albumin and H_2O_2.
Fr 806,904 12/29/36	Tyberghein, E. C. E., & Backer, P. J.	Same as Br 439,617/35 above.
Fr 742,684 3/14/38	Coffex, A. G.	Heat green coffee with 16 per cent water in autoclave; clave; extract with dichlorethane; heat to remove solvent.
Belg 430,910 1/31/39	Cafe H. A. G., S.A.	Caffeine-free coffee and tea. Caffeine decomposed by aeration of moist beans or leaves.
2,151,582 3/21/39	Block ,D. J.	Treat coffee brew with unactivated carbon, then nontoxic alkaline solution.
2,157,956 5/9/39	Hasselborn, W. C., & Thompson, J. J.	Cold water, steam, hot solvent, steam (green coffee).
Ger 675,471 5/9/39	Scheele, E.	Extract green coffee with emulsion of trichlorethylene or chloroform.
Fr 845,118 8/11/39	Cafe Sanka, S.A.	Decomposition of caffeine and/or theine by aeration in presence of water, electric current, and ultraviolet rays.
Ger 685,367 12/16/39	Coffex, A. G.	Water extraction of green coffee; decaffeination of extract by activated charcoal; re-use of extract.
2,198,859 4/30/40	Bürgin, E.	Decaffeination of aqueous extract of coffee by adsorbing agent in liquid permeable vessel.
Belg 440,644 1/31/41	Cafe H. A. G., S.A.	Caffeine-free coffee by aeration of moist beans with lactic acid bacteria.
Sw 211,646 2/2/41	Bürgin, E. (M. Brunner Co.)	Same as U. S. 2,198,859/40 above.
2,233,033 2/25/41	Robinson, F. W.	Moisten green coffee; steam, 10 lb; solvent extraction; steam.
Ger 709,365 7/3/41	Kirschbaum, E.	Decaffeination of coffee extracts. Extract R & G coffee with water; distill until residue is dry; collect aromatic distillate; free dry residue from caffeine under vacuum; combine with aromatic liquid distillate.
Dutch 51,215 10/15/41	Koffie, H. A. G.	Extract green coffee with water or coffee extract in air stream, electric current, ultraviolet light.
2,284,033 5/26/42	Berry, N. E.	Soak green coffee in solution of coffee solubles.

Number and Date	Inventors	Title or Description
Ger 722,132 5/14/42	Roselius, W.	Aeration of green coffee in presence of water; reuse of extraction water.
Dutch 53,500 11/16/42	Kaffee, H. A. G.	Caffeine destroyed in wet green coffee by air current, fermentation, oxidation, lactic acid bacteria, and yeast.
2,309,092 1/26/43	Berry, N. E., & Walters, R. H.	Continuous countercurrent aqueous extraction of green coffee; decaffeination of extract; recycling decaffeinated extract.
2,309,139 1/26/43	Rector, T. M.	Continuous process and apparatus. Moistening, countercurrent solvent extraction.
2,324,594 7/20/43	Polin, H. S.	Extraction solvent mixture for green coffee: small amount of chloroform for caffeine and large amount of hydrocarbons for oils.
Ger 740,900 9/9/43	Roselius, W.	Extract R & G coffee with water; collect gases; remove CO_2 from gases; return remaining gases to extract.
2,375,550 5/8/45	Grossman, H.	Decaffeinate coffee extract by contact with Al or Mg silicate.
Sw 239,206 12/17/45	Forster, O.	Decaffeinate coffee (?) with methylene chloride under alternating pressure changes in N_2 to exclude air.
2,391,981 1/1/46	Kremers, R. E.	Extract green coffee with chlor-organic solvents of low polarity; decaffeinate on clay; remove caffeine from clay by non-chlorinated solvents of high polarity; recover caffeine.
2,472,121 6/7/49	Ornfelt, J.	Extract caffeine from 40 per cent R & G coffee extract with organic solvents until 90 per cent of caffeine is removed.
Can 492,560 5/5/53	Ornfelt, J.	Same as 2,472,121/49 above.
2,472,881 6/14/49	Bender, C. R.	Extract green coffee with organic solvents; extract solvent with water to obtain bulk of caffeine by cooling; extract aqueous extract with organic solvent to obtain remainder.
Br 635,185 4/5/50	Durrenmatt, H. K.	Extract R & G coffee with water; distill.
Dutch 65,777 4/15/50	Hendrix, W. H.	Decaffeinating green coffee beans. Steam; extract with benzene; extract residue with water and ether.
2,508,545 8/28/50	Shuman, A. C.	Process of recovering caffeine.
Br 700,598 12/2/53	Blench, R. O.	Drive off aroma from R & G coffee by heat, then extract caffeine from de-aromatized coffee; add-back aroma to coffee or extract. 12 claims.
Ital 549,808 10/18/56	Conte, G.	Caffeine removal from coffee infusions.
2,802,739 8/13/57	Nutting, L.	Steam distill R & G coffee and condense; remove caffeine; add condensate back to extract.
2,817,588 12/24/57	Barch, W. E.	Immerse green coffee in water; extract caffeine with organic solvent; reuse decaffeinated aqueous extract.
2,933,395 4/19/60	Adler, I., & Earle, E. L.	Evaporate volatiles from thin film of R & G coffee extract at proper temperature and pressure; extract aqueous extract with organic solvent; decaffeinate and return to extract.

Alphabetical List of Inventors—Decaffeination

Adler, I.	2,933,395	Lifebelt Coffee Co.	Br 5,827/10
Backer, P. J.	Br 439,617/35	Lombaers, H. C. E.	Br 144,998/20
	Fr 806,904/36		Br 206,145/22
Barch, W. E.	2,817,588	Maatsch, C.	Br 397,323/32
Bender, C. R.	2,472,881		Fr 743,900/33
Berry, M. E.	2,284,033	MacLang, L.	2,023,333
	2,309,092	Meijer, F.	2,007,405
Blench, R. O.	Br 700,598/53	Merkel, H.	2,036,345
Block, D. J.	2,151,582	Metzger, F. J.	1,123,827
Brumund, D.	Ger 597,001/34	Meyer, J. F.	Br 6,375/06
Brunner, M.	Sw 166,486/34		Fr 364,189/06
	Sw 167,162/34		897,763
	Fr 768,452/34		897,840
Bürgin, E.	2,198,859		
	Sw 211,646/41	Neustadt, G.	Br 314,304/28
Cafe, H. A. G., S. A.	Belg 430,910/39	Neustadt, I.	Br 314,304/28
	Belg 440,644/41	Nutting, L.	2,802,739
Cafesa	Belg 399,292/33	Ornfelt, J.	2,472,121
Cafe Sanka, S. A.	Fr 845,118/39		Can 492,560/53
Closmann, E. A.	Ger 562,863/31		
Coffex, A. G.	Fr 742,684/38	Paffgen, W.	Br 339,543/30
	Ger 685,367/39	Polin, H. S.	2,324,594
Conte, G.	Ital 549,808/56	Produits Silgelac	Fr 775,227/34
Darling, E. R.	2,335,206	Rector, T. M.	2,309,139
De Pury, R.	1,041,160	Rennotte, J. F.	Fr 771,526/34
Durrenmatt, H. K.	Br 635,185/50	Robinson, F. W.	2,233,033
Earle, E. L.	2,933,395	Roselius, L.	897,763
Eden, F. R.	1,216,671		897,840
Farben, I. G.	Fr 694,602/30		1,000,692
Forster, O.	Sw 239,206/45		1,414,096
Gassner, C. O.	Fr 665,082/28		Ger 722,132/42
Geisler, L. W.	1,015,271		Ger 740,900/43
Gilbert, P.	Br 404,228/33	Rosewater, N.	1,016,293,4
	1,964,814		1,073,929
Grethe, T.	Fr 764,456/34	Ruppert, F.	1,400,992
	2,016,634		Ger 598,379/35
Gross, R.	1,640,648	Scheele, E.	Fr 739,527/32
Grossman, H.	2,375,550		1,957,358
Hasselborn, W. C.	2,157,956		Ger 675,471/39
Helmer, W.	Fr 681,860/30	Schuman, A. C.	2,508,545
Helmke, W. A. C.	Br 442,230/34	Seisser, L.	Fr 396,679/08
	Br 439,617/35		953,643
Hendrix, W. H.	Dutch 65,777/50	Silgelac, Produits	Fr 775,227/34
Hoffman, W.	2,045,854	Thompson, J. J.	2,157,956
Hubner, R.	Br 1,328/10	Trillich, H.	950,357
	947,577		953,073,4
Kaffee, H. A. G.	Ger 515,604/23		964,944
	Ger 538,439/23	Tyberghein, E. C. E.	Br 439,617/35
	Dutch 53,500/42		Fr 806,904/36
Kallman, A.	Ger 632,208/36	Utescher, E.	Ger 219,405
Kirschbaum, E.	Ger 709,365/41		Ger 227,380
Klappreth, W.	Br 314,059/29		Ger 237,810
Klein, L.	Ger 276,014/09	Walliseller, F. K.	1,629,512
	Br 24,793/10	Walters, R. H.	2,309,092
	Br 8,815/11	Whitaker, M. C.	1,123,827
	1,039,961	Wilder, H. K.	1,977,416
Koffie, H. A. G.	Dutch 51,215/41	Wimmer, H. K.	Fr 384,273/07
Koro Kaffee Cie.	Fr 733,915/32		Ger 293,539/08
Kremers, R. E.	2,391,981		Br 2,035/08
Kundig, F.	Br 247,039/25		897,763
	Sw 128,984/27		897,840
Laitat, G.	Belg 373,515/30		936,392
Levelt, W. H.	Br 362,313/31		1,009,610
			1,502,222

CHAPTER 20

Soluble Coffee Plant Design

BASES FOR PLANT INVESTMENT

Although there is, at present, excessive instant coffee production capacity, there is a lively interest in further investment in processing plants. The reasons all relate to the fact that a better tasting instant coffee can be provided at an equal or lower price than now exists in the market. In other words, there are special situations in the instant coffee sales market that may offer encouraging returns. Generally these special situations are related to political advantage (even if temporary). But in other cases there are advantages in process "know-how" that result in improved instant coffee quality at a lower cost. The net effect is more unit value for the consumer, and a profitable operation for the new instant coffee processor.

The United States Market

This market offers the largest sales base; but it is also the most competitive. Although the United States market is the most difficult to enter, it may be profitable. The potential for increased rate of sales, however, is greater in other instant coffee consuming countries. Currently the instant coffee sales base in Europe is quite small but growing steadily.

The Coffee-Growing Countries

These are the most likely to have special situations that can make processing instant coffee profitable. Although these special situations have not yet materialized in many of the coffee-growing countries because of local political disagreements, their development is inevitable.

Engineering Inquiries

Often, persons making inquiries have not stated, and have not accurately assessed the feasibility of such a project. Nor do they provide an engineering firm with adequate background as to their interests, objectives, and facts. The net effect is poor communication and delays. It is the object here to point out the economic and technical limitations of such plans and to show situations with special advantages.

Engineering takes time, materials, and money. It is neither fair nor good business for the would-be instant coffee processor to try to extract technical details from the engineering firm that he may never be able to use. Once the potential owner has realistically assessed his position, it is good businss to discuss details honestly with the engineering firm hired to supply the equipment and process, and to pay for any preliminary cost estimates and specifications.

Value

It is appropriate to recall John Ruskin's statement, "There is hardly anything in the world that someone cannot make a little worse and sell a little cheaper—and the people who consider price alone are this man's lawful prey."

With this thought in mind, the cost of an adequately equipped soluble coffee processing plant, consumer product prices, competitive flavor quality, and marketing factors for a profitable operation must be considered.

Coffee Experience

In the past decade some poor quality instant coffee plants (and products) have been sold profitably, and the original investments have been paid off. It is unlikely that such situations will be repeated in the future. At the same time, some experienced roast coffee and instant coffee firms have made expensive mistakes. So coffee experience, per se, is not an assurance of success in a new instant coffee business.

Special Situations

When factors influencing the profitable processing and sale of instant coffee in a particular situation are evaluated and exploited, new soluble coffee processing plants may be successful today. Often, indeed, special situations are an outgrowth of timing. A few years' operation in a profitable market can create a sound foundation for future competitive strength.

The world coffee market from grower to consumer is full of special rules and exceptions. Those who have the ability to use these to their advantage are likely to make a successful instant coffee processing plant investment. New rules and new ideas are always being tested; not infrequently a successful product rises in the coffee industry.

Risk Factors Influencing Pricing, Sales, and Quality

The bases for minimal plant equipment and product quality given here are not necessarily in agreement with those given by others. It is up to the investor to know and judge his risk. There are no absolute formulas.

Factors Governing Successful Investment

Primary factors include: (1) quality of instant coffee powder produced relative to competition; (2) selling price of instant coffee powder produced relative to competition. This will, in turn, be governed by costs of green coffee, processing, and plant construction as well as profit margin and sales estimates; and (3) actual, committed, and potential sales.

These three related factors must be known to the investors with reasonable certainty. Guessing or unfounded estimates are dangerous. The safest situation is one in which a committed sales record, unit price, and product quality already exist. Even if the committed amounts are only a fraction of the projected soluble coffee plant capacity, they are better than none at all.

Processing that offers an exceptionally good flavor quality is not attractive unless it is competitively priced (except for premium brands in a limited sales market). On the other hand, low cost green coffee that makes a low quality instant coffee also finds only a limited market. A captive market for flavor quality at a reasonable and competitive selling price may often be profitable. For example, instant coffee in some parts of the world sells for two to three times as much as the retail price in the United States. Often this is due to shipping costs, high markups, limited supply, and high duties. Behind this barrier of national protection, some soluble coffee manufacturers can establish a profitable business provided the sales volume is large enough.

It is worthwhile to consider the concept of value in marketing coffees. Value must be equal to or better than competition in a free market in order to win new consumers. Value has to be communicated and reinforced with advertising, distribution, and product uniformity to win consumers away from existing brands.

OBSTACLES TO NEW PLANTS IN THE UNITED STATES

New instant coffee processing plants are faced with at least four serious obstacles apart from the competition from established market brands.

Lower Processing Costs in Large Plants

Over 85 per cent of United States instant coffees are processed in plants that have already paid off their capital investment and have productive rates of several million pounds of instant coffee per year. Paid-off plants do not add amortization to operating costs. Furthermore, large productive rates mean lower processing costs per unit of instant coffee, hence, lower selling prices in a very competitive market.

Lower Green Coffee Costs for Large Plants

The cost of green coffee beans may be 75 per cent of final soluble coffee cost depending on blend. See Smith (1959A and 1959B) and Rasmussen and Nielsen (1954). However, in the past 5 yr, million bag purchases have been negotiated from Brazil at about 25¢ instead of 30¢ per lb. In 1962, 160,000 bags of semi-roasted coffee from Salvador was imported into the United States at less than world prices. These periodic situations place the small coffee processor at a green coffee price disadvantage. The large green coffee buyer also is offered especially low prices on large lots of green coffee when dealing with brokers.

Intense Advertising and Sales Discounts by Large Processors

Reduced processing costs, lower green coffee bean costs, and perhaps better flavor quality from a given blend with more advanced processing equipment, allow more money for advertising as well as prolonged lower retail prices.

Excess Processing Capacity Over Demand

Excess capacity depresses selling prices in order to drive out marginal processors as well as to maintain a full level of processing in an existing plant.

Lower Instant Coffee Consumption Outside the United States

Whereas one-third of all coffee consumed in the United States is instant coffee, its use in the rest of the world is relatively small, representing only a few per cent of all cups of coffee consumed in many countries. (England is an exception.) The reasons are:

Poor Flavor: Instant coffee flavor quality outside the United States has, until recently, been less acceptable.

Tradition: The deeper influences of traditional eating and living, as in the Scandinavian countries and Italy, have worked against its acceptance.

Relative Cost: Coffee is relatively more expensive outside the United States in terms of purchasing power. In fact, the highest per capita consumption of coffee is in consuming countries that have the highest standards of living. Potential consumers of instant coffee have the desire but not the means to buy it.

Real Cost: Instant coffee outside the United States often sells for two to three times the United States retail price. The relatively lower value received, compounded by the larger human effort necessary to obtain it, strongly discourage its purchase.

Opportunity Factors for New Instant Coffee Plant Investments—

1. **Political.**—This corresponds to geographic, cultural and population areas within which there may be obtained:

(a) *Tariff protection* (or licensing allowances) on coffee imports as well as *tax exemption* on process equipment imported and profits for perhaps 5 yr. These laws are common in coffee-growing countries and to a lesser extent in coffee consuming countries.

(b) *Price concessions* may be granted by a government of a coffee-growing country to dispose of lower grade surplus coffees via assigned instant coffee plants. Such schemes have been developed in Brazil and Costa Rica, but the opposition from coffee growers is so strong that these plans have only slowly materialized.

(c) *An exclusive franchise* to process instant coffee. A coffee growing and consuming country may be large enough to support only one instant coffee plant. This happens infrequently, but may occur in a kingdom.

(d) *Low grade nature of the green coffee* within a political boundary may be such that its processing and sale as instant coffee on the world market are much more profitable, even to the point of limiting green coffee exports.

(e) *Political advantages* of any sort may crumble in an unstable political climate and can work to the disadvantage of the instant coffee processing plant, e.g., instant coffee export taxes may be imposed after the plant is established.

(f) *Free zone* plants that pay no taxes or only nominal taxes, and that have good transportation, skilled labor, and access to all Latin American coffees. Such plants can be ideally situated in the Panama Canal free zone.

2. **Marginal Quality Green Coffee.**—Associated with some political advantage, even if temporary, lies the real profit in using the about 15 per cent marginal quality green coffee that is part of every crop.

In general, the low to marginal quality green coffee brings a low price on local markets. Some qualities are not exportable. But when those coffees are sorted, the poorer grades converted to instant coffee, and the remainder sold as upgraded green coffee, the combined selling price is good, and a fair to good quality of instant coffee is produced. A few per cent of the lowest grades are discarded. In fact most of the soluble plants in the coffee-growing countries are not in themselves profitable to operate, but the price received from the green coffee makes the whole operation profitable. Usually the investors in the instant coffee plants are the green coffee growers. Profits can be especially good where the green coffee grading is integrated. The green coffee is graded for export and for use in the soluble coffee plant. If, in addition, a large fraction of the instant plant's production capacity is committed to a "private label" contract in the coffee-consuming country, a wholly integrated operation from growth to consumer is realized.

Sales of instant coffee locally may bring larger profits per unit than sales to the world market. Thus local profits when tariff-protected, may be an important financial support to the new instant coffee plant. If local instant coffee sales as well as export sales are planned, flavor quality, price and sales volume must be taken into consideration in overall product marketing.

3. **Existing Facilities that Reduce Initial Investment.**—If the plant investors have existing facilities useful to the instant coffee process, the initial investment is reduced accordingly. Table 96 lists such possible facilities or situations. A combination of such available factors can reduce initial investment risk by as much as several hundred thousand dollars.

TABLE 96

EXISTING FACILITIES AND/OR SITUATIONS THAT REDUCE INITIAL INSTANT COFFEE PLANT INVESTMENT

(1)	Land with little or no site development
(2)	Green coffee bean handling, roasting, and grinding equipment
(3)	Green coffee warehousing
(4)	Instant coffee powder packaging equipment and housing
(5)	Existing building to house instant coffee plant
(6)	Suitable utilities: water supply, electricity, and gas
(7)	Suitable storm and sanitary drainage
(8)	Office, toilet, storage, locker, shops, and lunch room
(9)	Furniture and supplies for offices and laboratory
(10)	Available skilled labor and industrial supplies
(11)	Good communications by telephone, cable, and mail
(12)	A friendly political atmosphere in regard to tariffs, taxes, and franchises
(13)	A guaranteed sale of a substantial fraction of the plant's instant coffee output to a consuming country as a "private label" product with that firm's contribution of a significant portion of the initial plant investment
(14)	An experienced instant coffee plant engineer and/or superintendent

Limits on Plant Capacity

The instant coffee plant processing capacity must be related to estimates of sales volume, processing costs and plant investment as well as product selling price.

Estimating Selling Volume.—In an openly competitive broad sales (relatively elastic) market for competitive flavor quality, as unit price is reduced, sales growth increases at a rate influenced by advertising, distribution, brand image, public traditions, etc. For a new brand of instant coffee to wedge sales into an existing and saturated market is expensive. Assuring a portion of new instant coffee sales through existing marketed brands, displaces a supplier. It does not fully depend on broadening a retail market, which is more difficult. A tariff can practically prohibit imports into a coffee-growing country.

Even if better flavor quality and/or lower prices are demonstrated, sales growth is a slow process in competitive markets. In the United States no startling quality or price changes are likely because most instant coffee quality is acceptable, prices are reasonable, and the market is competitive.

In Europe and the rest of the world, profit margins are greater. Improved instant coffee flavor quality and markedly reduced prices will increase sales growth.

The size of the instant coffee market must be known or judged accurately and realistically, for the rate of sales fixes initial plant productive capacity. Normal sales also influence the future potential instant coffee sales.

Sales *must* actually equal the estimates plus commitments to buy. Otherwise, the investment cannot be profitable and may even fail. Success and failure also depend on the difference attained between selling price and processing costs. As lower cost producers successfully carry on their business, the older higher cost producers will fall by the wayside in a market with more supply than demand. Reasonable selling prices may or may not have a bearing on sales volume, depending as they do on freedom of market, types of coffees, surpluses, shortages, and living standards.

Estimating Processing Cost.—The following must be considered:

(1) Cost of green coffee beans.

(2) Yield of soluble coffee from green beans. Bean cost divided by solubles yield gives raw material cost. For example:

$$\frac{24\cancel{c} \text{ per lb}}{0.30 \text{ yield}} = 80\cancel{c} \text{ per lb instant coffee}$$

(3) Amortized cost of plant and buildings: if the plant cost to productivity ratio is 1.0 or $1,000,000 for 1,000,000 lb per yr, then the 10 yr amortization is $0.10 per lb of instant coffee.

(4) Administration is 2¢ per lb of instant coffee.

(5) Insurance, taxes, and overhead account for 2¢ per lb of instant coffee.

(6) Sales-advertising-posters, etc. are 3¢ per lb of instant coffee. Except for raw material the above costs are fixed.

The following costs are variable; all are per lb of instant coffee.

(1) Labor (partly fixed) is 4¢ per lb.
(2) Utilities are 4¢ per lb.
(3) Supplies and services are about 3¢ per lb.
(4) Bulk shipments of powder are 8 to 10¢ per lb.
(5) Jar packaging and delivery to retailer are about 20¢ per lb.
(6) United States import duty is 3¢ per lb.

Summarizing:

(1) Green coffee	$0.80 per lb instant coffee
(2) Fixed charges	0.17 " " " "
(3) Operating charges	0.38 " " " "
Total	$1.35

Of course, these figures vary from place to place in the world, but they demonstrate the methods of calculation and offer a point of reference until specific local costs are obtained from experience.

Estimated Selling Price.—Instant coffee selling prices (for the sales area chosen) for flavor quality that is acceptable to the consumer vary throughout the world. For example, current United States competitive prices are about $1.00 per 6 oz (170 gm) instant coffee, and $1.40 per 10 oz. This is about ½¢ per gm or 1¢ per cup which is equivalent to about $2.20 per lb of instant coffee retail. Discounting 30¢ per lb for the retailer and 25¢ per lb for jar packaging and delivery to retailer, the instant coffee must cost less than $1.70 per lb after entering the United States port. With a 50 to 60¢ per lb processing cost, the equivalent green coffee cost per pound of instant coffee must be a dollar or less.

In Europe (1962), with allowances for duties, taxes, etc., instant coffee usually retailed above $2.20 per lb. For Robusta quality, this is equivalent to green coffee costs of about 60¢ per lb of instant coffee.

In Central America, where the coffee is grown, instant coffee sells at about $4.80 per lb retail. The profit and amortization received on each pound of instant coffee sold locally are about 20 times that received from export bulk instant coffee.

From these examples, the cost of processing instant coffee in some new part of the world, as well as prevailing selling prices can be calculated. It should be apparent whether it is profitable to process instant coffee in that locality and whether the processed instant coffee should be for local use, export, or for both markets.

Basic Data for Instant Coffee Processing Plant Projections

(1) Committed and/or expected sales of instant coffee per year, as well as rate of sales growth expected

(2) Costs for processing instant coffee

(3) Initial capital investment required for the instant coffee processing plant

(4) Assessing and committing existing facilities useful to the instant coffee plant

(5) Deciding what features above minimal are desired in the design of the plant

(6) Gathering sources of capital investment, especially from coffee growers, coffee importers, and others who can help the establishment of an integrated operation

(7) Organizing the company under local political laws with local capitalization and officers

(8) Establishing tentative plant site, utility needs, and preliminary engineering data

(9) Securing an engineering firm dealing in construction and startup operation of instant coffee plants to discuss plant design, equipment, construction schedule, operation and training of personnel, as well as work contract. It is highly desirable to obtain, at a nominal cost, preliminary plant cost estimates associated with equipment and process descriptions

The best opportunities for new successful instant coffee processing plants lie in processing marginal quality coffees in the coffee growing countries both for export sale and for local consumption. Depending on the size of the instant coffee plant and its location, a plant can be placed into production in 14 to 20 months from the date of contract and commitment of funds.

Basis of Minimal Plant Size, Product Flavor Quality, and Plant Cost

In the following equipment costs cited for several sizes of instant coffee processing plants, the quality of the instant coffee product in regard to aroma, cup flavor, solubility, appearance, powder flow, and powder bulk density are held high, so that instant coffee quality from any size plant is competitive with any product in the world starting from the same green coffee blend.

Technically, this means that the portion of the plant cost for spray drier is higher (about 25 per cent) for the smallest capacity plant (333,000 lb per yr). At the same time this allows four-fold expansion of spray drier capacity.

For the plant producing 667,000 lb of instant coffee per year, the spray drier cost is 20 per cent of the plant cost, but allows doubling spray drier capacity without future investment.

The largest instant coffee plants are the cheapest based on the investment to productivity ratio as shown in Fig. 315. Still, the smaller plant can be profitable in its own local market or even in the world market. Articles in this field have been presented by Hardy (1955 and 1957), Smith (1959A), and Rasmussen and Nielsen (1954).

Production that falls below estimated plant capacity may be very costly in processing. For example, a 333,000 lb per yr instant coffee plant

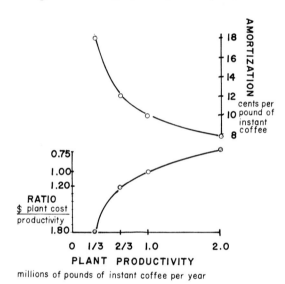

FIG. 315. INSTANT COFFEE PLANT PRODUCTIVITY VS RATIO OF PLANT COST TO PRODUCTIVITY (BELOW). INSTANT COFFEE PLANT PRODUCTIVITY VS TEN-YEAR AMORTIZATION COST

that only sells half that amount of instant coffee per year, must double the unit amortization costs. That is, a 36¢ per lb amortization cost makes that product much more difficult, if not impossible, to meet competitive pricing. Even at 18¢ per lb amortization costs, the added cost to the product for the small plant is considerable. Such costs could probably be tolerated only in a market with high prices, low cost coffees, some tax concessions, or special situations.

The Minimal Cost Instant Coffee Plant Does *Not* Include:

(1) Green coffee warehouse.

(2) Spent coffee grounds dewatering, drying, furnace and boiler.

(3) Vacuum water chiller to utilize excess fuel; disposal of coffee grounds.

(4) Shop.

(5) More than 1,000 sq ft office space, or 12,000 sq ft of plant floor area.

(6) Security fences, alarms, etc.

(7) Special provisions for earthquake, lightning, pilings, etc.

(8) Main electrical transformer and tie-in costs.

(9) Elevator for the spray drier tower.

(10) Site development, landscaping, water system for fire fighting.

(11) Emergency electrical generator.

(12) Land costs exceeding minimal requirements.

(13) Restaurants, locker, or furniture facilities and supplies.

(14) More than one gasoline engine fork truck.

(15) Extra expenditures for export crating, consular fees, shipping, etc. Although these expenses are nominal, they may amount to 10 per cent of plant equipment costs.

(16) Organizational and pre-operational expenses.

A minimal cost instant coffee plant involves some higher operating costs than those already listed. For example, trucking away grounds, thereby losing the fuel value of the spent coffee grounds, higher labor costs per unit of product, higher per cent wastage due to spills and washdown, relatively higher engineering costs, more crowded working conditions, etc. Powder would probably be handled manually in drums instead of Tote-bins. Pumps would be individual, not paired. Spare parts would be minimal. More reliance would be placed on manual process control than on instrument records and control.

TABLE 97

INSTANT COFFEE PLANT PRODUCTIVITY, INITIAL COST, AND AMORTIZED COST

	Plant Cost, Dollars	Produc-tivity, lb per yr	Ratio Cost to Capacity	10 yr, Amortization Cost, Cents per lb	Pounds of Instant Coffee Per 24 hr	Per hr
(1)	$1,500,000	2,000,000	0.75	7.5	9,600	400
(2)	$1,000,000	1,000,000	1.00	10.0	4,800	200
(3)	$ 800,000	667,000	1.20	12.0	3,200	135
(4)	$ 600,000	333,000	1.80	18.0	1,600	67

Plant Costs, Content, and Productivity

The complete soluble coffee plant with buildings, land, and site (from minimal to maximal, for the 500,000 lb per yr to 5,000,000 lb per yr soluble coffee production) will range for initial investment from almost $1,000,000 to $2,500,000, based on starting with bare land. Costs range from the minimum figure for absolutely essential equipment to expenditures for a first class properly equipped plant. The real attraction to the investor with limited funds is the small, low cost plant. The really good investment is the large, high quality plant.

Cost figures alone for finished plants are usually incomplete and misleading without detailed specifications. Frequently warehouse costs are omitted. Costs incurred shortly after plant completion for shortcomings, as well as costs for land and land development may not be included. Use of existing roasting, packaging, or other facilities and company subsidized engineering services are often not included.

Soluble coffee plants sized for 1,000,000 lb per yr or less have a small spray drier. This gives a smaller average spray-dried particle with less flavor retention. The soluble coffee plant market in the less than 1,000,000 lb per yr sizes has the greatest investment per unit of production. Until spray drying of instant coffee is achieved on lower cost driers and with better flavor retention on smaller driers, which is unlikely, the current relation of plant cost to plant productivity is not likely to change much.

Factors Influencing Minimal Productive Capacity

A million dollars today may construct a complete plant producing 1,000,000 lb of instant coffee per year, but the plant equipment will be marginal and the product quality will not be able to compete in the free world market against powder from larger spray driers. Thus, the product quality and costs of large producers set the competitive market situation. The small producer must make almost as good a quality at about the same selling price and this is almost impossible. Hence, soluble coffee plants are usually built for more than 1.5 million lb of instant coffee per year.

Future Capacity

In establishing the producing capacity of a soluble coffee plant, allowances are made for future increased production. One way is to build a 50 per cent increase in production into the plant or space. Facilities are allowed for future installation of percolation and spray drying equipment. When a soluble coffee plant operates five days per week, it is only operating at 70 per cent of rated capacity. Some soluble coffee plants are built without any area for expansion. Eventually congestion and increased sales may necessitate a more expensive separate process installation. Doubling soluble coffee production in a plant that has planned expansion facilities, can be done at perhaps $1/4$ to $1/3$ the cost of placing a new process plant on a bare piece of land. The site procurement and development as well as the green and roast equipment and utilities constitute a major part of plant costs.

Minimum Facilities Plant

Rasmussen and Nielsen's article (1954) on the economics of processing soluble coffee well illustrates what is provided in a Niro plant to minimize initial plant investment. It is risky to use overall cost figures for soluble coffee plants, because the quality and quantity of contents can vary the amount of initial investment considerably. Further, first costs are not last costs. And the quality of the final instant coffee is strongly influenced by the scope and content of the initial investment. For persons interested in the minimum plant investment, the following factors contribute to a low cost plant regardless of production capacity.

(1) **Minimal Facilities.**—These cover storage, instruments, services, standby equipment, air conditioning, grounds disposal, boiler, building structure, land and land development, barrels. They do not include Tote-Bins, hand trucks, batch roasters and coffee conveyors, office, laboratory, shops, stores, or utilization of fuel value of spent coffee grounds, flexibility or allowance for expansion.

(2 **Fast Percolation.**—A design factor rarely used is the ability to percolate at 20 min instead of 1 hr cycles. At three times the speed of percolation in the average plant the size of the percolator vessel is reduced to $1/3$, and this results in a more natural flavor, and more coffee flavor recovery in the extract.

(3) **Size and Quality of Packaging Machinery.**—This may sometimes make a $100,000 difference. There may be a manual line in one plant with no packeting machines, while in another plant there is a fully automatic packaging line and a first class packeting machine. Also the space allotted to packaging and the amount of air conditioning can affect the housing costs for the packaging system.

(4) **Services.**—Air conditioned offices, tile floors, adequate locker and toilet space, stores and shops can make at least $100,000 difference. Architecturally, a plant can be overdesigned as well as insufficiently designed. A minimal facility often cannot be readily changed into an adequate facility. Lack of eating facilities means further savings. Diminution of such services usually results in higher operating costs and employees that are less satisfied.

(5) **Elevator or Man-Lift.**—These services to the top of the spray tower are not provided in a minimal cost plant. Stairways may be narrow and steep, hence, not safe.

(6) **Bustle.**—Spray driers may have small bustles or none at all. Such driers are not so tall. This saves on structural steel and building height but causes a large carry over of fine powder.

(7) **Lighting.**—Inside and outside lighting can be minimal in quantity and quality; accidents in dark yards occur under such circumstances.

(8) **Spent Grounds Disposal.**—Trucking grounds away is expensive as is outside storage of raw and finished materials. Minimal stores and use of outside shops make the plant operation vulnerable to shutdown with an equipment failure.

(9) **Minimal Laboratory Facilities.**—This can result in loose product standards and poorer process control.

Table 98 lists some comparative cost items for soluble coffee plants. Table 99 lists factors that lower plant cost.

If a plant is not operated at full capacity or near full capacity the fixed costs per unit of production rise. Thus, without even an exhaustive

TABLE 98

COMPARATIVE ITEM EXPENDITURES FOR SOLUBLE COFFEE PLANTS[1]

(1)	Pre-operational and organizational	$100,000
(2)	First class green and roast processing system	
	(a) vs second class system	75,000
	(b) vs an existing one	200,000
(3)	Warehousing 15,000 sq ft or 30,000 bags vs none	100,000
(4)	Export crating on $1,000,000 equipment	50,000
(5)	Shipping (depending on destination) and documentation	100,000
(6)	Land procurement	100,000
(7)	Land and site development	100,000
(8)	Design-Engineering firm	200,000
(9)	Soluble plant technical personnel salaries, moving, and travel	50,000
(10)	Size of process building, e.g., 35,000 vs 20,000 sq ft	150,000
(11)	Office building vs use of available space	50,000
(12)	Spent coffee grounds boiler vs flash evaporation boiler	100,000
(13)	Standby generator system (300 kw)	30,000
(14)	Packaging jars vs outside contractor	140,000
(15)	Packeting machinery vs outside contractor 10,000 to	35,000
(16)	Startup expenses 5,000 to	50,000
(17)	Flexibilities in design, up to	200,000
(18)	Minimal vs adequate laboratory facilities	25,000
(19)	Spent grounds steam utilization chilled water system	40,000
(20)	Spray drier elevator vs stairs	20,000

Of course, at times when proper engineering and proper processing conditions are not covered by the original investment, later expenditures become very large, but these beforehand are only speculative and thus are not listed here.

[1] Basis: Several million pounds of instant coffee productivity per year.

analysis of factors influencing minimal initial cost it can be seen that these factors permeate the whole character of the plant operation. They influence personnel safety, comfort, and working conditions. They also influence product quality and product costs, as well as ability to expand and to upgrade minimal design situations. Minimal initial costs mean that day-to-day operating costs are higher and product quality is lower. It is easy to underestimate the value of product quality because it is a non-numerical factor and only can be verified in the market place, but it may be disastrous to do so. Some minimal cost plants have been wholly abandoned in favor of new plants which can produce a better quality instant coffee at a lower price, or partly abandoned to upgrade processing facilities and product quality.

It takes someone skilled in soluble coffee operations to lower the initial plant cost without losing a great many positive values of a well equipped process. Currently, several soluble coffee plants are being built in Brazil. Most of these have been purchased on a minimal cost basis. The initial results will show whether a second round of improved plants will be needed.

Summary: All Soluble Coffee Plants and Products are not the Same

The best plants and products are the result of conscientiously applying engineering and "know-how" to every step. There are no short cuts in

TABLE 99

FACTORS THAT LOWER INITIAL COST OF SOLUBLE COFFEE PLANT

(1)	Establishing management decision and approval on scope and cost of project	$ 75,000
(2)	Fiscal controls by preliminary budgeting, purchases, engineering, equipment, erection, etc.	75,000
(3)	Minimal green roast and ground coffee systems	70,000
(4)	Sub-contract engineering design on buildings, drier structure, electrical system, air conditioning, etc.	50,000
(5)	Engineering firm used should be located near management	50,000
(6)	Utilization of soluble firm's experienced engineers (key staff) early in project, thus minimizing training of engineering firm	50,000
(7)	Use of *foreign* steel, shop drawings, and erection	25,000
(8)	Consolidation of warehouse, process, and office space under one roof	10,000
(9)	Air-conditioned green coffee warehouse in hot humid climate	25,000
(10)	Use of equipment fabricators near engineering firm	15,000
(11)	Boiler for burning spent grounds later with water chiller and cooling tower system	150,000
(12)	Use of local shops at first	20,000
(13)	Consolidation of shipment to minimize shipping costs	20,000

costs or techniques that will not impair plant performance and product quality. The coffee, equipment, and personnel put into a plant determine its product. The excess of soluble coffee producing capacity in the world today is already causing the elimination of the low quality producers. Low quality may come from green coffee quality and/or plant processing. Usually a poorly equipped or poor processing plant that is unable to bring natural coffee flavor through to the instant coffee tends to use lower grade green coffees which insures a thoroughly low grade instant coffee.

Approvals

Some important factors in a soluble coffee plant project are prompt approvals of plans and expenditures and an organized management. Delays on these basically essential matters can increase costs $100,000 in a short time. A lack of proper cost controls and budgeting also allows costs to run more than $100,000 in excess before they are recognized and controlled.

Building Costs

Separation of offices or warehousing from the central process building also adds to building costs. Green coffee beans deteriorate in warm, humid climates, so that in a few weeks the coffee loses its most desirable flavor properties. Thus, an air-conditioned warehouse for green coffee beans is justified in some cases. This adds to the initial investment at a rate of about $10 per sq ft of floor area, including air conditioning equipment.

World Purchasing

Notable savings can also be made in buying concrete, reinforcing steel, and structural steels in the world market. For example, economies can be effected by procuring these materials from Belgium, Italy, Japan, or Mexico. In fact, in Mexico the whole steel structure can be designed, built, and erected under a single contract. Not all world purchases are as economical as they seem initially. For example, European bids on electrical substations will invariably be cheaper than in the United States. But the European transformers may burn out at only a few per cent overload; the United States transformers will not. They have a larger safety factor. Such a failure may cost more money in plant down time than the whole substation bid. Engineering decisions in these areas may make a plant operation reliable or erratic.

Each soluble coffee plant, as any other plant when it is related to its local environment is unique. The numbers of special situations and problems that may result will vary from plant to plant, but in the end each situation must be resolved to make the plant operate efficiently and to produce a good flavored product.

Quality built into a soluble coffee plant is hard for the untrained to see. A Volkswagen and a Cadillac are both cars and afford a means of transportation. But in space, power, safety, and stability, they are quite different.

Estimating the Costs of a Soluble Coffee Plant

It is not possible to lay down any firm rules on cost estimating because the purchaser requirements, location needs, and supplier offerings must be brought into harmony. However, for purposes of citing orders of magnitude in plant cost, the following figures are given.

(1) *Buildings,* including architectural and structural plans, civil engi-

neering, drawings, materials, and erection will cost about 30 per cent of complete plant costs.

(2) The complete *roasting* equipment, including green and roast bean storage facilities, grinders and conveyors up to the percolators will be about 10 per cent of total plant cost.

(3) The *percolation equipment* with all accessories such as pumps, heaters, coolers, tanks, instruments, valving, and platforming will cost about 15 per cent of plant cost.

(4) *Utilities and services* are about 15 per cent of total cost. The utilities include excess steam recovery for air conditioning or spray drier air heating, burning of spent grounds and a modest shop and stores.

(5) *Spray drying* (structural steel included above) is about 10 per cent of total cost.

(6) *Packaging* is about 5 per cent.

(7) *Engineering* would be about 10 per cent, and the remaining 5 per cent would include salaries, overhead, travel, communications, supervision, reports, and liaison.

(8) *Startup*—A not infrequently incurred expense is loss of quality and/or coffee during start up of the plant which can run into tens of thousands of dollars.

Accountability.—A simple way to run cost accounting during the planning and construction period, if it is not completely sub-contracted, is to have IBM[1] or similar cards for each class of purchase and expense and to summarize the committed and actual expenditures periodically. Similarly, the transit position of each order can be catalogued as to promised delivery dates, actual shipping dates, arrival at transfer points, arrival at site, etc.

The listed references by Bauman (1959A, 1959B, 1959C) show project cost control. Sweet (1959A) illustrates the factors affecting the cost of engineering. Tielrooy (1956) shows the importance of capital cost estimates and their subsequent effect on the profitability of the project. Hardy (1955A and 1955B) presents cost of soluble coffee plants and spray drier systems. However, his costs compared to actual outlays by many firms are low by factors of 3 to 6.

Manufacturing Cost of Soluble Coffee Product

The cost of the instant coffee product may vary. One plant may do no research or development. Under some circumstances advertising costs may be nil. Plant services may be minimal. Low initial investment reduces amortization rate. In other words, there are no absolute formulas for costing the instant coffee product. In general terms, it can be

---

[1] International Business Machines, Inc.

said in 1962, that for the average size of soluble coffee plant operating three-fourths of the work year, the green coffee will represent two-thirds to three-fourths of the final product cost, assuming that a blend slightly better than 100 per cent Brazilian coffee is used. In cost analysis, the productivity of the plant is a significant factor, especially when it falls below about 75 per cent. The skilled employees cannot be let go; their salaries continue. In terms of cost of processing, above the green coffee cost, this will vary with labor rates, utility rates, uniformity of operation, and yield of solubles, maintenance, and services. For example, labor rates may be low, utilities high, and maintenance high. Low initial costs on cheaper, less durable machinery may raise maintenance costs. In the coffee-growing country, the green coffee used may be cheaper, but inferior in quality. If imported into the United States, a 3¢ per lb duty must be added to the instant coffee cost.

In talking about costs of instant coffee, it is essential to list all the factors being considered; otherwise distribution costs may be obscured. A cost may exist in one category, but it may actually be allocated to another. For example, while obtaining consumer acceptance, a processor may be willing to discount product selling price for long periods of time. At the same time, he claims to be making no money. This is only a half truth as he is investing his money in the hope of a return.

The cost of labor, utilities and services are about 10 to 15¢ per lb of instant coffee.

A processing cost can be calculated on the basis of 33¢ per lb for green coffee at a 0.30 solubles yield from green coffee in packaged powder. This means a $1.00 per lb cost for the raw material coffee. Actually some Robusta-Brazilian blends may run at about half this cost. Yield represents the most significant cost after the cost of the green coffee beans.

To the $1.15 raw material and processing cost must be added about 20¢ per lb for packaging into jars and local transport to retailers. Amortization of plant may cost 5¢ per lb for 10 yr at three-quarters capacity. Fixed overhead may be about the same, raising the total cost to $1.45 per lb of instant coffee. Taking 3¢ per lb for research and development and 5¢ per lb for advertising raises the cost to $1.53 per lb. With a 9¢ per lb profit, the $1.62 per lb cost becomes a wholesale price of 90¢ per 6 oz (170 gm) jar which might retail for 95¢. Obviously, these figures can be moved about one way or the other, depending on actual costs and circumstances in any particular situation. However, the figures will serve as a basis for discussion and are representative of a particular situation. As in any business, if the end product quality and price cannot meet competition, sales and operating time go down, and costs rise. Thus far in the United States, only one failure in the soluble coffee business has occurred.

Table 100 illustrates a reasonable cost breakdown for a soluble coffee plant outside the United States shipping to consumer countries. Today there is relatively no risk in soluble coffee plant equipment obsolescence compared to 10 yr ago, but profits are also a fraction of what they were then. Research and development costs are also less. Any soluble plant that has an assured market outlet is still a good investment, especially if it can tap marginal quality, lower priced coffees in the coffee growing country to make a product of good flavor quality.

TABLE 100

APPROXIMATE COSTS IN PROCESSING[1] SOLUBLE COFFEE OUTSIDE THE UNITED STATES

Full Use of Plant Production Capacity

A.	Green Coffee—(price taken as 32c per lb)			$1.00
	(Yield of solubles from green coffee taken as 0.315)			
B.	Processing			
	(1) Labor			0.03
	(2) Utilities			0.04
	(3) Supplies and services			0.03
	(4) Sales expense			0.03
	(5) Depreciation (building and equipment—10 yr)			0.06
	(6) Insurance, taxes, overhead			0.02
	(7) Administration			0.03
				0.24
C.	Bulk Shipment to United States			
	(1) Carton, liner, seals, straps, etc.			0.02
	(2) Handling, freight and insurance			0.05
	(3) U. S. import duty			0.03
				0.10
D.	Financing. (Green and Instant Coffee)			0.05
	Sub-total			$1.39

		24/2 oz	24/6 oz	24/10 oz
E.	Cost per lb of soluble packaged and distributed	$ 1.85	$ 1.62	$ 1.58
	Cost breakdown of packaged jar and distribution cost in United States			
	(1) Soluble coffee lb, net wt; 3, 9, 15 lb per case	$ 4.17	$12.51	$20.85
	(2) Jars, caps, labels, and cartons	1.00	1.50	2.25
	(3) Packaging (private)	0.27	0.27	0.20
	(4) Packaging loss (0.3 per cent)	0.02	0.07	0.10
	(5) Freight, truck, shipment, etc	0.10	0.20	0.30
	Total cost per case	$ 5.56	$14.55	$23.70
X.	Cost per jar	$ 0.23	$ 0.61	$ 1.00
Y.	Wholesale price per jar	0.40	0.90	1.30
Z.	Retail price per jar	0.45	1.00	1.45

[1] For plants producing several million pounds of instant coffee per year.

Equipment Choice Limits Process and Product

There are three main objectives in soluble coffee plant design: yield, flavor, and physical properties. Many soluble coffee plants, including those of major producers, have been to a greater or lesser extent designed by engineers who knew little of the processing. This is especially true of some package plants that are engineered to perform the mechanics of soluble coffee manufacture, but with little regard for factors affecting quality and efficiency. The real finesse in soluble coffee plant design comes not only from processing experience but from keen perception of what is happening in the process as revealed by personal tasting as well as by consumer acceptance tests and sales.

In the past, and even now, soluble coffee plant design and investments have been poorly made. This results in poor taste quality of instant coffee produced and early process and equipment obsolescence. This has occurred in spite of the adequacy of process and equipment "know-how." Sometimes it is due to poor communications between investor and process engineer, and at other times to overconfident private ownership. Whatever the reason, millions of dollars have literally been wasted by numerous coffee companies on mediocre process plants.

Many investors in soluble coffee plants, who should know better, have been influenced strongly by low initial investment. The flavor quality of the resulting product and the operating costs have not been fully considered. Initial plus operating costs are total product costs. The equivalent dollar value of coffee flavor quality lost in some process plants is a surprising annual total. This type of plant is now being abandoned at considerable cost for a better processing plant. *There are significant differences among plants, equipment, processes, and products.*

Although the investor often is not technically capable of evaluating his purchase, he is afraid to delegate the responsibility to a hired employee. The investor may say that he has been in the *roast* coffee business for 40 yr, and he knows coffee, implying that he knows *soluble* coffee processes and product. Nothing could be farther from the truth, as experience has shown. The owner often injects his limited process "knowledge" into plant design. This covers some of the organizational pitfalls and unsound thinking that have existed. In addition, the scope and content of the soluble coffee process plants are often loosely defined when engineering contracts are drawn.

Engineering

It takes an experienced engineering firm to apply efficiently the required hours or months of various engineering skills and to release the personnel when the design aspects of the job are done. Similarly, in construction there must be the gradual application of one class of work skill at first and others later.

Since the late 1950's the risk in building a well engineered soluble coffee plant has become much less than in prior years. Many more engineers and contract firms with demonstrated experience are available for design engineering, construction, and plant operation. The soluble coffee plant and process have become fairly well standardized throughout the world using percolation and co-current spray drying. One trend since 1955 has been the progressively greater number of soluble coffee plants built in the coffee-growing countries.

There may be special problems like earthquakes, lightning, brackish water, drainage disposal, rain water diversion, dust, roads, bridges, and railroads sidings, that require special engineering. There are also numerous detail sketches that are never formally set apart in engineering but develop in purchasing and in the field during equipment erection and process startup, for example, diaphragm pressure gauges (see Fig. 316) for the extract lines and a dead weight pressure gauge tester (see Fig. 317).

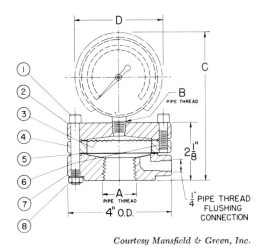

Courtesy Mansfield & Green, Inc.

Fig. 316. Diaphragm Type Pressure Gauge

Depending on the size and scope of engineering in a plant, engineering costs may be about 10 to 15 per cent of the total plant cost, depending on plant size and complexity. Unless one has reasonable acquaintance with specific engineering work in the translating of an idea into tangible equipment and process, it is hard for the layman to see what special service the engineer performs. But this becomes apparent in a process plant that has not been engineered properly so that there are continual electrical failures, safety hazards, heat, fuel, and labor waste as well as product and product flavor losses.

Acquiring a Soluble Coffee Plant

Some of the more common ways to acquire a soluble coffee plant are as follows:

(1) Outright contract for a complete soluble coffee plant with an engineering firm that has made successful installations, provided the buyer is satisfied with the "guaranteed" quality of the product. Actually, the final product taste quality is never guaranteed. The plant is purchased on the basis of a limited proposal, and the buyer always assumes most of the risks. This proposal is often attractive because the total costs are stated. The investment group will understand costs even when it does not understand the technical aspects of the plant.

(2) Partial contract for the soluble coffee plant portion, especially the percolation and spray drying portions, with the green and roast processing,

Courtesy Mansfield & Green, Inc.

FIG. 317. DEAD WEIGHT TESTER FOR PRESSURE GAUGES

boiler and utilities, packaging, building, etc. sub-contracted under the owner's engineering group.

(3) Development of one's own process, equipment, and engineering.

(4) Purchase of all or part of an existing operating soluble coffee plant.

The "Package" Soluble Coffee Plant.—One purchasing attraction is the low cost of the low capacity package plant. Usually product samples are provided from a similar plant. The suppliers of the plant may have sold several such soluble coffee plants which are in operation. A closer study of the plant proposal may reveal that the soluble coffee product is not the best. *The plant "package" is in fact expedient to relieve the owner of a lot of technical details* that somehow in fact *constitute the essence of the soluble coffee plant's value.* In other words, "packages" are not altogether safe investments because the purchaser must know the process and equipment he is buying and the quality of instant coffee it can produce. Thus the whole plant package is subject to breakdown into process and equipment steps. Equipment specifications are in order to analyze properly all of the constituent parts. Some day package soluble coffee plants may be safe investments; but for now the plant design, equipment, and processing engineering offered must be evaluated by engineers experienced in soluble coffee plant design and operation.

Consultant.—Services of a technical consultant experienced in soluble coffee plant construction are often used. Coffee firms that contract their plants to an experienced outside supplier usually feel this to be sufficient warranty. However, in the early design stages especially, the consultant can act on management's behalf in technically evaluating the soundness of the design and the projected costs. The consultant's fee for part-time service may be several thousand dollars, but the capable consultant can often save the investors many times his fee. The consultant can also guide the plant design and equipment specifications so that a better process and instant coffee will result. The outside advice of the independent experienced soluble coffee engineer can reinforce and help decide unsettled matters. The consultant acts not only as a contributor of technical "know-how" but as a tempering element between the exaggerations and vague commitments of some suppliers and management's lack of experience. The project has a better chance of starting more quickly and properly with such outside aid. Reinforced suggestions lend confidence to the project. There are many plant investors who wish they had gained their knowledge across the table rather than in the plant itself.

The consultant can do his job in several ways: (1) he can work behind the scenes with management in their proposed or existing plant; (2) he can survey plans or process plants and make recommendations regarding their improvement and the improvement of the product. The consulting engineer can follow up the changes in equipment and processing. Management may keep the consultant on a retainer for a specified time, usually until the project is complete.

Attention to details and the control of the choice of plant equipment and processing conditions produce the best coffee; there are no other secrets. The less experienced owner can upgrade his plant and process from consultant process "know-how," which is cheaper than floundering about on his own.

Plant Site Location.—Every type of processing plant must be suitably located for most economical operation.

Geographically.—Soluble coffee plants are usually located near a center of population in coffee consuming countries, or near the political coffee centers in the coffee-growing countries. Cost of product transportation is important in coffee-consuming countries, especially in the United States where there are long distances between plants and consumers. Many United States soluble coffee plants are in coastal ports, e.g., New York; Philadelphia; Jacksonville, Florida; New Orleans, Louisiana; St. Louis, Missouri; Houston, Texas; and San Francisco, California. For example, many gulf ports in the United States which are closest to green coffee growing countries have lower than average wage rates.

Labor.—After the specific city for a plant is chosen, educated labor and schools should be available. Unions should have a record of fair dealing if they exist. There should be no labor unrest. Low labor costs are desirable.

Utilities and Services.—There should be a good quality, low cost, and adequate water supply and low cost fuel and electricity. The plant should be so situated as to cause no neighborhood nuisance, (odor, smoke, noise, drainage, dust, etc.). In Gulf ports there is usually plentiful water (if not always of good quality) and drainage contamination regulations are not enforced so strictly near the mouth of a river. No foul odors from nearby industries should enter the soluble coffee plant. Strong, steady winds help dilute any odor or smoke.

Communication and Transport.—Good communications and transportation are important. The plant should be conveniently located not only for trucking in and out, but for ready and safe access by employees on shift work. For example, there must be public bus service, space for parking, safe conduct on lighted adjoining streets, and well paved roads.

Zoning.—Zoning and building height restrictions can directly determine whether the plant should be located in an otherwise desirable area.

Taxes.—Fair local taxation, political honesty and local inducements are important influences.

Stewart's Plant Site Selection Guide (1957) covers these and other useful points as do some engineering handbooks.

Environmental Factors.—These will influence soluble coffee plant design and will vary with the objectives sought and the plant location. However, the following considerations generally prevail. Roaster gases may have to pass through an after-burner in most urban locations, or the plant should be built upwind from unoccupied controlled property. Drainage fields for plant waters may be mandatory in some locations. Trucking spent coffee grounds may or may not be practical from a cost and sanitary viewpoint. Nearness to industry and supplies influences the amount of stores and shop equipment required. Neighboring population density and wind conditions influence stack heights, odors, dust, and noise levels tolerated. Inducements by local government may be substantial in selecting a plant location. Or local government authorities may be so antagonistic as to warrant seeking another location. Climate, ambient temperatures, sunlight angle, and intensity will govern the needs for heating or cooling and natural lighting. In the tropics prevailing rains, lightning conditions, rot, and insects may require suitable construction materials and a natural ventilation. Excessive tropical rains may require special storm sewers for water runoff. Low level locations may have to be avoided where flooding or isolation due to flooding may occur. Dust conditions may require totally enclosed fan cooled (TEFC) motors, more filtering or intake process air than normal. A thorough study of the plant's process needs in its considered location is vital to an overall satisfactory result. Oversights can cause continual expense.

In the Coffee-Growing Country

Some of the obstacles in building a soluble coffee plant in the coffee-growing rather than in the consuming country are differences in culture, language, customs, import holdup of equipment (which slows down construction rate), and shortage of skilled laborers who may have to be brought to the plant site. Examples of specialized skills are field supervision of erection of steel structures, boiler, spray drier, and installation of instruments. Export prices on equipment are sometimes 10 to 15 per cent less than in the United States. This saving is usually used up in special crating and shipping costs. It is usually desirable to obtain a duty waiver when importing a soluble coffee plant into a coffee-growing country. The erection of a soluble coffee plant there may be cheaper than in the United States, but the overall plant costs due to the need for better equipped stores and shop—possibly a Diesel generator and other supplies —result in a soluble coffee plant cost that may be 15 per cent more than in the United States. For such plants, equipment of the best quality is often warranted. This is because the somewhat higher initial costs are far offset by reduced maintenance and outage costs during use. In such cases the best available equipment is none too good.

The advantages of placing a soluble coffee plant in the coffee growing country is that it may be used in conjunction with a "beneficio" or green bean processing and grading plant. There are about 10 to 15 per cent of rejected green coffee beans that are unexportable in almost every coffee growing country. From a taste viewpoint, some of these rejected green beans are not tolerable in roast coffee use, but are acceptable for instant coffee processing. By grading green coffee beans for export, for soluble coffee plant use and for local use, a nice upgrading of marginal quality green coffee can be made.

One major disadvantage of a soluble coffee plant in the coffee-growing country is the political limitation on sources of green coffee; a "free zone" plant in Panama is ideal in being able to draw upon all Latin American coffees as well as African coffees if necessary.

ARCHITECTURAL FEATURES

Floor Tile

Certain features of the soluble coffee plant need special treatment. For example, the corrosive properties of coffee extract call for use of quarry or acid-proof floor tile in areas where extract or powder is likely to be spilled. See Fig. 318. Other concrete floor areas will be durable

Courtesy Atlas Mineral Products Company

FIG. 318. TILE FLOORS

if given a smooth, dense concrete finish or if given a special monolithic corrosion and wear-resistant finish. Firms specializing in this type of protective flooring are Murray Tile Co. of Lewisport, Ky.; Atlas Mineral Products Co., Mertztown, Pa.; Burmar Chemical Corp., Brooklyn, N. Y.; L. Sonneborn Sons, New York; Master Mechanics Co., Cleveland, Ohio.; Pennsalt Chemical Corp., Natrona, Pa.; and Tufcrete, Des Moines, Iowa. The really effective floor finishes are costly but are less costly than tearing up a corroded concrete floor and replacing it with quarry tile a year or two after plant startup.

Doors.—For entering air-conditioned areas, automatic opening doors, rubber doors or air curtains are used; the last is the preferred method. Roll-up metal doors are used for building and storage truck entrances.

Pre-Fab Structures.—Portions of or entire ground level soluble coffee plant designs can be built of standardized steel framing such as is provided by the firms Butler, StranSteel, Soule, and others. Costs for frame, roof, and siding, fully erected, may be less than $10 per sq ft. However, tall steel structures are not suited to such standardization and must be specially designed and purchased from standard rolled steel configurations.

Natural Lighting.—Translucent fiber glass and polyvinyl plastic corrugated colored sheets save markedly on building interior lighting costs. However, care must be taken in positioning such light transmitting panels that sunlight does not strike on Tote-Bins and cause heating of contents, building interiors, or glare.

Natural Building Ventilation.—In hot climates this is an important factor in keeping tolerable temperatures in work areas.

Insulation.—Acoustical tile is essential to quiet offices, just as wall and ceiling insulation is important to retard the flow of heat and cold.

CONTRACTING WITH AN ENGINEERING FIRM

Whether the whole soluble coffee plant is contracted for or not, the mechanics of engineering design, purchasing, expediting, shipping, erection, training, and operating the plant must be evolved in a systematic manner. These steps are presented here.

If there is no pattern of authority and procedure in developing the project, problems will arise which may lead to delays, additional costs and confusion, with duplications or omissions. In essence, the engineering design, erection, and operation must be evolved under control.

Engineering procedures for a soluble coffee plant are similar to those for any plant in the chemical, process, or power industries. Hence, controls and procedures are simply applied to the specific details of a soluble coffee plant. Nevertheless, the processing idiosyncrasies of coffee and coffee flavor must be provided for and coordinated by the owner's engineering representative skilled in the process being applied.

Cost Estimate

Usually the group investing in a soluble coffee plant has considered the project for months, if not years, and has developed a fair general knowledge of the process and the magnitude of costs. A cost estimate, prepared at this point, that includes specifications can save a great deal of difficulty later.

Acquiring a cost estimate reveals the bare facts not only of cost but also of scope and content of the plant facility. The cost estimate, when understood and approved, constitutes a relatively firm basis of part of the plant. It may even define the equipment quality and, in some cases, specify suppliers. The cost estimate constitutes the working budget and directly reflects investment requirements. The price of a good cost estimate may be as much as $25,000, but this is money well spent.

By-products of a cost estimate are an engineering design and a procurement and erection schedule. A realistic cost estimate must include expenses in shipping, duties, and field erection. Thus the cost estimate and plant erection schedule are the key factors. They indicate how much the plant will cost and when it will operate. Normally, if an engineering and construction contract is awarded on these conditions to a reputable firm with demonstrated experience, the rest of the work will be largely carried out by the engineering firm. However, some rules on the project work must be established that go beyond the approval of the original plant and engineering costs and time schedules. These are listed in Table 101.

Scope and Content of Plant and Engineering

The initial and future production capacity of the plant as well as storage requirements for green and roast coffee and the product must be specified. The quality of green coffees to be used and the quality of the soluble coffee to be produced should be stated. The scope of plant equipment will have been defined with the cost estimate. Burning facilities for spent grounds, the size and type of boiler, the make and general description of the spray drier and percolators, will be noted; a roast coffee plant may or may not be necessary; excess steam heat may or may not be used; laboratory and office space may be nominal; packaging and powder handling equipment may be minimal; etc. The investors may request a continuous roaster instead of batch roasters, which would initially increase the investment. In addition, the contract may cover only engineering, not construction.

All these facts establish a working agreement between the soluble coffee plant owners and the engineering firm. Answers to certain questions such as who trains operating personnel; when engineering and/or construction are considered complete and to what extent is startup assistance to be furnished are included in the agreement.

Contract

After the general operating features of the plant have been agreed to by the owner-management and the consultant and/or engineering firm, the contractual features must be worked out. These usually cover the

TABLE 101

BASIS OF SOLUBLE COFFEE PLANT DESIGN

Rate of Productivity
1. Plant capacity:
   (a) Initial production: lb per hr or bags per yr
   (b) Future production
   (c) Storage: instant and green coffees
Flavor
2. Quality of green coffee, roast, solubles yield, equipment, etc.
Scope of Project
3. Initial investment—projected budget
   (a) Defining objectives in regard to location (industrially forward or backward areas)
   (b) Minimal cost vs adequacy and flexibility
   (c) Next to existing roasting facility or bare land
   (d) Burning spent grounds; effluent drainage
4. Basis of equipment and plant specifications: minimal or otherwise
5. Engineering project type
   (a) Package plant
   (b) Part package plant
   (c) Mostly engineered
6. Engineering contract: Time, scope, work content, costs, specifications, purchases, field work, inspection, etc.
Time
7. Time Schedule:
   (a) Engineering
   (b) Purchasing
   (c) Shipping
   (d) Erection
   (e) Check-out and startup
Project Rules
8. Clearly defined areas of responsibilities: approvals, and prompt decisions
9. Budget and cost accounting including controls continually throughout project
10. Technical progress account, continually throughout project
11. Personnel needs: staff, supervisory, shift, operating, maintaining, semi- or unskilled (changes with stage of project)
12. Communications: meetings, phone, cables, letters, reports, memos, preliminary definitions of scope and content of work
13. Liaison and co-ordination between separate working groups
14. Site location, utility procurement, site development, building and equipment layout; aisles and paths of traffic

type of payment, fixed fee, labor rate, or cost plus. The scope of engineering services regarding drawings, purchasing, expediting, erection, installation, startup, training, etc. must be defined. The time schedule is vital. Sub-contracts for electrical system, structure, piping, plumbing, air conditioning, painting, furnishings, and utilities must be specified as to division of labor and responsibility. The cost of the plant and product should be projected in terms of plant location and environmental factors. The architectural features in regard to site size and development, building layout and types, earth properties, water supply, power supply, and grading must be discussed, and some agreed projections made by the engineering firm. Obviously not all design aspects can be covered in even several preliminary meetings and a written proposal. But enough of a working basis is established so that there will be no unpleasant surprises for management or for the engineering firm.

Engineering

Erection of a complete soluble coffee plant on bare land takes many engineering disciplines. In some cases exact process equipment may be specified such as spray drier, packager, and boiler. Parts of the plant may be engineered on a package basis. The plant will be no better than its overall engineering. Physical properties of coffee in process must be known to prepare heat and material balances. The engineering, shipping, and erection schedules need to be projected to arrange for skilled manpower and draftsmen. Budget and cost controls must be set up. Special situations (dust, drainage, a standby electrical generator) must be considered, and standardization of certain items (motors and lighting fixtures) is desirable. Shop, stores, spare parts, safety, reliability, instruments, construction materials, scales, water treatment, files, and manuals must be brought into the plant.

ENGINEERING EFFORT AND PLANT SIZE

The Hoboken expansion (early 1957), as reported by the Maxwell House Division of General Foods, illustrates the scope of the job of building a soluble coffee plant even when technical talent, drawings, and design experience are available. "This expansion took about 12 to 13 months for two units employing five construction firms, 275 people and 530 different manufacturers of equipment and materials." This job, although somewhat larger than usual, was close to all equipment resources and skilled construction and operating labor. In most cases, months of preliminary work and meetings are held so that the project is initiated at a high level of effort as soon as funds are approved.

Plant Models.—Models are not normally necessary for a soluble coffee plant as it is not very complicated. However, models are useful during design, erection, and training as well as for visitor demonstration.

The basic cost of engineering lies in the fundamental plant. Designing and erecting a 50 to 100 per cent larger capacity plant may only increase engineering costs a few per cent. It takes just about as much engineering to design, specify, buy, ship, and install one heat exchanger as another with 50 or 100 per cent more heat exchange capacity, and the cost of the large unit is usually less than proportionate.

Excess or Plant Overload Capacity.—The minimal cost plant will produce only what it is rated for. The adequately designed plant may be able to operate at 15 to 20 per cent higher than rated capacity. This built-in reserve capacity reveals itself in more uniform productivity, and fewer equipment failures (e.g., duplicate pumps) and less lost capacity from corrosion, scaling, and wear.

Minimum Soluble Coffee Plant Productivity.—This is often stated to be about 1,000,000 lb of instant coffee per year. The cost per unit of productivity of smaller sized plants rises sharply. Usually small plant costs are quoted without building or other supporting facilities. This can be quite misleading for smaller plants because the associated facilities may cost as much as the process equipment but only about 25 per cent of the cost of larger soluble coffee plants. This depends on factors such as the size and type of buildings, choice of land, and amount of site development. There really are no rules for such plant costs because the plant location and building requirements can be so variable and so important.

If a plant is built on a bare piece of land, with no prior engineering drawings, but with experienced direction and no outstanding delays, (strikes), an average sized (several million pounds soluble coffee per year) plant can be built and in operation in a coffee-growing country in 18 to 24 months. It will take about 20,000 engineering and draftsman man-hours and about 6 to 9 months' time. There will be produced about 25 architectural and/or civil drawings, over 100 structural drawings, and about 20 electrical, 20 mechanical, and 25 piping drawings. There will also be at least three comprehensive flow sheets (fuels, water, coffee, heat, steam, percolation, and spray drying).

In addition there are summary lists for motor pumps, fans, steel, purchases, spare parts, etc.

Specifications, Bids, and Purchases.—Every purchase order must have a specification. As many as 25 items may need special specifications of considerable length. Such items would be the green and roast coffee systems, spray drier, boiler, spent coffee grounds handling system transformer, motor starters and breakers, structural steel, percolator vessels, vacuum-chiller system, air conditioning systems, water treating systems, and any part of the plant jobbed out as a unit. There are also water and air purification systems, lighting, laboratory cabinets and facilities, glassware, instruments, and supplies.

Major purchases require at least two bids in order to verify prices and quality. Thus every purchase requires correspondence, explanations, and conversation from each potential supplier as well as delivery dates, crating, routing, and sometimes checking equipment before shipment and after receipt for fulfillment of purchase order specifications and safe arrival. Choosing the number and type of spare parts can sometimes be a problem that only an experienced maintenance and process engineer can competently judge. Excess spare parts tie up money for inventory. Inspection of fabricated equipment before shipment from factory as well as inspection of equipment arriving at the site must be done by an engineer acquainted with the technical features of the equipment. For example, incompetent inspection can result in acceptance of a faulty piece of vital machinery. Its defective quality may not be discovered until the machine is installed and operated. This can result in weeks or months of delay with additional operating expenses and/or delayed starting of production.

Projects such as this require over 400 purchase orders, apart from local orders for miscellaneous supplies. In addition, manuals must be assembled that pertain to every piece of plant equipment, process and utility procedure, product quality measurement and materials accountability.

In a "package plant" much of this information is often withheld by the seller because this is his "stock in trade." For the buyer this means an incomplete view and control of equipment on hand.

The buyer is responsible for getting all this technical information. The buyer must also set up his own files on project equipment, engineering data, supplies, personnel, costs, and correspondence.

A roasting plant is described in Chapter 8. Such systems can be purchased in their entirety as a package from Jabez Burns & Sons, Inc. in New York City, Probat-Werke in Emmerich, Germany, and other firms. In the case of a soluble coffee plant the green bean movement, roasting, grinding, storage, and conveying can all be sub-engineered as a package unit.

Sub-contracting of field installation of pipe, electrical conduit, wiring and control centers, steel structures, concrete work, and site development is normal procedure.

Equipment Layout and Floor Area

An important part of soluble coffee plant design is equipment layout. Most plants are built either vertically for a multi-story building or are laid out substantially horizontally on ground level with several mezzanines. Figure 319 shows a vertical multi-level design. Figure 320 shows a horizontal plant layout. Plant equipment layouts must be approved early enough in the project so that there will be no delays in engineering and purchases.

Plant floor area depends on how much green bean and instant coffee is kept in storage within the soluble coffee plant. For the plant ranges considered in Fig. 315 and without crowding, a minimum of 25,000 sq ft is used. With one month's supply of green coffee and finished powder,

40,000 to 50,000 sq ft are needed.   This area would include shop, stores, utilities, lockers, and offices at about 4,000 sq ft.

Utility Needs and Flowsheets

Utility requirements vary with the type of fuel, climatic locations, plant design, and plant productive capacity.   For example, air conditioning may be more critical and of different magnitude in one geographical area than in another.

Water.—There are usually several flowsheets for water use, and these are important.   For example, there may be raw water supply, softened

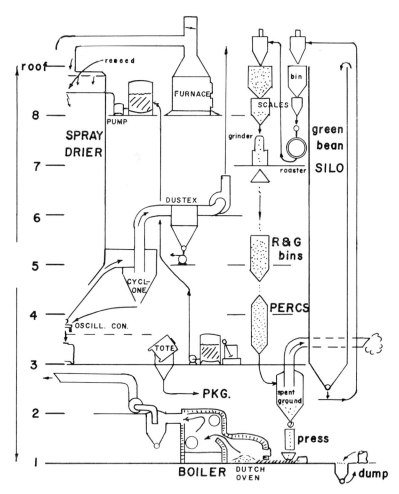

FIG. 319.   MULTI-LEVEL SOLUBLE COFFEE PLANT

water, demineralized water, deaerated water, acidified cooling tower water, domestic water, hot process water, chilled waters, purge waters, make-up waters, water for fire protection, etc.

The rate of water usage in a soluble coffee plant is widely variable. The maximum rates of water usage are attained during wash water use (e.g., for spray drier or floors). Fires create large water demands. In order to take care of such circumstances, and this influences design, it is best to have a water storage tank (e.g., 50,000 gal) in reserve. Depending on the plant productivity in the range of 2 to 5 million lb of instant coffee per year, a 50 gpm average water make-up rate may be used and 100 gpm

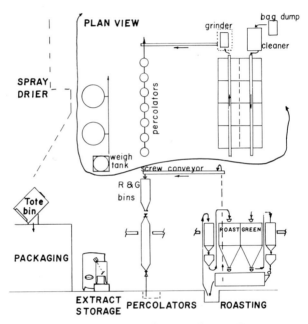

FIG. 320. TWO LEVEL SOLUBLE COFFEE PLANT

is ample. If a plant well is used, it is desirable that the pumping depth be shallow when choosing the plant site. Otherwise pumping costs over the years may be important.

Steam and Condensate Return.—Steam distribution may also be extensive. For example, steam from the boiler header goes to water heaters, to pressure reducing valves, to vacuum ejectors, to air heaters, for laboratory services, to percolator vessels and so forth. This is accompanied by many steam condensate lines. In the soluble coffee plant that burns spent coffee grounds, there may be an excess of steam heat available. This can be used for vacuum water chillers which provide chilled water for cooling in air conditioning systems. The steam can also be used for pre-heating spray drier air. These steam heat recovery uses are important since fuel costs are cumulative year after year. Such facilities are not normally provided for in a minimal cost soluble coffee plant. Figure 321 shows an example of a heat and steam balance in a soluble coffee plant. These

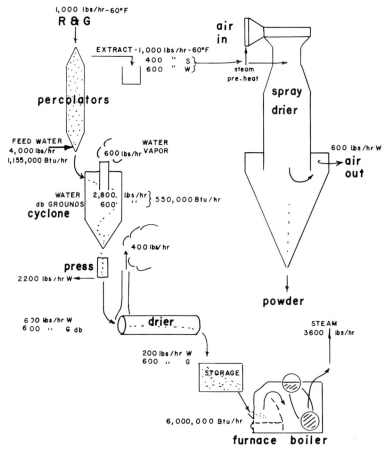

FIG. 321. FLOWSHEET: MASS AND HEAT BALANCE IN SOLUBLE
COFFEE PLANT

fuel savings are especially important in coffee-growing countries that must import fuels which are usually expensive.

Fuels

Gas and/or oil may be used for the coffee roaster, boiler, spray drier burner, laboratory coffee roaster, and other purposes.

Spent Coffee Grounds Used as Boiler Fuel.—Percolator spent coffee grounds are not always given the consideration and use they deserve. Some soluble coffee plants simply wash grounds down to a nearby sewer, creek, or river until local public health authorities stop such practices. Others truck the grounds away, spreading them on fields and incorporating them into the soil. Other plants simply incinerate the grounds. All these means of disposal are wasteful because no value is obtained from the spent coffee grounds. Trucking grounds away may be expensive. Incinerator systems are also investments requiring more than $25,000 for burning 2,000 lb spent coffee grounds (dry basis) per hour.

Incineration Systems.—These vary but, in general, require part of the fuel value of the grounds to dry the entering grounds enough to maintain combustion. Because combustion principles have been misunderstood, inadequate systems have been built. The recovery of heat from the hot combustion gases from the burning spent grounds in a steam generating boiler system is simply an extension of the incineration process. Some systems built to incinerate coffee grounds have been so poorly designed that they actually consume large amounts of fuel to dry the grounds so that they will burn. After a decade, such a system results in a large dollar loss that could otherwise have been applied to profit, plant improvements or lower product price. Unless heat is recovered from the incinerator system hot gases, the system is not efficient. Where the spent coffee grounds supply rate (dry basis) is less than 500 lb per hr, the boiler cost takes longer to amortize. In any case, the heat recovery system pays for itself in less than 10 yr and often in less than 5 yr. This is especially true for areas where fuel costs are high as in most of the coffee-growing countries.

The flowsheet (Fig. 321) clearly shows the disposition of water and grounds during processing. Some concentrations and moistures have been rounded off for simplicity, but the order of magnitudes are correct. A noteworthy point is that more steam can be formed from the combustion of the grounds than can be used for percolation and grounds drying. Therefore, the excess may be used for pre-heating spray drier air and for making vacuum chilled water. Pressed grounds enter the rotary steam tube drier at about 50 per cent moisture and leave at about 25 per cent moisture. The conversion of grounds combustion into steam is about 60 per cent efficient. The 3,600 lb/hr of steam can be used as follows: 1,150 lb/hr for heating percolator feed water, 400 lb/hr to dry spent grounds, 50 lb/hr (intermittent use) for the vacuum ejector, 800 lb/hr for preheating spray drier air (about half the heat load of the spray drier), 200 lb/hr for pre-heating boiler feed water, and 1,000 lb/hr to operate a 40 ton refrigeration unit for the vacuum water chiller.

Fuel Costs.—Since the economics of fuel costs, investment costs for boiler, presses or driers, trucking costs, size of soluble coffee plant, and consistency of processing all enter into the economics of spent grounds disposal, each plant situation must be evaluated separately. A minimum cost soluble coffee plant with initial low investment does not include spent coffee grounds heat recovery. The investors have chosen higher operating costs in order to lower initial investment. In the long run, the least efficient soluble coffee plant must compete against the most efficient plants, and such displaced costs cannot be ignored.

To ascertain the order of magnitude of such fuel costs, take the example of fuel oil cost at 16¢ per gal or 2¢ per lb, giving 18,000 Btu heat per pound of oil. For every pound of coffee solubles, there are 1.5 lb of dry spent coffee grounds. The spent grounds, after accounting for associated moisture, have about 7,500 Btu of heat value per pound. Hence, the fuel value associated with every pound of soluble coffee is about 1.25¢. In countries that import fuel, the heat value cost could be double the example given. A saving of 1 to 2¢ per lb on instant coffee is significant. A 2¢ per lb saving for each million pounds of soluble coffee production is $20,000. In addition to fuel savings, expenses for trucking grounds are eliminated. Trucking costs, especially in cities, can run to tens of thousands of dollars per year for plants processing only a few million pounds of instant coffee per year.

The E. D. Jones Corp. (1961), manufacturer of the Zenith press for dewatering spent coffee grounds, shows that overall economies in burning of grounds for a plant processing about 3,000,000 lb soluble coffee per year will amortize the whole boiler, press and accessories in 3 yr. Doubling the plant size reduces the amortization time almost to half.

Grounds Heat Value.—The important questions are: "How much heat is available from the spent coffee grounds?" "How much heat is needed to operate the soluble coffee plant?" On a dry basis the spent coffee grounds have a heating value of about 9,000 Btu/lb dry. The heating value with moisture is simply reduced by the heat required to evaporate the associated water.

For example, spent grounds with 50 per cent moisture have a heating value of 9,000 minus 1,000, or 8,000 Btu per lb dry; 75 per cent moisture spent grounds have a heating value of 6,000 Btu per lb of dry spent coffee grounds. Seventy-five per cent is about the moisture of the spent coffee grounds as discharged from the coffee percolator. Vibratory screening of the discharged wet coffee grounds may reduce the associated moisture to 70 per cent (or 67 per cent minimum). In the minimal screened moisture case, the heating value of the spent coffee grounds is 7,000 Btu per lb, dry basis. The Zenith press is guaranteed to deliver 50 per cent moisture in the squeezed spent coffee grounds. This gives the squeezed coffee grounds a heating value of 8,000 Btu per lb, dry basis.

If the pressed grounds are dried in a drier to 25 per cent moisture content, as will be discussed below, they will have a heating value of about 8,700 Btu per lb, dry basis.

Heat for Feed Water.—The 6,000 Btu per lb of dry spent grounds as heat value available from grounds containing 75 per cent moisture is equivalent to developing (at 67 per cent boiler heat conversion efficiency) 4.0 lb of steam per lb of dry spent grounds. Each pound of dry spent grounds is equivalent to 1.61 lb of fresh R & G coffee at 38 per cent solubles yield. In percolation, about 4 lb of water are needed per pound of R & G coffee. Raising the percolator feed water temperature by about 300 F (167 C) takes 300 × 6.4 or about 2,000 Btu, or, if used in the form of steam, 3,000 Btu per pound of dry spent grounds. Thus 6,000 minus 3,000 leaves 3,000 Btu available for other uses.

Heat for Drier Air.—One major heat use is for spray drier air. Each pound of coffee solubles has 2 lb of associated water to be evaporated. One lb of dry spent grounds is equivalent to 0.61 lb of solubles which are associated with 1.22 lb of water. To evaporate this would require 1,220 Btu per lb of dry spent grounds or, if steam were used at 67 per cent boiler efficiency, 1,830 Btu per lb of dry spent grounds. The 3,000 Btu available after heating the percolation feed water would be more than enough for the purpose, but practical limitations of steam pressures and temperatures would prevent heating the air above about 325 F (163 C) compared with the air operating temperature of 550 F (288 C).

Steam for Evacuation.—If steam heating of the drier air is not used, the excess heat as steam can be designed into a vacuum ejector system that chills water for plant and office air conditioning. A plant that processes 1,200 lb per hr dry spent grounds would have about 2,400 lb per hr of steam available for chilling. This is equivalent to 100 tons of refrigeration. Cooling the percolated extract (800 lb solubles with 1,600 lb water per hr) 60 F (33 C) takes about 100,000 Btu per hr or 8 tons of refrigeration. If heating of the plant is required in the winter, the surplus steam can be used for that purpose. The surplus steam is also used for vacuum loading R & G coffee into the percolator columns and for miscellaneous heating, e.g., utility water. Figure 322 shows a vacuum water chiller system.

Drying and Burning Spent Coffee Grounds.—So far only the economics of burning spent coffee grounds and the heat value recovery and use have been covered. Now it is important to consider the manner in which the grounds are prepared for burning and the design of the burning system. Boiler plants can burn wet grounds just as they are discharged from the percolators. But this takes a large enough combustion chamber and an excess of supplementary fuel and air to sustain temperatures to dry the grounds in the same chamber in which they burn. The net effect is that supplementary fuel costs are high, and moisture laden combustion gases require a wastefully large combustion furnace volume and gas blower

Courtesy Graham Mfg. Company

Fig. 322. Vacuum Chiller

capacity. In other words, this type of wet spent grounds combustion is inefficient and, consequently, expensive.

Grounds Fuel Feeders.—The furnace-boiler units are similar to those that burn sawdust, bagasse, coconut shells, walnut shells, etc. One is a Canton screwfeed; the other is a Detroit stoker.

One widely used type of feeder, but not the most thermally efficient, is the under-feed screw type used in a Dutch oven furnace. The spent coffee grounds are usually fed from a Zenith press at 50 per cent moisture. Grounds enter under the hearth via a screw conveyor into the center of the combustion chamber. Here the grounds form a mound as they rise up from the screw discharge. Figure 323 shows the side and end view of this feeder arrangement. The Canton Stoker Corp. of Canton, Ohio, builds these feeders for coal and other granular fuels. It is important that the screw drive bearings, especially the one under the hearth, be kept water cooled to prevent thermal warpage, loss of lubricant, and damage. The rotational speed of the screw governs the rate of grounds fuel feed. As the moist grounds rise to the top of the pile, they are drying. When they come to the pile surface, they have less than 25 per cent moisture and burn on the pile surface. At 50 per cent grounds moisture, the com-

Courtesy Canton Stoker Company, Canton, Ohio

FIG. 323. SECTION THROUGH DUTCH OVEN WITH SCREW GROUNDS FEED

bustion gases (with 50 per cent excess air) carry about 15 per cent moisture. Dry grounds contribute about another 7 per cent moisture. The leaving combustion gases contain about 22 to 25 per cent by volume of moisture. The fan work load due to the 50 per cent grounds moisture is increased 15 per cent. This is not important in a Dutch oven type furnace if it is designed for this purpose. But gas flow and fan capacity are important when a standard boiler package is obtained. A package boiler is designed specifically for fuel oil or coal combustion. There is no provision for excess water from fuel. Fuel oils and coal do not have an 80 per cent carbohydrate ($C_6H_{10}O_5$) content as do the dry spent coffee grounds. The combustion of one mole of carbohydrate produces 5 moles of water.

Combustion.—To illustrate the combustion chemistry, one mole of carbon (coke or coal) requires one mole of oxygen and yields one mole of

CO_2 gas. But when considering the same one mole of carbon in carbohydrate, the resulting one mole of CO_2 gas is associated with one mole of H_2O. Thus nearly 2 moles and 2 volumes of combustion product result where there was one with coke or coal. Standardized boiler-furnace systems are specifically engineered for oil or coal service. Therefore, so as to avoid raising boiler costs, it is permissible to consider a soluble coffee plant boiler of less capacity than is normally rated by the manufacturer for oil or coal. In any case, this point needs to be thoroughly reviewed with the boiler supplier so that a suitable design and warranty are specified. It would waste heat simply to use a larger blower system on the boiler-furnace. This would result in less heat transfer from combustion gases to boiler water tubes and would exhaust hotter flue gases.

In addition, a furnace combustion chamber held at about 2,000 F (1,093 C) is not an efficient place to dry moist coffee grounds. It is more efficient and economical to dry the grounds elsewhere at lower temperatures before burning them in the furnace. In order to do this, it is desirable to use a different type of coffee ground fuel feeding system than the underground screw feed. A Detroit stoker is used for this service.

Stoker Grounds Feed.—The second system is an oscillating or air-veyor type of stoker that throws the dry spent grounds into the hot combustion chamber. With spent grounds moistures less than 30 per cent, preferably 20 to 25 per cent, particle combustion is instantaneous as they enter the furnace. Hardly any unburned particles fall to the furnace grate.

Moisture Removal

Figure 324 shows the layout of such a spent coffee grounds disposal, drying, storage, and burning system. Grounds moistures below 15 per cent are undesirable since spontaneous combustion may occur. Figure 325 shows the stoking furnace and boiler section. Percolator spent coffee grounds contain about 75 per cent moisture and can be screened free of their free water to 67 to 70 per cent moisture or be pressed to 52 per cent moisture. Then the coffee grounds can be dried to 25 per cent moisture by means of several types of driers. The ones used to date are rotary steam tube types. Figure 326 (A, B, and C) shows the feed end, inside and discharge end of a rotary steam tube drier. Where hot gases up to 1800 F (982 C) can be obtained from furnace flues of an incinerator, the rotary louver type of drier is feasible. Dorr-Oliver (1961) developed an incinerator that fluidizes spent coffee grounds while drying and burning them to give a self-sustained incineration working with 67 per cent moisture in the feed coffee grounds. In late 1961, Louisville Dryers Division of General American

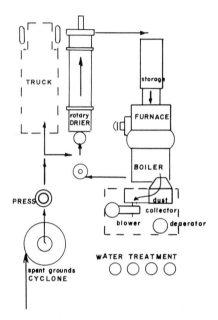

FIG. 324.   LAYOUT SPENT GROUNDS DISPOSAL

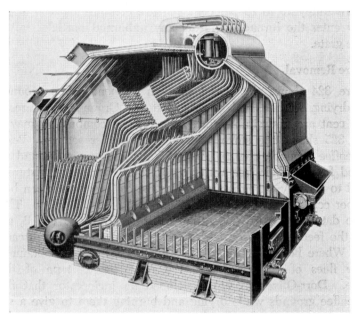

Courtesy C. C. Moore and Babcock & Wilcox Company

FIG. 325.   SECTION THROUGH WATER TUBE BOILER WITH STOKER

Transportation Corp. introduced a fluidized granular bed drier for wet spent coffee grounds; it dries grounds from 70 to 25 per cent moisture, and the drier is shown in Fig. 327. Combustion Engineering Corp. also makes a fluidized type of drier.

Courtesy General American Transportation Corporation

FIG. 326A.   FEED-END OF ROTARY STEAM TUBE GROUNDS DRIER

Courtesy General American Transportation Corporation

FIG. 326B.   INSIDE OF ROTARY STEAM TUBE GROUNDS DRIER

The two furnace-boiler systems in general use are the screw stoked Dutch oven and the more efficient method in which dried grounds are stoked into a package furnace-boiler.

The Zenith press section shown in Figs. 137 and 138 in Chapter 9 shows the outlet floating head which governs the release of pressed spent coffee grounds at back pressures of 50 to 90 psig. At these low pressures coffee grounds are squeezed enough to express water from interstices as well as from the particles. This demonstrates the effect of pressure differentials that occur during percolation that cause re-

Courtesy General American Transportation Corporation

FIG. 326. DISCHARGE END OF ROTARY STEAM TUBE GROUNDS DRIER

striction of flow passages, which in turn causes further excessive pressure drops, further reduced flow, and hence lengthening of percolation time cycles and accompanying loss of operational control.

Spent Coffee Grounds Briquettes

A feasible, but not yet applied by-product use of spent dry coffee grounds, is to briquette them into small logs or units. These are convenient, clean burning, and have higher heat value than sawdust. Spent coffee grounds contain 15 to 20 per cent oil and are drier than sawdust which has about 50 per cent moisture.

Effluent Drainage and Disposal

In many localities the spent coffee solutions associated with percolator discharge may have up to 5 per cent solubles. These solubles are
mostly simple sugars in nature. If such solubles as well as plant wash-
downs are allowed to flow into the public water supplies, they may cause
a high biological oxygen demand. Public health authorities may stop
such pollution. This is not an uncommon problem in sugar beet, fruit
juice, and other food processing industries.

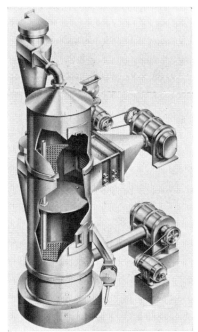

Courtesy General American
Transportation Corporation

FIG. 327. FLUIDIZED SPENT GROUNDS DRIER

One way in which these effluents have been freed of organic matter
is to divert their flow to open fields where they may be sprayed into
the air and then allowed to percolate through the soil from lagoons.
The bacterial and fermentation action in the soil decomposes some
solubles, while other solubles are absorbed on the soil. Fair and Geyer
(1958) and Parker and Litchfield (1962) discuss waste water disposal.
The net effect is that none of the solubles will normally leave the percolation field and lagoons and the soluble plant is not a source of contamination of nearby water supplies.

No set rule can be given as to the amount of land required for this disposal. This will depend on the soil available, the size of the soluble coffee plant, the quality and quantity of effluent, rainfall, winds, odors, isolation, etc. However, with suitable development of procedures and enough land area for this purpose, the effluent disposal problem can be solved. In extreme disposal cases it may be necessary to install a system to oxidize the organic sugars solutions much as sanitary sewage is processed in industrial or municipal sewage systems.

The soluble coffee plant drainage piping for this purpose may have to be dual: one for clean waste water and the other for water laden with coffee solubles to minimize the size and cost of the treatment system.

Boiler.—In a minimum size soluble coffee plant where facilities for burning of grounds are not provided, a skidded boiler of 75 to 125 hp (2,600 to 4,300 lb steam per hour) capacity generating 125 psig steam pressure can be obtained for less that $10,000. In a standard water tube boiler with grounds dewatered to 50%, or grounds drying facilities, the cost of all equipment installed may run to $150,000. This would be for a rate of about 1,000 lb grounds per hr (dry basis) and a generating rate of about 7,500 lb steam per hr.

Heating Value of Spent Coffee Grounds vs Moisture Content.—For example, at the 75 per cent moisture level and 6,000 Btu per lb dry basis, heat value is reduced to 4 lb steam per lb dry fuel. A 2,000 lb per hr R & G coffee process rate at 37.5 per cent solubles yield will supply enough spent coffee grounds to make 5,000 lb steam per hr. Reducing grounds moistures to 67 per cent increases heat value to 7,000 Btu per lb dry or steam generation to about 5,800 lb per hr. Use of a grounds press to reduce moisture to 50 per cent increases heat value to 8,000 Btu per lb (dry) or steam generation capacity to 6,700 lb per hr. At 25 per cent moisture, achieved through drying the spent coffee grounds, the net heating is the same (8,000 Btu per lb, dry) because it takes the increased steam production to dry the grounds. However, the actual heating value will rise to 8,700 Btu per lb.

"Why dry the spent coffee grounds after pressing to less than 50 per cent moisture?" The answer lies in the kindling temperature of the coffee grounds. Grounds of higher moisture content do not give up their moisture fast enough to burn promptly. The particles must either be dried on a pile in the Dutch oven furnace or dry after falling on a furnace grate. Even partial direct drying with 1800 F (982 C) furnace gases is not as efficient as indirect drying with 125 psig steam in a rotary tube drier. Dried grounds have the advantage of introducing less moisture into the furnace gases. Grounds at 50 per cent moisture in order to dry in the furnace (while still generating full furnace temperatures and steam generating capacity) require supplementary oil heating to sustain furnace temperatures. When the grounds are at 25 per cent moisture, combustion is in seconds, and furnace temperatures are self-sustained without supplementary fuel heating. The excess fuel costs to sustain furnace temperatures with grounds moistures over 30 per cent will pay for a drier in less than one year. Herein lies the importance of proper preparation of spent coffee grounds for retaining its full fuel value.

Spent grounds storage and feeding into the boiler furnace must be such as not to cause spontaneous combustion of the dried grounds in the entering ducts that are near the furnace. Provisions should be made with low pressure steam to quench any fires that may occur here or in the exhaust cyclone dust collectors.

In procuring a spent grounds drier or press, the grounds moisture entering and leaving should be specified and guaranteed by the supplier.

The larger volumes of gas from the burning of spent grounds requires assurance in the design that a fan suction is maintained in the furnace. Otherwise the rated capacity of the furnace-boiler system will not be obtained and such a design cannot be readily altered.

In the case of high fraction of water makeup to the boiler (due to a large fraction of the generated steam going into vacuum ejector use for refrigeration) it is important to provide continuous boiler water blowdown or demineralized water make-up to the boiler. Otherwise even softened feed water will result in a very high solubles content in boiler water. The alkaline nature of the water may then cause caustic embrittlement and/or tube scaling.

Dual Fuel.—Spent coffee grounds fuel systems for boilers are usually designed to operate both with spent coffee grounds fuel and/or oil or coal fuel. Usually the boiler furnace will use spent coffee grounds as the base fuel load and take up any overloads with fuel oil or coal; the load system may also operate vice versa. Coffee grounds leave negligible ash. Heat recovery from the flue gases is not usually worth the extra heat exchanger investment. Sometimes high fuel costs and a large enough boiler system make heat recovery desirable.

Air.—A diagram for compressed air flow may be extensive. Air is compressed to 100 psig pressure. It may be kept oil-free by using carbon pistons. The compressed hot air is cooled to reduce saturated moisture content. Then the air is distributed for use on drier wall vibrators, pneumatic machines and, after drying, for use with numerous instruments. Air packing of the R & G coffee in the percolators is intermittent. Air pressure is also used to tilt Tote-Bins, to clean jars, to clean shop work, and in the laboratory.

Electrical.—Depending on the size of the soluble coffee plant and how it is operated, a 300 to 500 kw demand load is usual. Since many electrical rates are determined by demand use, and systems must be designed for demand use, these indices are more important than actual average power use. In the coffee-growing countries, it often becomes practical to use a standby Diesel generator during peak demand periods for electricity to reduce the otherwise high electrical demand rates. Average electrical use is usually about three-quarters or two-thirds of peak demand. Where public power fails frequently, emergency Diesel power is justified to save coffee in process and, if necessary, to shut down the soluble process under control. Battery charging stations are usually required for electrically operated fork trucks. Outdoor and security lighting systems are usually desirable. Sometimes designers like to use ratios of utility requirements per unit of soluble coffee product. Due to marked variances in such figures, these are not cited here.

Flowsheets of electrical wiring distribution in conduits, to sub-stations, to control centers, to lighting panels with corresponding equipment areas must be prepared and must show every electrical outlet.

Similarly, the instrument systems for controlling the process steps at every stage in the soluble coffee plant must be specified. First, verbally, then by electrical diagrams and then by electrical working drawings used for shop preparations and assemblies. If standby electrical power is supplied, it must be tied into the normal electrical supply system.

SCHEDULING, AND LIAISON BETWEEN CUSTOMER AND CONTRACTOR

The *project rules* must clearly define areas of responsibility for approvals or engineering decisions and equipment purchases. Delays in decisions may be costly when engineers and draftsmen are neither fully nor productively employed. Throughout the project *cost accounting* must be made in accordance with the *budget* breakdown. Explanations must be reported for cost variations. Periodic technical *progress reports* must tell what has been done and how the design engineering, shipments and deliveries, erection, etc., are falling in with projected plans. At the beginning of the project it is useful to have a brief reference description of the plant as it will operate with personnel. This gives a common evaluation of ultimate working objectives as well as a guide to the type and caliber of persons required in processing.

The plant site location must be reported in full detail as a means of visualizing any unusual problems that may occur as a result of such factors as political situations, water quality and abundance, earthquake hazards, weather conditions, communications, power, and fuel costs.

The key to keeping the whole project under control is *communication* and *liaison* through a competent *project manager* or engineer. This calls for meetings, letters, phone calls, cables, memos, visits, and reports. Thorough *coordination* of all sectors of the project must be maintained to avoid errors, duplication, inefficiency of effort and, especially, timing of results.

Table 102 indicates the sequencing of events on this type of project from contract award to process flowsheet and plans approval by the customer, through specifications, drawings, procurement, shipping, erection, and finally operation. Figure 328 illustrates the magnitude of men vs months required. Engineering effort peaks at about one-third project time and construction effort peaks at about two-thirds project time.

SAFETY IN THE SOLUBLE COFFEE PLANT

Although insurance companies will monitor employee working conditions and safety of operating equipment, real safety originates from

TABLE 102

SOLUBLE COFFEE PLANT PROJECT MASTER SCHEDULE
Qualitative

Client——————————————   Start date—————————
Location—————————————   Net time req'd—————————

Per cent of time allotted	10	20	30	40	50	60	70	80	90	100
Engineering Contract Award	(x)									
(preceded by estimate and proposal)										
Process Engineering	x									
Planning and Analysis	x	x	x (CP)							
Working Drawings and Specifications				x	x	x	x			
Sub-Contracts Equipment										
Spray Drier			x	x	x	x	x			
Percolators and Accessories				x	x	x	x	x		
Boilers and Accessories				x	x	x	x	x	x	
Sub-Contracts Erection										
Site, grades, roads			x	x	x	x	x	x	x	x
Building steel and foundations					x	x	x	x		
Piping and electrical						x	x	x	x	x
Construction										
Site	E	E	E	P	P	P	P	C	C	C
Foundations		E	E	P	P	C	C			
Underground			E	P	P	C				
Steel				E	E	P	P	C		
Building					E	E	P	P	C	C
Instruments				E	E	P	P	P	C	C
Check-Out for Start up							x	x	x	x
(manuals and procedures)										
Operation										x (ready)
Costs										
Estimated (budget)	x	x	x							
Incurred			x	x	x	x	x	x	x	x
Operating personnel								x	x	x

Key points: contract award, client approval and ready for operation. Key to abbreviations: E = engineering, P = procurement, C = construction, x = work in progress.

management, supervisory attitudes and overall co-operation and employee education. As strange as it may seem in this day, there are many soluble coffee plants that are literally strewn with hazards. Municipalities have not taken legal action on building code violations. Poor and

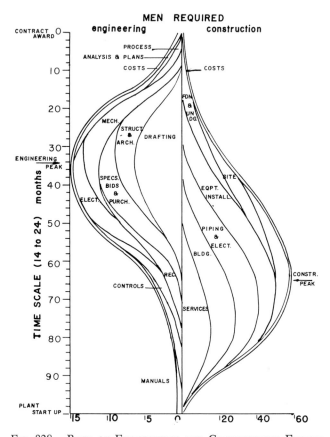

FIG. 328. RATE OF ENGINEERING AND CONSTRUCTION EFFORT

For a several million pound per year soluble coffee plant the engineering effort (area under curve) will be about 20,000 man-hours while the construction effort will be 75,000 to 100,000 man-hours.

hazardous working conditions are an invitation to lawsuits and labor union action.

Safety features are designed and built into the original soluble coffee plant with proper lighting, drainage, corridor space, strong ladders, adequate stairs, etc. It is surprising that many plants have high staircases, ladders without backing, stairs that are too steep, and staircases that allow insufficient headroom. Sometimes proper lighting is not provided in original plant installations and often lighting is not maintained. As a result serious accidents may occur. Open floor pits and balconies that have no barriers are also hazards. Buildings may be marginally built with no lightning protection or earthquake safety factor considered in structural design. Local drainage may cause foul odors and breeding of insects. Because ventilation may be inadequate, foul odors accumulate and working areas are so hot that they cause personnel fatigue. This can and does contribute to errors in work. Acid eaten floors may not be repaired or tiled. Wet floors, if not promptly squeegeed dry, leave slippery, dangerous walkways. Electrical systems may not be adequately protected for overloads nor adequately grounded. Layout of paths for transport trucks and fork trucks may be hazardous to pedestrians. Separate, isolated, and ventilated buildings should be provided for flammable and toxic solvent storage. Fire protection and first aid facilities may be minimal and inadequate.

Machinery must be maintained, and rotating machine parts must be covered to prevent contact by clothing. Motors should have an electrical lock-out so that the respective machinery can be worked on without the danger of accidental starting. Utility headers or mains should have shut-offs in case of local valve or switch failures.

There is a tendency to hire low paid and unskilled labor for menial tasks about a roast coffee plant. Similar labor has been placed in some soluble coffee plants. The latter process is considerably more complex and hazardous. There are high pressure steam and pressurized hot water lines, percolator vessels, more instrumentation, etc. To place an uneducated employee or untrained man in such a job may endanger the man and the plant. Accidents have happened with caustic soda boiling over on employees who were unaware that the solution of caustic soda in water is an exothermic process. Men have been obliged to work with Dowtherm water heaters that leak. These men did not appreciate the potential explosion hazard that existed when water leaked into the low pressure high temperature Dowtherm boiler. Men have cleaned out blow lines while the percolator operator has blown a column causing the cleaning men severe injury. Percolators under high pressure, and sometimes under assumed low pressure have been opened with blast injury. In 1957 a major decaffeination firm had a severe trichlorethylene leakage overcoming dozens of employees.

An interesting case occurred in 1961 when a percolator ruptured in the Granite City, Nescafé plant. This was the first case that warned that the safety element designed and built into a percolator vessel must be subject to close scrutiny and repeated testing. Some percolators have been built for temporary pilot use and have become production units. Further, test equipment installed on a temporary basis may be operated under circumstances so different from normal production that the average operator is not qualified to oversee such special conditions.

Often management and the operating foreman, who are not technically competent to use equipment, accept it at face value, and assume it is sturdy and will work safely. Such assumptions may result in failures of various sorts. Other sources of danger are inadequate instrumentation and careless keeping of records that are theoretically designed to show actual operating conditions at any moment as well as changes in these conditions over the weeks, months, and years.

Personnel must be qualified to maintain soluble coffee plant equipment. In some apparently well run plants, shockingly inadequate maintenance is a hazard to the plant and to the maintenance personnel. Care must be exercised in handling fuels, acids, solvents, caustic, gases, pressure vessels, gasketing, lubrication, and safety valves.

The National Safety Council

This council, with its main offices in Chicago, has prepared an *Accident Prevention Manual* which goes into many details of causes of accidents based on industrial experience. It also provides other literature, books, and posters in English and Spanish.

A common occurrence in the soluble coffee plant is the scalding of an employee with steam or hot water. The Mine Safety Appliances Company of Pittsburgh, Pa. provides a spray salve that, if applied promptly, can reduce a potentially serious burn to a minor injury. The plant personnel should have access to and be instructed in the use of the burn spray, safety glasses for grinding, tinted goggles for welding, safety shoes and helmets, electrical grounding dangers, eye wash fountain and safety showers, rubber, leather and asbestos gloves, etc. In the United States safety is so often emphasized, that the enforcement of safety rules is taken for granted. But in industrially backward countries, where people's lives are often looked upon as cheap and expendable, men climb barefooted hundreds of feet up steel structures, without belts or other safety equipment.

Physical Tests

Personnel in the soluble coffee plant should be tested for vision, color discrimination, hearing, general health, tuberculosis, or any other chronic or infectious infirmities. If a person cannot understand and follow instructions, he should not hold a skilled job that can cause harm to others. With the use of chlorinated solvents for decaffeination and CO_2 gas for inert gas pack, special plant hazards exist and these must be recognized. In addition, simple rules against smoking, wearing rings or loose clothing, and eating on the job must be continually enforced.

BIBLIOGRAPHY

ANON. 1959. Accident Prevention Manual for Industrial Operations. 4th Edition. National Safety Council, 425 N. Michigan Avenue, Chicago.

ANON. 1961. Coal slurry burns without drying. Chem. Eng. News 39, No. 46, 35.

ANON. 1961. General Foods prefabricates instant plants for off shore sites. World Coffee and Tea 2, No. 1, 21.

ANON. 1960. Latin costs are hard to figure. Chem. Eng. News 38, No. 27, 22.

ANON. 1954. Manual of Industrial Water. D-19. American Society for Testing Materials, 1916 Race Street, Philadelphia.

ANON. 1959. Models cut construction costs. Chem. Eng. News 37, No. 37, 64–65.

ANON. 1960. United Instants. Instant coffee blending. Tea and Coffee Trade J. 118, No. 5, 36, 38.

ARIES, R. S.. and NEWTON, R. D. 1955. Chemical Engineering Cost Estimation. McGraw-Hill Book Company, New York.

BASS, M. S. 1960. Multiple pitch screw equalizes discharge. Chem. Eng. 67, No. 1, 11.

BAUMAN, H. C. 1959A. Capital cost control. Ind. Eng. Chem. 51, No. 5, 69A–72A.

BAUMAN, H. C. 1959B. Measuring cost elements. Ind. Eng. Chem. 51, No. 11, 63A–64A.

BAUMAN, H. C. 1959C. Project cost control. Ind. Eng. Chem. 51. No. 7, 67A–69A.

CHILTON, C. H. 1960. Cost Engineering in the Process Industries. McGraw-Hill Book Company, New York.

DALY, T. P. 1956. Planning manufacture of soluble coffee. Tea and Coffee Trade J. 111, No. 2, 18, 66.

FAIR, G. M., and GEYER, J. C. 1958. Elements of Water Supply and Waste Water Disposal. John Wiley and Sons, New York.

HARDY, W. L. 1955A. Costs of process and construction of soluble coffee plants. Plant. Ind. Eng. Chem. 47, No. 8, 79A.

HARDY, W. L. 1955B. Costs of process and construction of soluble coffee plants. Spray drier. Ind. Eng. Chem. 47, No. 10, 73A.

HARDY, W. L. 1957. Manufacture of instant coffee. Coffee and Tea Inds. 80, No. 10, 11–16.

HETTIG, S. B. 1962. Dealing with an outside designer. Chem. Eng. 69, No. 6, 101–104.

IMHOFF, K., and FAIR, G. M. 1956. Sewage Treatment. John Wiley and Sons, New York.

PARKER, M. E., and LITCHFIELD, J. H. 1962. Food Plant Sanitation. (See chapter on Waste Disposal and Utilization.) Reinhold Publishing Corporation, New York.

PETERS, M. S. 1958. Plant Design and Economics. McGraw-Hill Book Company, New York.

PINCUS, L. I. 1962. Practical Boiler Water Treatment. McGraw-Hill Book Company, New York.

RASMUSSEN, E. H., and NIELSEN, H. B. 1954. Economics in processing soluble coffee. Tea and Coffee Trade J. 107, No. 5, 20.

SCHWEYER, H. E. 1955. Process Engineering Economics. McGraw-Hill Book Company, New York.

SMITH, D. A. 1959B. Green bean price a major soluble coffee manufacturing cost. Tea and Coffee Trade J. 116, No. 3, 46.

SMITH, D. A.   1959A.   Economics of soluble coffee manufacture.   Tea and Coffee Trade J. *117*, No. 1, 26, 88.

STEWART, O.   1957.   Plant site selection guide.   Factory, May.

SWEET, R. E.   1959A.   Factors affecting the cost of engineering.   Ind. Eng. Chem. *51*, 989–990.

SWEET, R. E.   1959B.   Operating cost estimates.   Chem. Eng. Progress *52*, No. 5, 179–182.

TIELROOY, J.   1956.   Importance of capital cost estimates.   Chem. Eng. Progress, *52*, No. 5, 187–190.

TYLER, C., and WINTER, C. H.   1959.   Chemical Engineering Economics.   McGraw-Hill Book Company, New York.

VILBRANDT, F. C., and DRYDEN, C. E.   1959.   Chemical Engineering Plant Design. McGraw-Hill Book Company, New York.

WEAVER, J. B.   1961.   Profitability measure.   Chem. Eng. News *39*, *No.* 39, 94–104.

WISEMAN, J. P.   1962.   Eight tips toward a better plant.   Chem. Eng. *69*, No. 6, 105–106.

CHAPTER 21

Conclusion

In Volume I of this book we have tried to present a brief historical survey of coffee, a summary of outstanding horticultural problems—what men have done to grow the huge tonnages of coffee fruit demanded by the modern world and how they have processed the fruit.

Here the main problem is to conserve the excellent quality that coffee has when it is ripe on the tree, and we have pointed out the fundamental principles involved in obtaining a dry, stable, high quality product at the lowest cost. Then we have described its safe handling from the grower to the man who roasts it; and here again the main consideration is the conservation of its quality.

Now our roasted product takes one of two paths. It is delivered to the ultimate consumer in the roasted and ground form or its soluble constituents are extracted and it reaches the consumer as the dry, soluble powder. A small and diminishing portion reaches him as liquid extract. In both cases, our constant struggle to conserve quality has involved intricate problems of packaging. This, in summary, is the content of Volume I.

Volume II deals with the engineering, chemical, physical, and physiological problems of rendering soluble (instant) coffee, as dissolved in the cup, more nearly like the freshly brewed beverage from freshly roasted coffee. From the accounts in this volume, it can be seen that an immense amount of highly skilled work has been and is being expended on this problem and that it is an extremely difficult one. Like many problems of this kind, it is gradually yielding to analysis and study, and, although it is far from a complete solution, much progress has been made and we may confidently expect that the pressure of public demand, the commercial rewards for success, and the immense resources available in the industry because of its magnitude, will eventually result in a high degree of success. The existence of nearly 600 patents on soluble coffee directly or in closely allied fields shows that a strong effort is being made.

We know a great deal about exactly what chemical compounds constitute the flavor and aroma of coffee. Sometime, we shall be able to put them in the cup at the right time for maximum enjoyment.

In the meantime, about two-thirds of our coffee is brewed just prior to drinking and we need to know how to do this dependably and with maximum satisfaction. This book has presented the latest and best work in this field. It takes more, however, than the brewing itself. For the finest cup of coffee, the fruit must have been grown on a healthy tree at optimum altitude in a favorable climate and soil; it must have been harvested and processed skillfully, freed of all imperfections, transported with loving care and roasted under the strictest controls. Only then is it really ready to be brewed. Every factor and every step are important. The problem is complex and difficult, and much work will be required for a long time to come.

It is hoped that this book will be of service to all types of coffee people who deal with this elusive and challenging commodity at any stage of its production.

Chronological List of Soluble Coffee Patents

Number and Date	Inventors	Title or Description	Chapter[1]
		United State Patents	
4,922 1/7/1847	Remington, J. R.	Roasting coffee. Wheel of buckets dump into heating trough; condensing vessel for aroma.	8 14
21,066 8/3/1858	Dealey, J. & Heberling, T. H.	Apparatus for making coffee.	10
48,268 6/20/1865	Gale, L. D.	Preparing coffee. Steam distill R & G coffee; press out residue; mix extract and distillate with sugar and form into solid cakes for shipping without boxes or cans.	10 13
95,015 9/21/1869	Galloway, J.	Coffee roaster and brewer sphere. Roast green coffee, then immerse in water in same container to obtain brew.	8 10
115,302 5/30/1871	Galloway, J.	Autoclave steam roast for even roasting and to conserve aroma.	14
116,298, 9 6/27/1871	Gillies, J. W.	Coffee roaster; two-stage roast with intermediate cooling; removal of silver skin to improve flavor.	14
119,959 10/17/1871	Ashcroft, J.	Roasting in sealed cylinder; aroma gases highly heated and driven back into roasted coffee.	
177,592 5/16/1876	Underwood, J. B.	Condensing roast aroma on roast beans. Cool R & G coffee in closed chamber.	8 14
228,889 6/15/1880	Gue, D. J. & Grant, J. C.	Coffee extract. Cold, then hot water extractions of R & G coffee.	10
229,697 7/6/1880	Gue, D. J. & Grant, J. C.	Coffee extract. Cold infusion plus cooled decoction of R & G coffee.	
243,521 6/28/1881	Davidson, S. C.	Infusions, extracts, or essences of tea, coffee, and cocoa. Treat with sugar, Al(OH)$_3$, glycerin, and salicylic acid which clarifies and preserves.	
246,274 8/23/1881	Jennings, R. S.	Method and apparatus for collecting aromatic coffee volatiles.	8 14
268,869 12/12/1882	Conroy, A. & Conroy, M.	Coffee compound or substitute. Dried roast coffee extract with raw and roasted malt.	
270,787 1/16/1883	Groff, C. R.	Coffee compounds. Brewing coffee with alcohol, glycerin, and burnt sugar.	14
324,050 8/11/1885	Thew, W. H.	Condensed milk with coffee. Condensed peptonized milk with coffee and sodium phosphate.	14
339,114 3/30/1886	Rundel, T. J.	Roast volatiles condensation and return.	8 14
344,597 6/29/1886	St. Aubin, A. L.	Volatiles recovery and return.	8 10 14
358,300 2/22/1887	Samelson, M.	Manufacturing liquid coffee extracts. Extract R & G coffee with cold, warm, and near boiling water; combine extracts.	
439,318 10/28/1890	Barotte, H.	Steam distillate added to instant coffee powder.	14
474,531 5/10/1892	Salomon, C.	High temperature, fast roast to drive off empyreumatic substances and to develop aromatic compounds as indicated by alkaline reaction of gases; quick cooling.	8 14
488,801 12/27/1892	Trillich, H.	Coffee substitute. Roast moist malt; extract malt with coffee extract and sugar; dry, coat with fat.	
513,252 1/23/1894	Trillich, H.	Coffee substitute. Impregnate malt with extract of raw coffee waste products and roast.	
543,299 7/23/1895	Drake, J. B.	Coffee surrogate (substitute). Roast mix of sugar, caffeine, cream of tartar, caffeol, and cornstarch.	
617,322 1/10/1899	Duke, J. F.	Apparatus for making fluid extracts. Countercurrent successive extraction; 9 movable vessels.	
617,434 1/10/1899	Brougier, A.	Double roast. Partially roast to 200 C; cool; finish roast.	8 14

Number and Date	Inventors	Title or Description	Chapter[1]
680,889 8/20/01	Schutz, J. M.	Coffee compound and process. Roast coffee powder with sugar, dried milk, and CaCO₃ to absorb coffee oils.	
686,689 11/12/01	Eschwege, H.	Coffee extract. Extract coffee with water below 100 F; seven steps countercurrent.	
701,750 6/3/02	Maxim, H. S.	Volatiles recovery on roasted beans.	8 14
723,152 3/17/03	Gürber, A.	Process of concentrating solutions. Freeze concentration of milk.	14
726,279 4/28/03	Giacomini, L.	Volatiles condensed; sugar dissolved; solution used to glaze roasted beans.	8 14
731,028 6/16/03	Eschwege, H.	Apparatus for making coffee extract. Similar to 617,322 above.	
735,777 8/11/03	Kato, S.	Coffee concentrate and process. Roast coffee and grind; extract oils; distill off solvent; extract coffee with water and dry; add oil back.	10
754,943 3/15/04	Timby, T. R.	Return volatiles to roasted beans.	8 14
758,384 4/26/04	Reichert, F. J.	Coffee extract. Low roast; grind; extract with water; dry; finish roasting.	
829,649 8/28/06	Herron, J. M.	Coffee preparation. Mixture of 1 part R & G coffee, 1 part raw cocoa beans, 1/2 part cocoa butter.	8
893,073, 4 7/14/08	Herron, J. M.	Coffee preparation and process. Extract R & G coffee; immerse raw, ripe cocoa beans; dry and grind beans. Mix roast coffee with raw cocoa beans; heat; remove coffee; use cocoa.	8
955,659 4/19/10	Monti, E.	Freeze concentration. Complex apparatus for freeze concentration of solutions; no product mentioned.	14
981,860 1/17/11	Jackson, W. B.	Freeze concentrating fruit juices.	14
997,431 7/11/11	Winter, H.	Absorb sugar into green coffee before roasting; improve yield and flavor.	8 14
1,002,137 8/29/11	Carreras, L. B.	Coffee tablet.	14
1,026,971 5/21/12	Bullard, A. H.	Coffee beverage powder: soluble coffee, dry milk, malted milk, sugar, salt.	
1,058,279 4/8/13	Volkers, G.	Making coffee extract tablets with sugar.	14
1,063,188 6/3/13	De Simone, M. G.	Coffee making machine. Roast coffee, distill essence, grind, mix distillate and ground coffee in one machine.	8
1,079,474 11/25/13	Davis, J. T.	Extract R & G coffee at 165 F; evaporate to dryness under vacuum.	
1,093,962 4/21/14	Allison, J. M.	Beverage extract. Dry soluble powder mixture of roast coffee germs, roasted cocoa, and milk.	
1,137,265 4/27/15	Hubner, R.	Coffee tablet. Extract R & G coffee with ether; saponify; remove soaps; make tablets; cover.	10 14
1,157,947 10/26/15	Merrell, I. S.	Box dryer-collecting apparatus.	12
1,158,431 11/2/15	Benjamin, G. H.	Soluble coffee process. Germinate coffee partially; heat to 150 to 160 F; extract and dry.	
1,175,091 3/14/16	Vietinghoff, K.	Aromatic, clear, soluble coffee extract. Second roasting of soluble coffee powder; 10 min at 225 C.	10
1,214,875 2/6/17	Åslund, K. & Boberg, T.	Aromatizing dry coffee extract. Add finely ground R & G coffee to soluble coffee powder to aromatize.	14
1,229,052 6/5/17	Ewing, W. J.	Carbohydrate soluble coffee. Add water soluble starch to concentrated (syrupy) coffee extract and dry.	
1,237,931 8/21/17	Malvezin, P.	Gas pressurized roast with condensed volatiles.	8 14
1,240,020 9/11/17	Boberg, T., Soderlung, O., & Åslund, F.	Concentrated food product. Dry R & G coffee extract to 5 to 10 per cent moisture; heat to 90 C under reduced pressure while tumbling to get porous, dry granules.	
1,251,359 12/25/17	Etaix, L.	Coffee extract, (CO₂ solvent). Pass cold gas saturated with coffee volatiles through dry soluble coffee powder in series of vessels.	14
1,255,816 2/5/18	Fletcher, J. D.	Coffee. Beverage mixture of caffeine, caramel, and coffee extract.	
1,271,761 7/9/18	Phillips, W. G. & McKenna, W.	Extract R & G coffee with water; evaporate to dryness; mix residue with coffee oil; pelletize.	

Number and Date	Inventors	Title or Description	Chapter[1]
1,292,458 1/28/19	Hamor, W. A. & Trigg, C. W.	Preserving fugacious components. Absorb caffeol into petrolatum; extract jelly; concentrate solvent; extract; combine extracts.	14
1,324,538 12/9/19	Boyles, F. M.	Powdered flavors. Pasty oleoresin composition concentrated for use as food flavor.	14
1,324,662 12/9/19	Goldsworthy, W. J.	Grind green coffee before roasting; roast in perforated containers; seal after cooling.	8 13 14
1,359,911 11/23/20	Öman, E.	Separating water from solutions by freezing.	14
1,365,443 1/11/21	Anhaltzer, H.	Making soluble coffee. Steam R & G coffee; extract with ethyl alcohol; dry with exclusion of air.	14
1,367,715, 6 2/8/21	Pratt, D. S. & Trigg, C. W.	Adding aromas to coffee extract. Use of lactose as aroma absorbent.	14
1,367,724, 5, 6 2/8/21	Trigg, C. W.	Recovery of coffee aroma and flavor. Condense aroma under pressure; grind in closed system.	14
1,376,870 5/3/21	Graff, F. W. & Oppel, J. V.	Beverages. Germinate coffee or cocoa beans; extract; ferment, and dry.	
1,381,821, 2 6/14/21	Greenberg, J.	Dry coffee substitute. Dry soluble coffee and dry skim milk mixture. Dry soluble vegetable extract (imitative of coffee) and skim milk mixture.	
1,393,045 10/11/21	Scott, J. W.	Producing soluble concentrated coffee. Countercurrent extraction of R & G coffee with falling water temperatures; spray rapidly at high temperature using air containing grinder gas.	10 14
1,398,115 11/22/21	Prell, H.	Roaster design; close roaster after moisture removal to retain aroma.	8 14
1,402,004 1/3/22	Mack, H.	Confectionary. Ingredients: sugar, butter fat, soluble coffee extract; hard protective coating of dextrose.	14
1,428,256 9/5/22	Romero, L. A.	Making coffee extract. Paste of soluble coffee powder and milk sugar.	
1,465,020 8/14/23	Monti, E.	Apparatus for concentrating solutions. Distillation under vacuum.	14
1,478,940 12/25/23	Chalas, A.	Freeze drying soluble coffee extract.	12
1,504,459 8/12/24	Washington, G.	Amorphous powder with impalpable solids. Adding soluble saccharine matter and insoluble flavoring to soluble coffee.	14
1,507,410 9/2/24	Zorn, W. M.	Freeze concentration of coffee liquids with oils.	14
1,525,272 2/3/25	Darrah, W. A.	Extract R & G coffee with 30% glycerin.	
1,535,233 4/28/25	McColl, F. P. & Willison, W.	Coffee flavor process. Pellets from crushed roasted coffee.	
1,546,669 7/21/25	Monti, E.	Apparatus for concentrating solutions by freezing.	14
1,576,136, 7 3/9/26	Johnson, M. O.	Apparatus for concentrating solutions by freezing.	14
1,605,115 11/2/26	Kellogg, J. L.	Press out coffee flavor at moderate temperatures.	14
1,636,890 7/26/27	Zorn, W. M.	Freeze concentrating fruit juice.	14
1,641,429 9/6/27	Heyman, W. A. & McComb, W.	Freeze concentration.	14
1,641,446 9/6/27	McColl, F. P.	Coffee tablet. R & G coffee and concentrated extract.	14
1,687,112 10/9/28	Slocum, F. L. & Troutman, W. E.	Roast coffee oil flavor. Remove gases from R & G coffee; extract with cold water; partially recycle extract.	10
1,696,419 12/25/28	Staudinger, H.	Coffee aroma. Mercaptans and sulfides reacting with oxygen and nitrogen bearing coffee components.	
1,716,323 6/4/29	Rector, T. M.	Grind roast coffee beans in oil, use oil flavor.	
1,738,225 12/3/29	Baker, E.	Cold milk freeze dehydration process.	14
1,742,261 1/7/30	Klein, E.	Soluble coffee. Germinate green coffee; treat with acid and quinine, then alkali.	
1,770,118 7/8/30	Williams, W. M.	Quick-beverage cup. Nest of conical cups with tight spaces for flavors.	

Number and Date	Inventors	Title or Description	Chapter[1]
1,836,931 12/15/31	Meyers, A. W. & Haas, L. W.	Imparting coffee aroma to soluble coffee. Extract R & G coffee; mix with fresh R & G coffee; filter.	14
1,866,414, 5 7/5/32	Lorand, E. J.	Concentrated coffee product and process. Extraction with anhydrous glycerin.	14
1,891,383 12/20/32	Giffen, W. W. & Carter, C. W.	Making liquid coffee extract. Stepwise water (300 per cent by weight) infusion of R & G coffee at 30 to 50 C.	10
1,903,362 4/4/33	McKinnis, R. B. & Mellon Institute	Flaking R & G coffee.	
1,915,410 6/27/33	Decker, L. B.	Steam inlet used for wood pulp and coffee percolators.	10
1,925,159 9/5/33	Wendt, G. L.	Coffee extract. Extract R & G coffee with hot 20 per cent glycerin; evaporate water leaving concentrated glycerin solution.	10
1,930,257 10/10/33	Stelkens, W.	Beverages. Soluble coffee powder containing fine activated carbon and glycerin.	
1,932,769 10/31/33	Copes, L. G., Haurand, C. H. & Kellogg, E.	Coffee extract. Crush green coffee; extract with cold then hot water; combine and dry.	
1,933,049 10/31/33	Copes, L. G.	Coffee extract. Crush green coffee; extract with cold then hot water; combine and dry.	
1,933,960 11/7/33	Brabaek, J.	Apparatus for removal of volatile constituents from liquid, pasty or solid matter.	14
1,979,124 10/30/34	Tival, H. L. P.	Animal and vegetable powders by freeze concentration.	14
1,989,077 1/29/35	Bredt, O. P. C.	Acetic acid in coffee extraction feed water.	10
1,996,988 4/9/35	Badger, W. L.	Freeze concentration. Apparatus with wall scraping for freeze concentration of solutions.	14
1,999,712 4/30/35	Zorn, W. M. & Eickhoff, T. H.	Concentration of liquids by freezing.	14
2,001,554 5/14/35	Süssmuth, K. W.	Instant coffee. Saturated sugar solution of coffee enclosed in solid sugar wall.	14
2,017,892 10/22/35	Clary, P. T.	Roaster machine to apply moisture, and confine steam to impregnate coffee with aroma.	8 14
2,022,467 11/26/35	Heyman, W. A.	Instant and R & G coffee in bags.	13 14
2,036,345 4/7/36	Merkel, H.	More digestible coffee infusions. Adjust pH to 6.4 to 6.9 with non-injurious basic materials.	14
2,043,443 6/9/36	Meyer, G. L. M.	Two-step roast; second step in sealed containers.	8 13 14
2,054,689 9/15/36	Andresen, H. P.	Roasting coffee beans in oil.	8 14
2,062,109 11/24/36	Rogers, L. M.	Inert gas roast, grind, and packaging.	8 13
2,068,841 1/26/37	Bowen, W. S. & Freeman, J.	Belt delivery spray dryer.	12
2,071,011 2/16/37	Wendt, G. L.	Concentrating half of coffee extract.	10
2,077,564 4/20/37	Heuser, H.	Coffee extract. Heat and cool concentrated mixture of R & G coffee extract and reducing agent in sealed container; filter and package the liquid extract.	10 13
2,081,909 6/1/37	Bowen, W. S.	Apparatus for spray drying.	12
2,084,839 6/22/37	Dubois, E. F.	Coffee extract. Knead pulverized R & G coffee and water; press out air in a receptacle; extract with water for measured time.	
2,087,602 7/20/37	McCrosson, J. T.	Collect roast gases; purify; return to roaster under pressure.	8
2,088,622 8/3/37	Stokes, W. E. & Wenneis, J. M.	Gelatin flavor powders. Emulsify flavor with higher boiling ester; add hygroscopic carbohydrate.	14
2,090,985 8/24/37	Peebles, D. D. & Manning, P. D. V.	Evaporating apparatus and method.	14
2,091,493 8/31/37	Schuftan, P.	Freeze concentration of solutions by freezing into structurally stable solid mass then separating liquid and solid.	14
2,098,961 11/16/37	Fronmuller, D.	Coffee extract with recovered aroma.	14

Number and Date	Inventors	Title or Description	Chapter[1]
2,110,732 3/8/38	Kane, J. P.	Coffee ball. Porous container for R & G and soluble coffee for 1 cup brew.	
2,116,308 5/3/38	Gore, H. C. & Frey, C. N.	Three step extraction of coffee.	10
2,119,182 5/31/38	Schuftan, P. & Ranke, H.	Condensing liquids by freezing.	14
2,123,207 7/12/38	Rosenthal, H.	Coffee treatment. Crimp and roll raw coffee; extract with low boiling hydrocarbon solvent under pressure to remove oil and fat.	
2,130,154 9/13/38	Riley, C. L.	Heat treating powdered material. Heat treat powder with radiant heat by spraying in chamber in hot air.	12
2,145,395 1/31/39	Horvath, F. J.	Recycling solvent between R & G and instant coffee.	10
2,149,876 3/7/39	Wendt, G. L. & Fronmuller, D.	Condensation of coffee flavor volatiles.	10 14
2,152,602 3/28/39	Ott, E.	Coffee flavor. Aldose and ammonia reaction product as preservative.	
2,152,788 4/4/39	Burkhart, W. H. & Marceau, E. T.	Soap product and manufacture. Spray drying of soap to control particle size to 40 to 60 mesh.	12
2,154,447 4/18/39	Heyman, W. A.	Fractionating ground coffee for best roast flavor.	8
2,155,971 4/25/39	Houseman, P.	Steam distilling coffee aroma in making soluble coffee.	10 14
2,156,212 4/25/39	Wendt, G. L. & Fronmuller, D.	Collecting roaster gas on instant coffee powder.	14
2,159,027 5/23/39	Jalma, M. M. & Continho, H.	Purifying roasting gases.	8 14
2,159,248 5/23/39	Brabak, J.	Apparatus for desiccating liquids in thin films.	14 14
2,204,896 6/18/40	Kappenberg, W.	Stabilizing coffee extract in glycerol.	10 14
2,217,711 10/15/40	Shappirio, S.	Coffee flavor. Betaine as an antioxidant to improve coffee flavor.	
2,224,942 12/17/40	Weisman, M.	Preparing coffee. R & G coffee coated with coffee extract; dried to seal the particles.	
2,230,031 1/28/41	Fisher, G. A.	Deaerating water for brewing coffee.	
2,236,059 3/25/41	Heuser, H.	Coffee extract. Percolation of R & G coffee under pressure in high column.	10
2,241,726 5/13/41	Krause, G. A.	Process for separating ice from concentrate.	14
2,248,634 7/8/41	Krause, G. A.	Freezing, diffusion, and evaporating method of concentration.	12 14
2,258,567 10/7/41	Epstein, C. H. & Gotthoffer, N. R.	Gelatin flavor powders.	14
2,263,610 11/25/41	Cain, G. H.	Coffee extract. Cold slow extraction of R & G coffee by water.	10
2,270,768 1/20/42	Polin, H. S. & Aims, J. F.	Volatile acids roasting control (A. & P.).	8
2,282,138, 9 5/5/42	Kellogg, J. L.	Precooking R & G coffee. Treat roasted coffee in water with a converting enzyme.	14
2,286,334 6/16/42	Brandt, R. L.	Extraction process with ethylene oxide.	14
2,288,284 6/30/42	Kellogg, J. L.	Coffee extract. Mixing hydrogenated edible oil with brewed coffee to improve flavor and aroma.	14
2,290,470 7/21/42	Hall, J. M.	Co-current spray dryer.	12
2,291,604 8/4/42	Baselt, F. C.	Canning liquid coffee beverage. Extract R & G coffee excluding air; filter; apply vacuum; seal in can; sterilize.	13 14
2,301,901 11/10/42	McKinnis, R. B.	Apparatus for extracting fruit juice. Use of inert gas.	14
2,305,620, 1, 2 12/22/42	Kremers, R. E.	Flavored foods. Add stable non-volatile, non-oxidizable derivative of flavor or aroma bearing constituent of a volatile oil to coffee brew or R & G coffee.	14
2,306,061 12/22/42	Johnston, W, R.	Coffee grinder gas collection in extract at −15 C or lower.	14
2,314,988 3/30/43	Johnston, W. R.	Coffee oil unsaponifiables as antioxidants in drying soluble coffee. Drying conditions specified.	14

Number and Date	Inventors	Title or Description	Chapter[1]
2,317,479 4/27/43	Peebles, D. D. & Manning, P. D. V.	Spray drying corn sugars.	12
2,319,994 5/25/43	Ketchum, W. R.	Refining and preserving citrus fruit juices. Use of CO_2.	14
2,324,526 7/20/43	Morgenthaler, M. R.	Percolation hydrolysis (Inredeco). Extract R & G coffee; cool; add carbohydrate (not sucrose) 60 to 90% of dry solids content of extract; dry.	10 12 14
2,333,027 10/26/43	Morgenthaler, M. R.	Manufacturing soluble, dry extracts. Fifteen meter extraction vessels to filter and remove fat from extract.	10
2,333,333 11/2/43	Peebles, D. D. & Manning, P. D. V.	Spray dryer for corn sugars. Preheating syrup; tangential drying air.	12
2,334,171 11/16/43	Carter, C. W.	Liquid coffee extract. Add moisture absorbing inert substance to R & G coffee in percolator to permit expansion without compacting.	10
2,335,206 11/23/43	Darling, E. R.	Coffee extract. Remove gases and volatiles from roasted coffee, remove CO_2 from gases, return gases to extract. (Hills Bros. Company)	14
2,335,732 11/30/43	Bowen, W. S.	Drying and chilling chamber. Slowing fall of particles in spray drier by upward current of air to give more drying time.	12
2,337,317 12/21/43	Eggert, W. H.	Cooling apparatus for freeze concentration of solutions.	14
2,338,608 1/4/44	Weisberg, M. & Corman, L.	Percolation with high feed water temperature. Extract R & G coffee at 60 to 100 C; cool; store at 0 to 10 C to retain taste, flavor, aroma, and clarity.	10
2,340,235 1/25/44	Tribuno, M. P.	Roasting with glycerin and sugar.	8 14
2,340,721 2/1/44	Whitney, W. R.	Purifying water. Purify solvent (water) from solution by spraying cold solution (near freezing point) on cold surface (below freezing point) to prevent occlusion of impurities in frozen pure solvent.	14
2,340,758 2/1/44	Kappenberg, W. & Rameh, F. J.	Extraction of coffee. Wet R & G coffee with 50 per cent of its weight in water; extract with aqueous coffee extract.	10
2,341,723, 4 2/15/44	Kennedy, D. J.	Roasting green coffee. Treat green coffee with ultraviolet rays 6 min to reduce chlorogenic acid to obtain uniform flavor from different batches.	8
2,343,169 2/29/44	Burkhart, W. S.	Freezing method of concentration.	14
2,345,378 3/28/44	Brandt, R. L.	SO_2 as transfer solvent, R & G to instant coffee.	14
2,350,903 6/6/44	Kellogg, J. L.	Coffee extract enhanced with coffee oil and hydrogenated vegetable oil.	14
2,353,459 7/11/44	Gruber, M. F.	Spray agglomeration. (Inredeco). Design of spray drier.	12
2,360,342 10/17/44	Heyman, W. A.	Solid expanded coffee—corn syrup. Expanded dehydrated mixture of soluble coffee solids, volatile condensable and non-condensable constituents and corn syrup (Granular Foods).	14
2,361,940 11/7/44	Hall, J. M.	Two-stage spray drying.	12
2,367,269 1/16/45	Epstein, C. H. & Gotthoffer, N. R.	Powdered citrus fruit flavors. Use of gelatin.	14
2,368,113 1/30/45	Carter, C. W.	Liquid extracts. Mix finely ground R & G with roasted and flaked coffee while adding water; extract as usual.	10
2,369,847 2/20/45	Olsen, A. G. & Seltzer, E.	Powdered food flavors. Emulsify dry immiscible flavor into sheets of hydrophilic edible colloid (encapsulated flavor).	14
2,379,427 7/3/45	Fetzer, W. R.	Dehydrated coffee. Extract R & G coffee with corn syrup solution.	10 14
2,380,046 7/10/45	Hugeunin, R.	Coffee percolation and hydrolysis. (Inredeco).	10
2,380,092 7/10/45	Weisberg, M.	Coffee product. Two-stage extraction, one at 100 C, the other above 100 C to hydrolyze.	
2,389,732 11/27/45	Kellogg, J. L.	Organic liquids and coffee. Inhibit detrimental bacterial action by taka diastase. (7 claims).	14
2,393,562 1/22/46	Perech, R.	Preparing beverage concentrate. Add soluble salt of carboxymethyl cellulose to coffee extract.	

Number and Date	Inventors	Title or Description	Chapter[1]
2,395,498 2/26/46	Noyes, H. A.	Freeze concentration of plant products.	14
2,398,081 4/9/46	Carter, C. W.	Coffee concentrate. Mix 2 parts liquid coffee extract, 1 part fresh cream, and 1 part evaporated milk; dry.	
2,405,487 8/6/46	Brandt, R. L.	Extraction of R & G coffee with SO_2 and Et_2O. Mix and vibrate intensely at 500 to 5,000 frequency dry soluble coffee powder and liquid water insoluble constituents of roasted coffee to obtain water dispersible solid.	14
2,408,260 9/24/46	Kellogg, J. L.	Making coffee extract. Soak R & G coffee in cold water; freeze concentrate cold extract; extract hot; concentrate extract in vacuum pan; mix, and dry.	14
2,410,157 10/29/46	Fredrickson, W. S.	Processing liquid coffee extract. Extract coffee with cold water (0 to 4 C), then extract at successively higher temperatures; mix various extracts.	
2,416,945 3/4/47	Noyes, H. A.	Concentrating coffee. Extract R & G coffee hot; freeze concentrate; freeze dry partially to get scale-like arrangement of crystals; separate.	14
2,419,031 4/15/47	Pollack, P.	Adding $LiCO_3$ to R & G coffee to protect flavor.	14
2,419,909 4/29/47	Noyes, H. A.	Natural colored fruit juice. Fractional crystallization.	14
2,420,615 5/13/47	Palmer, E. & Schwartz, D. S.	Concentrating coffee extract. Extract R & G coffee with cold distillate from concentrated hot extract, then with hot water; mix.	10 14
2,422,145 6/10/47	Taylor, W. A.	Powdered flavors. Composition of solution of essential oil (e.g., coffee essence), hydroxypolyoxyethylene ether, and higher fatty acid ester.	14
2,424,663 7/29/47	Mantle, H. L.	Removal of water from aqueous solutions by freezing and pressing.	14
2,428,636 10/7/47	Perech, R.	Flavor retention additives. Use of amylopectin glycolate.	14
2,431,496 11/25/47	Natelson, S. & Weiss, M.	Coffee powder. Extract is made to foam under vacuum; foam is frozen and freeze dried.	12 14
2,432,698 12/16/47	Taub, A. & Simone, R. M.	Stabilizing vitamins by antioxidant, (no mention of coffee).	12 14
2,432,759 12/16/47	Heyman, W. A.	Coffee concentrates. Steam R & G coffee; condense volatiles; absorb gases in solvent; extract residual R & G coffee with hot water; mix.	14
2,436,218 2/17/48	Malcolm, W. E.	Freeze concentration of fruit juice.	14
2,437,768 3/16/48	Timberlake, J. F.	Making beverages. Apparatus and method for continuous percolation; R & G coffee moves through apparatus.	
2,443,620 6/22/48	Hubbard, J. W.	Continuous roaster for roasting in 1 to 3 min. Pass green coffee over heat-conducting surface at 500 to 800 F in hot gas stream.	8
2,444,217 6/29/48	Armentrout, A. L.	Vacuum drying green coffee beans, CO_2 roast at 200 lb per sq in.	8
2,448,802 9/7/48	Holzcker, R.	Concentrating aqueous suspensions. Freeze concentration of fruit juice.	14
2,453,109 11/9/48	MacDowell, L. G., Moore, E. L., & Atkins, C. D.	Full flavored fruit juice concentrations. Add fresh juice.	14
2,454,510 11/23/48	Heyman, W. A.	Coffee concentrate. Heat coffee to roasting temperature; quench with corn syrup solution; filter.	
2,457,036 12/21/48	Epstein, A. A.	Coffee concentrate process. Coffee extract fused into melted carbohydrate; cooled and solidified; melting point under 100 C.	14
2,457,315 12/28/48	Milleville, H. P.	Volatile flavor recovery process.	14
2,464,421 3/15/49	Torres, A. S.	Infra-red roast in 1 to 3 min.	8
2,469,553 5/10/49	Hall, J. M.	Single chamber spray dryer.	12
2,478,169 8/9/49	Kellogg, J. L.	Making and bottling carbonated beverages by freezing syrup in bottles.	19
2,480,954 9/6/49	Palmer, R. T.	Dehydration of foods by sublimation. Freeze in electrostatic field.	14

Number and Date	Inventors	Title or Description	Chapter[1]
2,481,470 9/6/49	Cohen, H.	Aromatic coffee extract with ethanol. Extract R & G coffee with alcohol; cool; precipitate fats and separate; extract with water; combine extracts (Medial Labs.).	14
2,482,507 9/20/49	Rentschler, H. C., & Nagy, R.	Sterilizing by ultra-violet light. 0.038 mu w per sq cm for 8 hr.	14
2,494,928 1/17/50	Cohen, H.	Three step solvent extraction of R & G coffee.	14
2,497,501 2/14/50	Himmel, L. B. & Bush, R. V.	Air suspension of green coffee beans in high frequency field to generate heat for roasting.	8
2,497,721 2/14/50	Foulkes, J. H.	Canned liquid coffee. Propylene glycol and sodium phosphate as preservatives.	
2,503,395 4/11/50	Leboeuf, J.	Freeze concentrating apparatus and method.	14
2,504,735 4/18/50	Schwartz, H. W., Hellier, E. G., & Schroeder, A. L.	Dried coffee extract. Vacuum drum drying of coffee extract with foaming at 4 mm Hg and 150 to 200 F for 4 to 8 min. (National Research Corporation).	10 12
2,511,712 6/13/50	Holzer, T.	Partial roast, extraction, drying, and heating of powder. Soluble aromatic coffee extract. Mix green coffee with carbohydrates (glucose, dextrose, or maltose); partially roast; extract; roast residue.	8
2,513,813 7/4/50	Milleville, H. P.	Recovering volatile flavors. Use of rectifying column.	14
2,513,991 7/4/50	Bradbury, S.	Desiccation of aqueous materials from frozen state. Vacuum freeze drying in electrical frequency of 200 megacycles for heating.	14
2,515,730 7/18/50	Ornfelt, J.	Coffee percolation. Extraction of fresh R & G coffee at 15 to 25 C; hydrolysis extraction at 125 to 150 C.	10
2,518,441 8/15/50	Schaeppi, J. H. & Mossimann, W.	Water soluble coffee extract. Remove albumen from coffee extract with $Ca(OH)_2$; filter; add lactose and gum arabic to retain aroma; pH adjusted to 4.7 to 5.4 with tartaric or citric acid.	
2,522,014 9/12/50	Bacot, P. A.	Coffee extract. Low temperature distillation of R & G coffee at 42 C; then extract as usual.	14
2,539,157 1/23/51	Page, P.	Vacuum roast and distillation. Roast under vacuum of 0.001 to 0.005 mm; distill at 350 to 500 C to collect aroma.	8 14
2,542,119 2/20/51	Cole, H. M.	Separation of coffee aroma from oil. Extract R & G coffee with volatile organic solvent; remove fat; add back volatile aromatics to soluble dry power. (General Foods Corporation).	14
2,550,615 4/24/51	Stansbury, J. H.	Method and apparatus for freezing foods. Freeze in liquid medium.	14
2,552,524 5/15/51	Cunningham, G. L.	Apparatus for extracting liquid to form concentrate.	14
2,552,525 5/15/51	Wenzelberger, E. P.	Dehydration. Extract in several tanks; centrifuge to remove solids; return liquid to extraction tanks; filter in tanks.	14
2,555,466 6/5/51	Bogin, H. H. & Feick, R. D.	Food composition (locked-in flavor). Soluble coffee powder and polyvinyl alcohol.	14
2,557,294 6/19/51	Kellogg, J. L.	Flavor-enriched coffee extract. Add coffee oil foots to soluble coffee.	14
2,562,206 7/31/51	Nutting, L.	Steam distilled aroma (Hills Bros. Company).	14
2,563,233 8/7/51	Gilmont, R.	Producing soluble coffee. Extract R & G coffee with solvent; fractionally distill to remove solvent; extract with hot water; combine.	14
2,564,332 8/14/51	Kellogg, J. L.	Soluble beverage extract. Add lecithin to coffee extract; heat to 140 F and dry.	14
2,566,410 9/4/51	Griffin, W. C.	Sorbitol coating of essential oils. (Atlas Powder Company).	14
2,569,217 9/25/51	Bagdigian, N. S.	CO_2 roast, grind, and packaging.	8 13 14
2,573,406 10/30/51	Clough, P. J., Morse, R. S., Stauffer, R. A. & Hellier, E. G.	Acid hydrolysis of spent R & G coffee, vacuum drying (National Research Corporation).	12

Number and Date	Inventors	Title or Description	Chapter[1]
2,585,473 2/12/52	Kennedy, A. B.	Extraction apparatus. Countercurrent extraction.	10
2,587,556 2/26/52	Weiss, M. & Natelson, S.	Coffee concentrate. Apparatus for continuous counter-current extraction; inclined cylinder.	
2,588,922 3/11/52	Haney, E. P.	Coffee flavor. One part asafetida gum resin, four parts edible gelatin, and 7,000 parts R & G coffee ground together improving coffee flavor.	
2,594,385 4/29/52	Blench, R. O.	Roasting in paraffin wax. Immerse green coffee beans in molten paraffin wax which is inert to coffee flavor and aroma; heat, strain, drain, and cool; remove wax.	8
2,607,689 8/19/52	Hale, W. J.	Treating green coffee beans before roasting. Impregnate green coffee with non-toxic oxygen-carrying por-phyrin; roast at 400 F to destroy chlorogenic acid and trigonelline.	8
2,614,043 10/14/52	Lenz, W. G.	Condense volatiles; return to roaster.	8 14
2,620,276 12/2/52	Heyman, W. A.	Packaged coffee drink. Seal coarse R & G coffee (larger than 10 mesh) in container hermetically and store.	13
2,626,558 1/27/53	Stein, J. R.	Preparing coffee. Add positively and negatively charged diatomaceous earth to R & G coffee extract; filter; add nordihydrogualaretic acid; pack in sealed containers.	13
2,629,663 2/24/53	Fogler, B. B. & Nugent, J. B.	Extracting R & G coffee. Continuous countercurrent extraction; R & G coffee moves through spiral pass-ageway which grows larger to accommodate swelling of coffee.	10
2,639,236 5/9/53	Zachary, J. H.	Water extract of alfalfa as coffee substitute.	
2,665,198 1/5/54	Harcourt, G. N.	Solvent extraction of coffee.	14
2,666,707 1/19/54	Beu, E. R.	Recovering esters and other volatile products. Vacuum removal of aroma with gas carrier.	14
2,680,687 6/8/54	Lemonnier, P.	Dry vacuum aroma from R & G coffee.	14
2,687,355 8/24/54	Benner, F. C. & di Nardo, A.	Coffee concentrate. Hydrolyze spent coffee grounds with phosphoric acid solution pH 1.5 to 2.0; neutralize with strongly basic Ca and Mg compounds then with neutral Ca and Mg compounds; filter; mix with first extract and dry. (National Research Corporation).	12
2,689,795 9/21/54	Olenikov, S.	Coffee roast with carbonaceous catalyst.	8
2,712,501 7/5/55	Hale, J. F. (Borden Co.)	Steam roast green coffee at 100 to 350 lb pressure 2 to 15 min.	8
2,720,936 10/18/55	Beu, E. R.	Add-back fruit juice condensates. Apparatus for re-covering volatiles; condense from N_2 stream by re-frigeration.	14
2,734,355 2/14/56	Wenzelberger, E. P.	Apparatus for separating fluids and solids by freezing and suction.	14
2,735,779 2/21/56	Wenzelberger, E. P.	Dehydration by freezing.	14
2,738,276 3/13/56	Blench, R. O.	Aromatization of instant coffee powders. Shower of sol-uble coffee powder dropped through aroma laden inert gas stream with gradually falling temperature.	14
2,746,866 5/22/56	Lee, S.	Inhibiting caking of soluble coffee with calcium gluco-nate.	
2,750,998 6/19/56	Moore, D. P.	Inert gas spray drying.	12 14
2,751,687 6/26/56	Colton, R. F.	Freeze dried coffee pellets.	12 14
2,758,927 8/14/56	Chase, F. A.	Soluble coffee concentrate. Extract green coffee while grinding with water at 60 to 212 F; spray dry; roast the powder.	14
2,765,234 10/2/56	Schmidt, R. G., Raddatz, H. W., & Swedberg, V.	Frozen fruit juice concentration.	
2,765,235 10/2/56	Wenzelberger, E. P.	Separation of ice and fluid.	14

Number and Date	Inventors	Title or Description	Chapter[1]
2,771,364 11/20/56	Chase, F. A. & Laursen, G. E.	Carbonation of coffee extract at 15 to 150 lb pressure before spray drying.	12
2,783,149 2/26/57	Epstein, A. A.	Coffee extract. Extract R & G coffee at 0 to 18 C with water containing CO_2 to displace air in the water, the coffee, and the atmosphere above the coffee.	
2,788,276 4/9/57	Reich, I. M. & Johnston, W. R.	Spray drying flavors. Aqueous extract foamed with air, N_2, and CO_2.	12 14
2,800,001 7/23/57	Wenzelberger, E. P.	Apparatus for dehydration of heat sensitive materials.	14
2,800,457, 8 7/23/57	Green, B. K. & Schleicher, L.	Oil in micro-capsules (National Cash Register Company).	14
2,801,920 8/6/57	Reich, I. M., Redfern, S., Lenney, J. F., & Schimmel, W. W.	Preventing gel in frozen coffee extract with mannanase preparation.	14
2,804,389 8/27/57	Tarasch, L. C.	Preserving macerated coffee with tartaric acid, sodium chloride and magnesium sulfate to solidify and remove fatty waxes.	
2,809,895 10/15/57	Swisher, H. E.	Solid flavoring composition. Corn syrup, essential oil, and antioxidant; extract with organic solvent.	14
2,816,039 12/10/57	Eskew, R. K.	Making powdered fruit juices. Evaporate in thin film under vacuum at 240 to 250 F.	14
2,816,840 12/17/57	Turkot, V. A., Eskew, R. K., & Aceto, N. C.	Full flavored powdered fruit juice. Add essence to concentrated fruit juice under pressure of 15 lb per sq in.	14
2,818,917 1/7/58	Vincent, D. B.	Two-stage drying.	12
2,824,805 2/25/58	Hale, W. J.	Treating coffee. Impregnate green coffee with oxygen-carrying porphyrin, sulphonated amino alcohol, or amidified fatty acids; roast at 400 F to destroy chlorogenic acid and trigonelline. (see 2,607,689). (Borden Company).	
2,826,504 3/11/58	Chase, F. A. & Lee, S.	Heat molten carbohydrate and soluble coffee at 135 to 225 to produce foam.	14
2,834,680 5/13/58	Jenny, H.	Preservation of R & G coffee. Roast; cool; apply vacuum; dry.	8
2,853,387 9/23/58	Nutting, L.	Steam distill R & G coffee; neutralize acidity; extract distillate with solvent; extract grounds with water; mix; dry.	14
2,863,774 12/9/58	Bonotto, M.	Extract roasted and partly roasted coffee. Oxidize latter extract to develop flavor and aroma.	10
2,864,707 12/16/58	Toulmin, H. A.	Dextran-coated particles of soluble coffee.	14
2,872,323 2/3/59	Perech, R.	Extract ground green beans; heat beans in air one hour; filter; dry; roast.	8
2,875,063 2/24/59	Feldman, J. R.	Remove H_2S from aroma with copper leaving other valuable S compounds.	14
2,881,079 4/7/59	Simijian, L. G.	Treat food articles with sound energy to aid subsequent processing.	
2,887,383 5/19/59	Kopf, J. L.	Roasting method. Burn and remove smoke; return gases (Jabez Burns).	8
2,887,390 5/19/59	Coulter, S. T. & Townley, V. H.	Method and apparatus for spraydrying. Conditions of air velocity and temperature are specified.	12
2,888,353 5/26/59	Toulmin, H. A.	Concentrate fruit and vegetable juices by freeze drying.	14 19
2,889,226 6/2/59	Hinkley, D. F.	Instant coffee tablet. Soluble coffee powder, polyethylene glycol, $NaHCO_3$, and alginic acid.	
2,897,084 7/28/59	Peebles, D. D.	Agglomerate soluble coffee by moistening and drying.	
2,899,313 8/11/59	Makower, B. & Schultz, T. H.	Solid flavor composition (locked-in flavor). Use of sugar.	14
2,903,359 9/8/59	Bonotto, M., Webster, R. M., & Gola, J.	Steam volatiles from R & G coffee on to silica gel to remove acid compounds.	14
2,903,371 9/8/59	Toulmin, H. A.	Inert gas guards flavor in fruit juice freeze concentration.	14
2,904,440 9/15/59	Dimick, K. P. & Makower, B.	Extract R & G coffee with organic solvent; add edible oil; remove solvent; incorporate oil and essence into molten sorbitol.	14

Number and Date	Inventors	Title or Description	Chapter[1]
2,906,630 9/29/59	Turkot, V. A., Eskew, R. K., & Aceto, N. C.	Add honey to R & G coffee extract; concentrate; add molten syrup; cool to brittle solid (U.S.D.A.).	14
2,911,308 11/3/59	Smith, P. L.	Inert gas in fruit juice add-back.	
2,915,399 12/1/59	Gugenheim, H. & Stinchfield, R. M.	Extraction with temperature control; intercolumn heaters (General Foods Corporation).	10
2,915,403 12/1/59	Clinton, W. P., Gugenheim, H., & Stinchfield, R., M.	Extraction with temperature control; First inlet 220 to 270 F; Second inlet 250 to 315 F; Third inlet 210 to 270 F; Last outlet 175 to 200 F (General Foods Corporation).	10
2,918,372 12/22/59	Blench, R. O.	Solvent extraction of R & G coffee before spray drying.	12 14
2,929,716 3/22/60	Barch, W. E. & Reich, I. M.	Fatty acids used to cut down instant coffee foam in cup (Standard Brands).	12 14
2,929,717 3/22/60	Eskew, R. K.	Thin film evaporation of concentrated coffee extract.	14
2,931,727,8 4/5/60	Franck, G. & Guggenheim, H.	Concentrated coffee extract. Pelletizing fines in percolation of R & G coffee (General Foods Corporation).	14
2,947,634 8/2/60	Feldman, J. R., Levenson, H. S., & White, W. V.	Distill expressed coffee oil under vacuum (General Foods Corporation).	14
2,949,364 8/16/60	Bilenker, E. N.	Ultrasonic extraction (Curtiss Wright Corporation).	10
2,950,973 8/30/60	Cameron, J. W.	Inert gas extraction and drying (Vitagen).	
2,953,199 9/20/60	Kohlins, W. D., Moore, J. G., & Montgomery, D. B.	Blaw-Knox horizontal spray drier.	12
2,957,519 10/25/60	Walker, A. M.	Box dryer with fines re-agglomeration.	12
2,975,056 3/14/61	Lombardi, E. H.	Sonic coffee foam reduction.	
2,976,158 3/21/61	Morgan, A. I. & Randall, J. M.	Drying instant coffee foam. (U.S.D.A.)	12 14
2,977,231 3/28/61	Fox, I. & Palley, S.	Packaging and dispensing beverage concentrate. Pressure can.	13
2,977,234 3/28/61	Wenzelberger, E. P.	Freeze concentrating juice.	14
2,978,328 4/4/61	Melzard, D. E., Kendall, D. A., & Karas, A. J.	Tea concentrate.	
2,981,629 4/25/61	Ginnette, L. F., Graham, R. P., & Morgan, A. I.	Dehydrating foam on perforated belt. (U.S.D.A.).	12 14
3,021,218 2/13/62	Clinton, W. P. & Pitchon, E.	Stable coffee aroma. Aroma gas condensed below −78 C; warm to vaporize CO_2 at −78 C and purge O_2; warm remaining frost to 70 C in CO_2 freeing aroma constituents from H_2O, O_2, and undesirable aroma components (General Foods Corporation).	14
3,022,173 2/20/62	Tiedemann, H.	Coffee and tea brews (1 to 10 per cent polyvinyl pyrrolidone).	
3,023,111 2/27/62	Huber, E. B.	Freeze concentration of fruit juice.	14

Foreign Patents[2]

Br 172,744 12/19/21	Mocha Mfg. Co.	Coffee essence paste consisting of melted sugar, chicory infusion, R & G coffee, and cocoa or coconut butter.	
Br 246,454 10/14/26	Staudinger, H.	Isolating coffee aromatics.	14
Br 260,960 2/22/28	Staudinger, H.	Artificial coffee oil mercaptans, pyridine, pyrrole, phenols.	14
Br 278,799 10/13/27	Heyman, W. A.	Improved apparatus for freeze concentration of fruit juice.	14
Fr 694,602 12/5/30	Farben, I. G.	Liquid ammonia extraction of R & G coffee.	14 19
Br 383,170 10/10/32	Closman, E. A.	Extracting vegetable matter with trichlorethylene.	14

Number and Date	Inventors	Title or Description	Chapter[1]
Br 413,617 10/10/32	Françon, J.	Coffee paste. High yield, full aroma extraction by grinding coffee in colloid mill with water; add gel to make paste.	
Sw[2] 165,813 3/1/34	Jemac, A. G.	Remove cellulose from coffee extract. Extraction of alkaloids from natural products without loss of character with water charged with CO_2.	
Br 408,613 4/11/34	Ornfeldt, O. & Loew, M.	Treat green coffee with aldehydes to improve taste and aroma.	14
Br 429,474 5/30/35	Krause, G. A.	Process and apparatus for separating liquid mixtures by cooling, crystallization, and centrifuging.	14
Br 438,613 11/14/35	Poultney, S. V.	Coffee extracts. Roast coffee (chicory, cocoa); while hot, place in water; heat under pressure separate by grinding, filtering, and pressing out oils.	
Br 442,232 2/5/36	Gebhardt, K.	Extraction of organic materials. Heat R & G coffee; pre-wet with small amount of water; heat several hours before percolation.	
Au 150,157 7/10/37	Mainl, J.	Coffee extract (Austrian). Powdered R & G coffee is extracted with such a restricted amount of water that subsequent concentration of the extract is unnecessary.	
Br 477,670 1/4/38	Fairweather, H. G. C.	Manufacture of concentrated coffee extract. Scrub difficultly condensible coffee vapors produced during extraction with cold, concentrated coffee extract.	
Br 485,540 5/20/38	Escher, Wyss, Machinenfabriken, A. G.	Continuous crystallization. Grow large ice crystals; skim ice off top.	14
Br 489,062 7/19/38	Societé d'Etudes et Applications Industrielles	Concentrated coffee extract. Percolate R & G coffee; cool; add concentrated acid hydrolisate of spent grounds; spray dry to powder; maltose or maltodextrine may be used.	
Ger 669,185 12/19/38	Krause, G. A.	Freeze concentrate solutions by forming ice layer 5 to 10 mm thick and pressure filtering. See Br 429, 474/35 above.	14
Can 389,192 6/4/40	Johnston, W. R., Landis, Q., Gore, H. C., & Frey, C. N.	Coffee oil unsaponifiables as antioxidants. (26 claims) (Standard Brands).	14
Can 394,579 2/11/41	Johnston, W. R.	Grinder gas adsorption on instant coffee powder. Revive stale, deteriorated liquid compounds containing essential oils from coffee, tea, fruits, etc. by catalytic hydrogenation.	14
Can 399,060 9/2/41	Johnston, W. R.	Coffee character determining method. Determination of O_2 absorption capacity under standard conditions.	8 14
Sw 216,406 12/1/41	Heitzmann, E., Séchaud, F. R., & Zobrist, C.	Apparatus for roasting coffee and recovering volatile aroma constituents from gases.	8 14
Sw 217,126 1/16/42	Societé d'etudes et Applications Industrielles	Preservation of aroma. Soluble carbohydrates (malt, dextrines, 18 per cent of extract) added to extract.	14
Br 548,889 10/28/42	Arndt, W.	Coffee essence. Extract R & G coffee; concentrate under vacuum; add H_2O_2, ozone, or nascent oxygen.	
Br 565,620 11/17/44	Kappenberg, W. & Rameh, F. J. (Coffee Products Corp.)	Extraction of coffee. Pre-wet R & G coffee with $1/2$ to 1 lb water to 1 lb coffee before percolation and compact it to 34 to 45 lb per cu ft; skimmed milk may be used.	10
Br 575,118 2/4/46	Reavell, J. A.	Selective isolation of volatiles from coffee extract.	14
Br 582,918 12/2/46	Granular Foods	Solid expanded coffee—corn syrup. Coffee flavor and aroma added to corn syrup; expanded under heat and 29 in. vacuum to get cellular structure.	14
Sw 250,804 7/1/48	Afico, S. A.	Preservation of aroma of dry, soluble coffee extracts by polyhydric alcohols; mannitol, erythritol or inositol added to extract in amounts equal to coffee solids. See Sw 201,940.	14
Br 614,139 12/9/48	Medial Laboratory	Three-step preparation of aromatic coffee extracts. Hydrocarbon solvents, non-hydrocarbon solvents; water; successive extractions.	14
Sw 255,956 2/1/49	Oswald, E.	Soluble aromatic coffee extract paste.	

Number and Date	Inventors	Title or Description	Chapter [1]
Br 620,383 3/23/49	Theodore, D. T.	Manufacture of coffee concentrate. Exclusion of air.	
Sw 262,262 9/16/49	Germinal, S. A.	Distillation of plant extract of R & G coffee. Coffee distilled in CO_2 at 130 to 150 C; distillate condensed at -25 to -80 C; extract of distillate mixed with sugar.	
Sw 263,267 00/00/49	Medial Laboratory	Ethanol coffee extract. See Sw 272,240/51.	
Br 630,153 10/6/49	Appareils & Evaporateurs Kestner	Soluble coffee powder. Grind green coffee to fine powder; extract with organic solvent; evaporate and recover solvent; extract with water; add residue from solvent to water extract; dry; roast powder in autoclaves. Apparatus and method.	
Sw 264,898 2/1/50	Giradet, A.	Coffee flavor. Same as Fr 963,554/50 below.	14
Fr 963,554 7/13/50	Laguilharre, P. R.	Distilling coffee extracts. Extract R & G coffee; dry with or without sorbitol; or R & G coffee is distilled under vacuum at 130 to 150 C in CO_2; distillate added back to dry powder.	14
Br 640,241 7/19/50	Nyrop, P. & Johan, E.	Stabilizing coffee against oxidation. Use of hexose phosphate and acid 1% of dry content of extract.	
Sw 269,390 10/16/50	Schott-Germinal	Coffee flavor (dry vacuum aroma). Distill R & G coffee at 130 to 150 C; condense at -25 to -80 C; extract with water; mix extract with sugar.	14
Sw 272,240 12/15/50	S. A. Schaeppi, J. H. & Mossimann, W.	Soluble aromatic coffee. Extract R & G coffee with Ca$(OH)_2$ at 100 C; add gum arabic and lactose; adjust pH to 5.0 with tartaric acid; evaporate under vacuum.	14
Sw 272,990 1/15/51	Schott-Germinal, S. A.	Coffee flavor. Extract R & G coffee with alcohol under reflux, then with boiling water; chill alcohol extract and filter; dry both extracts and combine; lactose added.	14
Br 654,950 7/4/51	Giradet, A. & Pouterman, E.	Aromatic vegetable extracts with added carbohydrate. Carry out grinder gases with CO_2; condense by cooling; add to coffee extract with sorbitol or any of several other carbohydrates.	14
Br 658,806 10/10/51	American Home Foods, Inc.	Percolation with controlled temperatures; use of CO_2 in extract; 40% final concentration.	10
Sw 277,290 11/16/51	Schott-Germinal, S. A.	Aromatic extract in hot water.	14
Br 734,546 8/3/55	Hatz, A.	Coffee flavor apparatus. Household coffee maker.	
Br 744,757 2/15/56	Aktieselkabet Niro Atomizer	Coffee extract in carbohydrate malt.	
Can 535,118 1/1/57	Lemonnier, P.	Dry vacuum aroma from R & G coffee. Distill at 50 to 70 C, 20 mm vacuum; condense at -180 C.	14
Dutch 59,834 8/15/57	Rutten, A. M. G.	Synthetic coffee aroma.	14 19
Can 572,026 3/10/59	Clinton, W. P. & Pitchon, E.	Grinder gas aroma recovered, heated, and added to vacuum packed instant coffee can (General Foods Corporation).	13 14
Can 575,517 5/12/59	Tesch, B. H.	Continuous grinding and packaging of R & G coffee. Vacuum and inert gas pressure packaging.	8 13
Can 575,697 5/12/59	Lee, S.	Inhibiting caking of soluble coffee with Ca gluconate.	
Can 576,810 6/2/59	Groneweg, A.	Stabilizing roast coffee beans during grinding; exclusion of air by cold inert gas.	8 14
Can 581,366 8/11/59	Selzer, A. H., Berry, E. G., & Williams, R. E.	Radiant circulatory roasting. Use of inert gas in roaster.	8
Br 822,335 10/21/59	Berghgracht, M.	Vacuum pack in perforated envelope.	13
Br 824,731 12/2/59	Brandl, W.	Atmospheric drying; roasting and cooling under pressure.	8
Br 826,415 1/6/60	Aagaard, B. M.	Grading green coffee beans in water by density. Apparatus for separation of pulps; use of $KMnO_4$.	
Can 593,006, 7 2/23/60	Guggenheim, H. & Stinchfield, R. M.	Percolation with intercolumn heating and controlled temperatures (General Foods Corporation).	10
Br 836,464 6/1/60	Perech, R.	Oxidation of water soluble instant coffee. Heating extract in contact with oxygeneous atmosphere.	

Number and Date	Inventors	Title or Description	Chapter[1]
Br 844,514 8/10/60	Blench, R. O.	Adding volatile solvent to extract before spray drying for better flavor.	14
Can 603,954 8/23/60	Feldman, J. R., Levenson, H. S., & White, W. V.	Vacuum distill expressed coffee oil. Pressure less than 50 mm, temperature less than 100 C. (General Foods Corporation).	14
Can 607,065, 7 10/18/60	Kraut, T., Franck, G., & Guggenheim, H.	Percolation of pelletized expeller cake and fine R & G coffee to reduce pressure losses (General Foods Corporation).	10
Ger 1,113,864 9/14/61	General Foods Corporation	Coffee extracts.	
Ger 1,114,074 9/21/61	General Foods Corporation	Coffee extracts.	
Can 654,696 12/25/62	Clinton W. P. & Pitchon, E.	Aromatizing soluble coffee by passing particles through a contact zone and plating them with aromatizing coffee oil. (General Foods Corporation.)	
Can 656,891 1/29/63	Mishkin, A. R.., Marsh, W. C., & Wertheim, J. H.	Aromatizing powdered coffee by stripping volatiles from roasted coffee, condensieg differentially, and adding them to coffee oil, then adding the latter to powdered coffee. (Inredeco.)	

[1] Also cited in the bibliography of the designated chapter.
[2] Sw denotes Swiss.

Alphabetical List of Inventors

Aagaard, B. M.	Br 826,416/60	Bradbury, S.	2,513,991/50
Aceto, N. C.	2,816,840/57	Brandl, W.	Br 824,731/59
	2,906,630/59	Brandt, R. L.	2,286,334/42
Afico, S. A.	Sw 250,804/48		2,345,378/44
Aims, J. F.	2,270,768/42		2,405,487/46
Aktieselkabet	Br 744,757/56	Bredt, O. P. C.	1,989,077/35
Niro Atomizer		Brougier, A.	617,434/1899
Allison, J. M.	1,093,962/14	Bullard, A. H.	1,026,971/12
American Home Foods	Br 658,806/49	Burkhart, W. H.	2,152,788/39
Incorporated			2,343,169/44
Andresen, H. P.	2,054,689/36	Bush, R. V.	2,497,501/50
Anhaltzer, H.	1,365,443/21	Cain, G. H.	2,263,610/41
Appareils & Evap-	Br 630,153/49	Cameron, J. W.	2,950,973/60
orateurs Kestner		Carreras, L. B.	1,002,137/11
Armentrout, A. L.	2,444,217/48	Carter, C. W.	1,891,383/32
Arndt, W.	Br 548,889/42		2,334,171/43
Ashcroft, J.	119,959/1871		2,368,113/45
Åslund, F.	1,240,020/17		2,398,081/46
		Chalas, A.	1,478,940/23
Åslund, K.	1,214,875/17	Chase, F. A.	2,758,927/56
Atkins, C. D.	2,453,109/48		2,771,364/56
Bacot, P. A.	2,522,014/50		2,826,504/58
Badger, W. L.	1,996,988/35	Clary, P. T.	2,017,892/35
Bagdigian, N. S.	2,569,217/51	Clinton, W. P.	2,915,403/59
Baker, E.	1,738,275/29		Can 572,026/59
Barch, W. E.	2,817,588/57		Can 654,696/62
	2,929,716/60		3,021,218/62
Barotte, H.	340,120/1890	Closman, E. A.	Br 383,170/32
	429,318/1890	Clough, P. J.	2,573,406/51
Baselt, F. C.	2,291,604/42	Cohen, H.	2,481,470/49
Benjamin, G. H.	1,137,431/15		2,494,928/50
Benner, F. C.	2,687,355/54	Cole, H. M.	2,542,119/51
Berghgracht, M.	Br 822,335/59	Colton, R. F.	2,751,687/56
Berry, E. G.	Can 581,366/59	Conroy, A.	268,869/1882
Beu, E. R.	2,666,707/54	Conroy, M.	268,869/1882
	2,720,936/55	Continho, H.	2,159,027/39
Bilenker, E. N.	2,949,364/60	Copes, L. G.	1,932,769/33
Blaine, J. E.	2,765,236/56		1,933,049/33
Blench, R. O.	2,594,385/52	Corman, L.	2,338,608/43
	2,738,276/56	Coulter, S. T.	2,887,390/59
	2,918,372/59	Cunningham, G. L.	2,552,524/51
	Br 844,514/60	Darling, E. R.	2,335,206/43
Boberg, T.	1,214,875/17	Darrah, W. A.	1,525,272/25
	1,240,020/17	Davidson, S. C.	243,521/1881
Bogin, H. H.	2,555,466/51	Davis, J. T.	1,079,474/13
Bonotto, M.	2,863,774/58	Dealey, J.	21,066/1858
	2,903,359/59	Decker,	1,915,410/33
Bowen, W. S.	2,068,841/37	De Simone, M. G.	1,063,188/13
	2,081,909/37	Dimick, K. P.	2,904,440/59
	2,335,732/43	Di Nardo, A.	2,687,355/54
Boyles, F. M.	1,324,538/19	Drake, J. B.	543,299/1895
	2,118,184/38	Dubois, E. F.	2,084,839/37
Brabaek, J.	1,933,960/33	Duke, J. F.	617,322/1899
	2,159,248/39		

349

I. G. Farben,	Fr 694,602/30	MacDowell, L. G.	2,453,109/48
Jackson, W. B.	981,860/11	Mack, H.	1,402,004/22
Jalma, M. M.	2,159,027/39	Mainl, J.	Au 150,157/37
Jemac, A. G.	Sw 165,813/34	Makower, B.	2,899,313/59
Jennings, R. S.	246,274/1881		2,904,440/59
Jenny, H. L.	2,834,680/58	Malcolm, W. E.	2,436,218/48
Johan, E.	Br 640,241/50	Malvezin, P.	1,237,931/17
Johnson, M. O.	1,576,136,7/26	Manning, P. D. V.	2,090,985/37
Johnston, W. R.	Can 389,192/40		2,317,479/43
	Can 394,579/41		2,333,333/43
	Can 399,060/41	Mantle, H. L.	2,424,663/47
	2,306,061/42	Marceau, E. T.	2,152,788/39
	2,314,988/43	Marsh, W. C.	Can 656,891/63
	2,788,276/57	Maxim, H. S.	701,750/02
Kane, P. F.	2,110,732/38	McColl, F. P.	1,535,233/25
Kappenberg, W.	2,204,896/40		1,641,446/27
	2,340,758/44	McComb, W.	1,641,429/27
	Br 565,620/44	McCrosson, J. T.	2,087,602/37
Karas, A. J.	2,978,328/61	McKenna, W.	1,271,761/18
Kato, S.	735,777/03	McKinnis, R. B.	1,903,362/33
Kellogg, E.	1,932,769/33		2,301,901/42
Kellogg, J. L.	1,605,115/26	Medial Lab.	Br 614,139/48
	2,281,138,9/42		Sw 263,267/49
	2,288,284/42	Mellon Institute	1,903,362/33
	2,350,903/44	Melzard, D. E.	2,978,328/61
	2,389,732/45	Merkel, H.	2,036,345/36
	2,408,260/46	Merrell, I. S.	1,157,947/15
	2,478,169/49	Meyer, G. L. M.	2,043,443/36
	2,557,294/51	Meyers, A. W.	1,836,931/31
	2,564,332/51	Milleville, H. P.	2,457,315/48
Kendall, D. A.	2,978,328/61		2,513,813/50
Kennedy, A. B.	2,585,473/52	Mishkin, A. R.	Can 656,891/63
Kennedy, D. J.	2,341,723,4/44	Mocha Mfg. Co.	Br 172,744/21
Ketchum, W. R	2,319,994/43	Montgomery, D. B.	2,953,199/60
Klein, E.	1,742,261/30	Monti, E.	955,659/10
Kohlins, W. D.	2,953,199/60		1,465,020/23
Kopf, J. L.	2,887,383/59		1,546,669/25
Krause, G. A.	Br 429,474/35	Moore, D. P.	2,750,998/56
	Ger 669,185/38	Moore, E. L.	2,453,109/48
	2,241,726/41	Moore, J. G.	2,953,199/60
	2,248,634/41	Morgan, A. I.	2,976,158/61
Kraut, T.	2,915,403/59		2,981,629/61
	2,931,727,8/60	Morgenthaler, M. R.	2,324,526/43
	Can 593,006,7/60		2,333,027/43
	Can 607,065,7/60	Morse, R. S.	2,573,406/51
Kremers, R. E.	2,305,620,1,2/42	Mossimann, W.	2,518,441/50
Laguilharre, P. R.	Fr 963,554/50		Sw 272,240/50
Landis, Q.	Can 389,192/40	Nagy, R.	2,482,507/49
Laursen, G. E.	2,771,364/56	Nardo, Di, A.	2,687,355/54
Leboeuf, J.	2,503,395/50	Natelson, S.	2,431,496/47
Lee, S.	2,746,866/56		2,587,556/52
	2,826,504/58	Noyes, H. A.	2,395,498/46
	Can 575,697/59		2,416,945/47
Lemonnier, P.	2,680,687/54		2,419,909/47
	Can 535,118/57	Nugent, J. B.	2,629,663/53
Lenney, J. F.	2,801,920/57	Nutting, L.	2,562,206/51
Lenz, W. J.	2,614,043/52		2,853,387/58
Levenson, H. S.	2,947,634/60	Nyrop, P.	Br 640,241/50
	Can 603,954/60	Olenikov, S.	2,689,795/54
Loew, M.	Br 408,613/34	Olsen, A. G.	2,369,847/45
Lombardi, E. H.	2,975,056/61		
Lorand, E. J.	1,866,414,5/32		

Walker, A. M.	2,957,519/60		
Washingtom, G.	1,504,459/24		2,800,001/57
Webster, R. M.	2,903,359/59	White, W. V.	2,977,234/61
Weisberg, M.	2,338,608/44		2,947,634/60
	2,380,092/45		Can 603,954/60
Weisman, M.	2,224,942/40	Whitney, W. R.	2,340,721/44
Weiss, M.	2,431,496/47	Williams, R. E.	Can 581,366/59
	2,587,556/52	Williams, W. M.	1,770,118/30
Wendt, G. L.	1,925,159/33	Willison, W.	1,535,233/25
	2,071,011/37	Winter, H.	997,431/11
	2,149,876/39		
	2,156,212/39	Wyss (Escher M. A. G.)	Br 485,540/38
Wenneis, J. N.	2,088,622/37	Zachary, J.	2,639,236/53
Wenzelberger, E. P.	2,552,525/51	Zobrist, C.	Sw 216,406/41
	2,734,355/56	Zorn, W. M.	1,507,410/24
	2,735,779/56		1,636,890/27
	2,765,235/56		1,999,712/35
Wertheim, J. H.	Can 656,891/63		

Sources of Information About Coffee

BOOKS

ANON. 1956. Coffee. 56 p. Merrill, Lynch, Pierce, Fenner, and Beane. New York.
ANON. 1954. Investigation of coffee prices. 300 p. U.S. Federal Trade Comm. Washington, D.C. (out of print–available in some libraries).
CHENEY, R. H. 1925. Species Coffea. 224 p. New York Univ. Press, New York.
CIUPKA, P. 1931. Coffee Pocketbook. O. M. Verlag, Hamburg Germany.
CIUPKA, P. 1949. Coffee, Substitutes and Additives. Bleckede (Elbe), Meissner, Germany.
CLANCEY, D. J. (judge) 1949. (Feb. 1 to 11) Patent Case: Inredeco vs Standard Brands. U.S. District Court, South District, New York.
COSTE, R. 1955. Coffee Culture and Coffees of the World. Tome 1, 384 p.; Tome 2,896 p. G. P. Maisonneuve et La Rose, 11 rue Victor Cousin, Paris.
HAARER, A. E. 1962. Modern Coffee Production. 495 p. Leonard Hill (Books) Ltd., London.
JACOBS, M. B. 1951. Chemistry and Technology of Food and Food Products. Vol. II, Coffee & Tea, p. 1656–1687. Interscience Div. John Wiley and Sons, New York.
KIRK, R. E., and OTHMER, D. F. 1949 and 1960 supplement. Encyclopedia of Chemical Technology. Vol. 3, Caffeine; Vol. 4, Coffee, and Supplement, Instant Coffee. Interscience Div. John Wiley and Sons, New York.
KOEHLER, F. A. 1957. Coffee for the Armed Forces. 134 p. U.S. Dept Army, Office of Quartermaster General, Washington, D.C.
LINDER, M. W. 1955. Coffee. 156 p. Verlag A. W. Hayn's Erben, Berlin.
MACKAYE, P. 1942. The Coffee Man's Manual. 75 p. Coffee & Tea Industries, 106 Water St., New York.
MARTINEZ, A., and JAMES, C. N. 1960. Coffee Bibliography of the Publications available in the Library of the Institute. 637 p. Inter-American Institute of Agricultural Sciences, Turrialba, Costa Rica.
OTIS MCALLISTER AND COMPANY. 1954. Coffee Facts. 140 p. Tea & Coffee Trade Journal, 79 Wall Street, New York.
PRESCOTT, S. C. 1923. Investigation of Coffee. Massachusetts Institute of Technology, Cambridge, Mass.; Reprinted by Jabez Burns & Sons, New York.
UKERS, W. A. 1962–63. Tea & Coffee Buyers' Guide. 508 p. Tea & Coffee Trade J., 79 Wall Street, New York.
UKERS, W. A. 1948. The Romance of Coffee. 280 p. Tea & Coffee Trade J., 79 Wall Street, New York.
UKERS, W. A. 1922 and 1935. All About Coffee. 818 p. Tea & Coffee Trade J., 79 Wall Street, New York.
U. N. AND F.A.O. 1958. Coffee in Latin America–Columbia and El Salvador. 1956. Coffee in Latin America–Brazil, two parts. United Nations Publications, New York.
URIBE, A. 1954. Brown Gold. 237 p. Random House, New York.
WILBAUX, R. 1956. Coffee Culture in the Belgian Congo. La Direction de L'Agriculture des Forets de L'levage. Brussells, Belgium.
WELLMAN, F. L. 1961. Coffee: Botany, Cultivation, and Utilization. 488 p. Interscience Div. John Wiley and Sons, New York.
WINTON, A. L. and WINTON, K. B. 1939. Structure and Composition of Foods. Vol. IV, p. 139–162. John Wiley and Sons, New York.
WICKIZER, V. D. 1943. The World Coffee Economy. Stanford Univ. Palo Alto California.

PERIODICALS

Tea & Coffee Trade J., 79 Wall St., New York.
Coffee & Tea Industries, 106 Water St., New York.
World Coffee & Tea, 129 Front St., New York.
George Gordon Paton & Co., Pine St., New York.
Coffee roasting company publications, e.g., Maxwell House Messenger, What's Brewing and Folger Way.
Coffee company annual reports, e.g., General Foods Corporation, Unilac (Nestlé), Standard Brands, Bordens.
Annual coffee crop estimates for world. U.S. Dept. Agriculture, Washington, D.C.
Quarterly coffee roasting reports (including soluble coffee) U.S. Dept. Commerce, Bureau of Census, Washington, D.C.
Coffee Annual. Pan American Coffee Bureau, 120 Wall St., New York.
Food magazines such as Food Engineering, Food Processing, Food Science, Food Technology.
General publications such as Time, Business Week, Chemical & Engineering News, Newspapers.
Specialized publications such as Modern Packaging, Perfumery & Essential Oil Record, J. American Oil Chemists.

SOCIETIES DEALING WITH COFFEE

National Coffee Association.[1]
Pan American Coffee Bureau.[1]
Coffee Brewing Institute (C.B.I)[1].
Brazilian Coffee Institute.[1]
National Federation of Coffee Growers of Colombia.[1]
Mexican Coffee Institute.[1]
Guatemalan Coffee Bureau, 111 Wall St., New York.
Salvador Coffee Growers' Association.[1]
Many individual coffee growing countries have representative offices in New York City and in the capital cities of their own countries.
European Coffee Bureau, Rue Capitaine Crespel No. 34, Brussels 5, Belgium.
Coffee Publicity Assoc. Ltd., 10 Eastcheap, London, E.C.3.
Related societies, e.g., Can Mfg. Institute, Glass Container Mfg. Institute, National Resturant Assoc., Nat'l Automatic Merchandising Assoc.
United Nations and the Food & Agricultural Organization.

OTHER SOURCES

Equipment suppliers.
Coffee processing engineering firms and consultants.
Green coffee exporters and importers.
Coffee roasters, packers (private label), and soluble coffee processors.
Port Authorities.
Research laboratories: A. D. Little, Cambridge, Mass.; Evans Research & Development Corp., New York, N.Y.; Mellon Institute, Pittsburgh, Pa.; Southern Research Institute, Birmingham 5, Ala.; Southwest Research Institute, San Antonio, Tex.; Mid West Research Institute, Kansas City, Mo.; Stanford Research Institute, Palo Alto, Calif.
Universities with Food Technology Departments: e.g. Massachusetts Institute of Tech.; Cornell Univ., Ithaca, N.Y.; Illinois Inst. of Tech., Chicago, Ill.; University of California, Davis, Calif.; Michigan State Univ., E. Lansing, Mich.; Ohio State Univ., Columbus, Ohio; Oregon State College, Corvallis, Ore.; Rutgers Univ., New

---

[1] 120 Wall St., New York 5, New York.

Brunswick, N.J.; Texas A. & M. College, College Station, Tex.; Univ. Florida, Gainesville, Fla.; Univ. Georgia, Athens, Ga.; Univ. Illinois. Urbana, Ill.; Univ. Maryland, College Park, Md.; Univ. Mass., Amherst, Mass.; Univ. Minnesota, St. Paul, Minn.; Univ. Missouri, Columbia, Mo.; Univ. Tennessee, Knoxville, Tenn.; Univ. Wisconsin, Madison, Wis.; Virginia Polytechnic Inst., Blacksburg, Va.

EXHIBITS

Coffee and Coffee By-Products at Each Process Step

Cherry fruit
Beans in hull (pergamino)
Hulls
Husks
Silver skins
Green coffee beans
Roast coffee beans: light, medium, dark, French and Italian
Grinds: regular, drip and fine; also pulverized
Instant coffee powder (spray dried and belt dried)
Extracted coffee grounds
Equivalent grounds mineral ash

CHEMICALS IN COFFEE

Volatiles

Acids—acetic, propionic, butyric, valeric
Aldehydes—acet, propyl, butyl, valer
Ketones—ketone, methylethyl, penetanone, diactyl
Ketone-alcohols—acetol, acetoin
Esters—methyl formate, methyl acetate, methyl propionate, propyl formate
Sulfides—hydrogen, dimethyl, methyl mercaptan, thiophene
Cyclic—furan, methyl furan, pyridine
Amines—trimethyl, dimethyl, ammonia
Hydrocarbons—isoprene
Unsaturates—acrolein

Non-Volatiles

	Soluble coffee, per cent	Roast coffee, per cent
Chlorogenic acid	17	7
Caramel	56	23
Mineral ash	12	3.5
Trigonelline	3	1
Caffeine	4	1.2
Oil	0.1	10
Caffeic acid	0.8	0.3
Quinic acid	0.8	0.3
Citric acid	1.5	0.6
Malic acid	1.5	0.6
Tartaric acid	1.3	0.5
Pyruvic acid	0.1	0.06
Guiacol	...	...
Nicotinic Acid	...	...

TYPES OF COFFEE BREWING APPARATUS

Steeping and straining or decanting
Boiling (driving off volatile flavors and aromas)

Percolation (recycling brew over spent grounds in air)
Drip (water once through shallow grounds bed)
Vacuum (slurry with straining)
Cold extractor (similar to drip but regulated cold water flow)
Pressure entraction with hot water (commercial soluble coffee)
Urn (batch rinsing of solubles from grounds in bag)
Tape (rinsing solubles from 1 cup equivalent of R & G coffee)
Espresso—domestic (upward or downward hot water/steam flow).   One cup per cycle.

Useful Tables

Table 103 is intended to give an overall view of the coffee industry from a financial standpoint, and to indicate the order of magnitude of its most important elements. It is obvious that costs and prices are constantly changing and will always vary considerably with the particular situation under consideration. The table is designed to give a sense of proportion in the whole picture. In many instances, the figures are given to show methods of calculation and should not be regarded as in any way precise. Statistics are lacking for items left blank.

TABLE 103

FINANCIAL ASPECTS OF COFFEE AND RELATED INDUSTRIES

		Estimated	
		Cost of Green Coffee, U.S. $ per lb	Annual World-Wide Millions, U.S. $
1.	Growing coffee cherries	0.15	300
2.	Transportation: man, mule, ox cart, truck, ship, plane	0.04	80
3.	Taxation, fees, duties, insurance, loans, etc. (varies greatly from country to country)	0.10	200
4.	Engineering and construction	...	...
5.	Processing green bean: fermentation, drying, milling, grading, and bagging	0.035	70
	(a) Labor		
	(b) Machinery: carts, pulpers, tanks, pumps, drying terraces, driers, hullers, huskers, graders, boilers, conveyors, baggers, sorters, etc.		
	(c) Materials: utilities, fuels, bags, stencils, chemicals, lubricants, wood, concrete, steel, etc.		
	(d) Buildings: land, surfaced yards, drainage, fencing, utility runs, warehousing, etc.		
6.	Exporters and importers: insurance, cables, etc.	0.04	80
7.	Processing roast bean: cleaning, conveying, blending, roasting, storing, grinding, extraction, and drying.	0.20	400
	(a) Labor		
	(b) Machinery: office, cleaners, blenders, roasters, incinerators, grinders, weighers, fillers, sealers, instruments, conveyors, etc.		
	(c) Materials: utilities, fuels, coolants, packaging laminates, cartons, bags, cans, jars, adhesives, caps, labels, packets, etc.		
	(d) Buildings: land, surfaced yards, drainage, fencing, utility runs, warehousing, etc.		
8.	Advertising: newspapers, magazines, radio, television, premiums, discounts, etc.	0.05	100
9.	Associations[1]: NCA, PACB, CBI, IBC, and others	...	...

358

TABLE 103 (Continued)

10.	Research and Development	. . .	. . .
11.	Distributor and retailer	0.09	180
12.	Brewing and dispensing equipment: water purifiers and heaters, filters, flasks, urns, cups, detergents, etc.	0.005	10

For the remaining items, the following assumptions are made:
Annual U.S. green coffee use .... 2 billion lb
Yield of R & G coffee .... 1.6 billion lb
Yield of brewed coffee from R & G coffee .... 50 cups per lb
Commercial sale price of coffee .... 10¢ per cup

		%	Millions of lb Green Coffee	Millions of lb R & G Coffee	Billions of Cups	Estimated Cost of Green Coffee, U.S. $ per lb	Estimated Annual United States Millions, U.S. $
13.	Vending machine sales	0.5	10	8	0.4	4.00	40
	Cost of machinery					5.00	50
14.	Restaurant sales	10.0	200	160	8.0	4.00	800
15.	Domestic use	89.5	1790	1432	71.6	0.80	1432
		100.0	2000	1600	80.0		
16.	Dairy cream and milk. Assume: 20 ml per cup; 50 cups per qt cream; 33¢ per qt; 1 billion qt; $333 million; 1250 million lb green coffee					0.16	333
17.	Sugar. Assume: 10 gm sugar per cup (all cups); 1 lb sugar per lb. green coffee; 10¢ per lb sugar					0.10	200
18.	Cost of fuel to bring water to boil. Assume: 1.6 billion lb. R & G coffee; 40 billion lb. water; 150 F temperature rise; 6,000 billion Btu; fuel oil 140,000 Btu per gal; 40 million gal; 25¢ per gal					0.005	10

[1] National Coffee Association, Pan American Coffee Bureau, Coffee Brewing Institute, Brazilian Coffee Institute, all at 120 Wall St., New York.

TABLE 104

UNIT CONVERSION FACTORS

Length	One centimeter (cm) = 10^{10} micromicrons (mu mu) = 10^8 Angstroms (A) = 10^7 millimicrons (m mu) = 10^4 microns (mu) = 10 millimeters (mm) = 0.3937000 inch (in.). One meter (m) = 100 cm = 39.37000 in. = 3.280833 ft = 1.09361 yard (yd). One kilometer (km) = 1,000 m = 0.62137 statute mile. One statute mile = 5280 feet (ft) = 1,760 yd = 1.60935 km. One nautical mile (1 min of arc at equator) = 1.1516 statute mile = 6080.2 ft. One ft = 0.3048006 m. One in. = 2.540005 cm. One rod = 16.5 ft.
Area	One sq mile = 640 acres = 2.59000 sq km. One acre = 160 sq rods = 4,840 sq yd = 43,560 sq ft = 0.404687 hectares (ha) = 4046.9 sq m = 208.71 ft squared. One ha = 100 ares = 2.471044 acres = 100 m squared. One sq ft = 929.0341 sq cm. One sq in. = 6.4516258 sq cm.
Volume	One U.S. gallon (gal) = 3.78533 liters (l) = 231.00 cu in. = 0.83268 British gal. One gal water at 59 F (15 C) weighs 8.337 pound (lbs). One British gal = 1.20094 U.S. gal. One U.S. quart (qt) = 0.946 l. One l = 1,000 milliliters (ml) = 1.056710 qt = 0.26418 U.S. gal. One U.S. qt = 32 fluid ounces (fl oz). One fl oz = 29.6 ml. One cu ft = 28.316 l = 7.481 U.S. gal. One cu m = 35.314445 cu ft = 1.307943 cu yd.

TABLE 104 (*Continued*)

UNIT CONVERSION FACTORS

Weight	One hundredweight (cwt) = 100 lb avoirdupois (avdp) U.S. = 112 lb avdp U.K. One oz avdp = 28.349527 grams (gm) = 437.5 grains (gr) avdp. One gm = 1,000 milligrams (mg) = 15.4324 gr. One lb = 7,000 gr. One Spanish lb = 1.014 lb avdp. One arroba = 12.5 kilogram (kg). One quintal = 100 lb avdp or 100 Spanish lb according to local custom.
Velocity	One ft per second (sec) = 0.681818 miles per hour (hr) = 1.09828 km per hr.
Density	One gm per ml = 62.426 lb per cu ft = 1,685.50 lb per cu yd = 2,204.55 lb per cu m = 8.345 lb per gal = 1000 kg per cu m.
Pressure	One atmosphere (atm) = 14.697 lb per sq in. (psi) = 1.0332 kg per sq cm = 760.00 mm = 29.921 in. of mercury (Hg) at 32 F (0 C) = 10.295 m = 33.899 ft of water at 39.1 F (3.94 C). One kg per sq cm = 14.223 psi. One psi = 0.070307 kg per sq cm.
Power	One horsepower (hp) = 745.70 watts (w) = 1.0139 metric hp = 178.130 gm calories (gm-cal) per sec = 0.7070 British thermal unit (Btu) per sec. One boiler horsepower (bhp) = 33,500 Btu per hr = 34.5 lb water per hr evaporated to steam from and at 212 F (100 C). One ton of refrigeration = 200 Btu per min = 12,000 Btu per hr = 288,000 Btu per 24 hr = latent heat of freezing of 1 ton of water frozen in 24 hr.
Heat	One Btu (1 lb water 1 deg F, mean value 32 to 212 F) = 252.00 gm-cal (1 gm water 1 deg C mean value) = 0.25200 kg-cal = 778 foot-pounds (ft-lb) One kilowatthour (kwhr) = 3413 Btu. One Btu per lb = 0.5556 kg-cal per kg = 0.5556 gm-cal per gm.
Heat Flow	One gm-cal per sec per sq cm = 13,272 Btu per hr per sq ft = 4.186 w per sq cm.
Heat Conductivity	One gm-cal per sec per sq cm per cm thickness per deg C = 4.186 w per sq cm per cm per deg C = 2,903 Btu per hr per sq ft per in. per deg F.

TABLE 105

RELATIONS BETWEEN TEMPERATURE, VAPOR PRESSURE, AND LATENT HEAT OF VAPORIZATION OF WATER[1]

Temperature		Vapor Pressure			Latent Heat	
F	C	mm Hg	psia[2]	kg/cm²	Btu/lb	kg-cal/kg
32	0	4.6	0.0886	0.00623	1072	595
77	25	23.7	0.4581	0.03221	1048	582
122	50	92.3	1.7849	0.12549	1023	568
167	75	289.0	5.589	0.3329	997	554
212	100	760.0	14.697	1.0333	970	539
338	170	5937.0	114.79	8.0705	880	489

[1] From steam tables.
[2] Absolute pressure in pounds per square inch.

TABLE 106

BOILING TEMPERATURES OF WATER AND BAROMETRIC PRESSURES AT VARIOUS ALTITUDES

Altitude		Temperature		Pressure		
ft	m	F	C	mm Hg	in. Hg	psia
0	000	212.0	100.0	760	29.92	14.70
3,000	914	206.4	96.9	677	26.65	13.09
5,000	1524	202.6	94.8	629	24.76	12.16
7,000	2134	198.8	92.7	582	22.91	11.25

TABLE 107

STEAM GAUGE PRESSURES AT VARIOUS ALTITUDES

Altitude		Pounds Per Square Inch			
ft	m	212 F/100 C	230 F/110 C	248 F/120 C	260 F/127 C
0	000	0	6.1	14.1	20.7
2,000	610	1.0	7.1	15.1	21.7
4,000	1219	2.0	8.1	16.1	22.7
6,000	1829	2.9	9.0	17.0	23.6

TABLE 108

ALKALINITY AND HARDNESS OF VARIOUS UNITED STATES WATER SUPPLIES[1]

Lake Waters From 8 Large Lakes, results in ppm	Lake Superior, Sault Ste. Marie, Mich.	Lake Huron, Port Huron, Mich.	Lake Erie, Buffalo, N.Y.	Lake Ontario, Toronto, Ont., Canada	Lake Mich- igan, Chicago, Ill.	Yellow- stone Lake, Nevada	Lake Champlain, New York & Vermont	Lake Oke- chobee, Florida
Total hardness as CaCO3	46	89	109	123	125	23	48	107
Calcium hardness as CaCO3	33	60	78	89	80	22	36	78
Magnesium hardness as CaCO3	13	29	31	34	45	1	12	29
Alkalinity as CaCO3	46	82	94	94	122	42	51	93
Sodium + potassium as Na	3	4	7	8	3	20	6	18
Chlorides as Cl	1	3	9	16	2	9	1	28
Sulfates as SO4	2	6	13	22	7	8	7	7
Nitrates as NO3	.5	.4	.3	1.3	...	..	..	.1
Iron as Fe	.06	.04	.07	.05	.03	..	..	.1
Silica as SiO2	7	12	6	8	5	42	1	8

Hardness of Nine Rivers	Average	Maximum	Minimum
Willamette at Salem	19	27	12
Raritan at Bound Brook	46	56	29
Hudson at Hudson	69	89	45
Potomac at Cumberland	79	149	41
Iowa at Iowa City	203	269	82
Missouri near Florence	246	412	154
Smoky Hill near Lindsborg	376	510	209
Brazos near Waco	481	652	176
Arkansas near Deerfield	721	1008	292

High Sodium Alkalinity Waters, results in ppm	Bryan, Tex., Well	Lufkin, Tex., Private Well	Waverly, Kan., Well	Cristfield, Md., Private Well
Sodium alkalinity as CaCO3	121	170	280	460
Total hardness as CaCO3	12	7	24	0
Calcium hardness as CaCO3	8	5	15	0
Magnesium hardness as CaCO3	4	2	9	0
Total alkalinity as CaCO3	133	177	304	460
Free carbon-dioxide as CO2	0	0	0	0
Chlorides as Cl	18	6	14	54
Sulfates as SO4	2	26	74	42
Iron as Fe	.5	.2	.1	.1
Silica as SiO2	35	12	7	0

[1] From Permuti Water Conditioning Handbook (1949).

(TABLE 108 Continued)

COMPOSITION OF TYPICAL U.S. WATER SUPPLIES[2]

					Composition, Parts per Million							
Location	Total Dissolved Solids	SiO₂	Fe	Ca	Mg	Na	K	HCO₃	SO₄	Cl	NO₃	Total Hardness CaCO₃
Augusta, Me.	31	3.8	0.01	5.0	1.0	2.4	0.8	15	5.8	1.4	0.50	17
Boston, Mass.	43	2.1	0.12	4.4	1.0		3.9	16	9.8	3.2	0.31	15
Providence, R.I.	54	11	.05	12	0.5	<5		17	12	4.4	0.53	32
New York, N.Y	31	2.4	0.14	5.8	1.4	1.7	0.7	14	9.7	2.0	.54	20
Trenton, N.J.	70	9.0	.07	12	3.3		5.4	46	12	2.9	1.1	44
Philadelphia, Pa.	99	2.4	.01	17	6.4	6.6	2.1	54	25	10	4.5	69
District of Columbia	130	7.0	2.7	34	1.9		6.8	79	34	5.2	...	93
Miami, Fla.	191	9.0	.02	35	4.8	12	1.5	47	61	20	4.5	107
Chicago, Ill.	157	6.4	0.2	34	9.7		5.1	146	12	4.5	...	125
St. Louis, Mo.	228	8.0	2.5	21	7.5	36		48	94	18	4.9	83
New Orleans, La.	158	7.8	...	17	7.1	23		45	43	28	...	72
Minneapolis, Minn.	210	9.7	0.07	44	15		4.0	167	36	3.8	.20	172
Omaha, Neb.	334	12	2.2	44	12	50		130	138	12	...	159
Tulsa, Okla.	98	4.0	0.1	30	1.3		4.7	93	7.5	4.5	Trace	80
Ponca City, Okla.	1005	8.5	0.1	143	20	157		306	133	276	...	440
Dallas, Tex.	1119	15	13	14	3.0	367		451	382	88	...	47
Los Angeles, Calif.	421	...	0	75	21	46		223	130	39	...	274
Tacoma, Wash.	76	25	.29	7.9	4.4	4.1	1.4	38	4.9	4.0	5.3	38

[2] From Kunin, R. 1958. Ion Exchahge Resins. John Wiley and Sons. New York.

TABLE 109

WATER ANALYSES CONVERSION UNITS (EQUIVALENTS OF CaCO₃)

	ppm	gr/gal U.S.	gr/gal English
Parts per million or mg/liter	1	0.058	0.07
Grains per U.S. gallon or German degrees (practically)	17.1	1.0	1.2
Grains per English gallon or Clark degrees	14.3	0.83	1.0

One French degree = one part per 100,000.

TABLE 110

SCREEN EQUIVALENTS

	Sieve Openings			
Screen No.	U.S. Standard Screens		Tyler Screens	
	in.	mm	mm	in.
8	0.0937	2.38	2.362	0.0929
10	0.0787	2.00	1.651	0.065
12	0.0661	1.68	1.397	0.055
14	0.0555	1.41	1.168	0.0459
16	0.0469	1.19	0.991	0.039
18	0.0394	1.00	...	...
20	0.0331	0.84	0.833	0.0328
25	0.0280	0.71 (24-mesh)	0.701	0.0276
30	0.0232	0.59 (28-mesh)	0.589	0.0232
35	0.0197	0.50	0.417	0.0164
40	0.0165	0.42 (42-mesh)	0.351	0.0138
45	0.0138	0.35	...	...
50	0.0117	0.297 (48-mesh)	0.295	0.0116
60	0.0098	0.250	0.246	0.0097
70	0.0083	0.210	...	...
80	0.0070	0.177	0.175	0.0069
100	0.0059	0.149	0.147	0.0058
200	0.0029	0.074	0.047	0.00185
325	0.0017	0.044	...	...

TABLE 111

ABBREVIATED STEAM TABLE

Absolute Pressure, lb per sq in.	Temperature F	C	Specific Volume, cu ft per lb-steam	Latent Heat of Evaporation, Btu per lb
1	102	39	334	1036
14.7	212	100	26.8	970
65	298	148	6.7	912
115	338	170	3.9	880
165	366	186	2.75	857
215	388	198	2.13	837
265	406	208	1.75	822

TABLE 112

TEMPERATURE CONVERSION CENTIGRADE/FAHRENHEIT

F	C	F	C	F	C	F	C
−459	−273	−166	−110	115	46	421	216
−454	−270	−148	−100	133	56	482	250
−436	−260	−130	−90	151	66	572	300
−418	−250	−112	−80	169	76	662	350
−400	−240	−94	−70	187	86	752	400
−382	−230	−76	−60	205	96	842	450
−364	−220	−58	−50	223	106	932	500
−346	−210	−40	−40	241	116	1022	550
−328	−200	−22	−30	259	126	1112	600
−310	−190	−4	−20	277	136	1202	650
−292	−180	14	−10	295	146	1292	700
−274	−170	25	−4	313	156	1382	750
−256	−160	34	1	331	166	1472	800
−238	−150	43	6	349	176	1562	850
−220	−140	61	16	367	186	1652	900
−202	−130	79	26	385	196	1742	950
−184	−120	97	36	403	206	1832	1000

Conversion Formulas:

$$C = \frac{5}{9}(F - 32) \qquad F = 1.8C + 32$$

TABLE 113

FREEZING TEMPERATURES OF SALT (NACL) BRINES

Approximate Salt, Per Cent	Freezing Temperature F	C	Specific Gravity	Grams NaCl per Liter Solution
5	24.8	−4	1.034	51.6
10	19.4	−7	1.071	107.1
15	12.2	−11	1.108	166.0
20	6.8	−14	1.148	230
25	−0.4	−18	1.189	292

TABLE 114

SPECIFIC GRAVITY OF AMMONIA 20 C/4 C

Specific Gravity	°Baumé	Per Cent NH₃	Grams NH₃ per Liter	Normality
0.977	13.1	5	49	2.75
0.958	16.2	10	96	5.62
0.923	21.7	20	185	10.84
0.892	27.0	30	268	15.7

TABLE 115

GAUGE AND THICKNESS U.S. STANDARD SHEET METAL

Gauge No.	Inches	Millimeters
3	0.250	6.35
6	0.203	5.16
8	0.172	4.37
10	0.141	3.58
12	0.109	2.77
14	0.078	1.98
16	0.062	1.57
18	0.050	1.27
20	0.0375	0.95
22	0.0312	0.79
24	0.0250	0.64

TABLE 116

SPECIFIC GRAVITY OF SOLUTIONS HEAVIER THAN WATER

°Baumé	Twadell	Specific Gravity	Per Cent by Weight				
			H₂SO₄	HCl	HNO₃	NaOH	Na₂CO₃
5	7.2	1.036	5.3	7.2	...	3.2	3.4
10	14.8	1.074	10.8	14.8	12.9	6.6	7.0
15	23.0	1.115	16.4	22.9	19.4	10.3	10.7
20	32.0	1.160	22.3	31.5	26.2	14.4	...
25	41.6	1.208	28.3	41.7	33.4	18.7	...
30	52.2	1.261	34.6	...	41.3	23.5	...
35	63.6	1.318	41.3	...	50.3	28.8	...
40	76.2	1.381	48.1	...	61.4	35.0	...
45	90.0	1.450	55.1	...	77.2	42.0	...
50	105.2	1.526	62.2	...	...	50.1	...
55	122.2	1.611	69.7	...	...	...	...
60	141.2	1.706	77.7	...	...	...	...
65	162.6	1.813	88.7	...	...	...	...

Conversion Formulas

Baumé heavier than water

$$\text{Bé} = 145 - \frac{145}{\text{sp gr}} \qquad \text{sp gr} = \frac{145}{145 - \text{Bé}}$$

Baumé lighter than water

$$\text{Bé} = \frac{140}{\text{sp gr}} - 130 \qquad \text{sp gr} = \frac{140}{130 + \text{Bé}}$$

Twadell

$$\text{Tw} = 200(\text{sp gr} - 1,000) \qquad \text{sp gr} = 0.005\text{Tw} + 1,000$$

TABLE 117

SOLUBLE COFFEE PLANTS IN THE WORLD

Maxwell House Soluble Coffee Plants
1. Hoboken, N.J. (Sanka)
2. Houston, Tex. (Sanka)
3. Jacksonville, Fla.
4. San Leandro, Calif.
5. Coburg, Ont., Canada
6. Cafe LEGAL, LeBlanc-Mensil (suburb of Paris), France
7. Helmshorn (near Hamburg), West Germany
8. Birmingham, England
9. Itami, Hyogo Prefecture, Japan
10. Cafes de Mexico (carretera Mexico-Laredo Km $17^1/_2$)

Nescafé Soluble Coffee Plants
1. Freehold, N.J. (Decaf), 1949 and 1953
2. Sunbury, Ohio, 1944
3. Ripon, Calif.
4. Granite City, Ill., 1944
5. Orbe, Switzerland, 1939
6. Chesterville, Ont., Canada (1948)
7. Hayes, England (1949), also Ashbourne
8. Mainz, West Germany (1961)
9. Hjørring, Denmark (1951)
10. La Penilla, Spain
11. Abbiategrasso, Italy
12. Hamar, Norway
13. Dennington, Australia
14. Marseille, France
15. Rotterdam, Holland
16. Ocotlan, Mexico
17. Bugalagrande, Colombia (1949)
18. Graneros, Chile (1945), also Los Angeles (1938)
19. Chiclayo, Peru
20. Argentina—Saavedra, Villanuevo (Cordoba), Magdaleno
21. Bayamo, Cuba (until 1958)
22. Gap, France, (1952)
23. Estcourt, South Africa
24. Pilot plants: Marysville, Ohio and Vevey, Switzerland
25. New plant in Brazil (1962)
26. Abidian, Ivory Coast (1962)

J. A. Folger Instant Coffee Plants
1. Houston, Tex.
2. San Francisco, Calif.

Chain Store Soluble Coffee Plants
1. Jewel Tea, Barrington, Ill. (1957)
2. Safeway, San Francisco, Calif. (1960)
3. Kroger, Cincinnati, Ohio (1957)

Private Label Soluble Coffee Plants
1. Tenco, Linden, N.J. (Div. Coca-Cola Corp.)
   Blending plants Hamburg, Germany, and San Francisco, Calif.
   Soluble coffee plant at Ajax, Canada (1961).
2. Sol Cafe, Jamaica, L.I., N.Y. (interest by Chock Full o' Nuts)
3. United Instants, Paterson, N.J.
4. Coffee Instants, L.I.C., N.Y.
5. Baker Importing, Minneapolis, Minn.
6. Schroeder Products Company, Woburn, Mass.
7. Sandra, Toronto, Canada

TABLE 117 (*Continued*)

SOLUBLE COFFEE PLANTS IN THE WORLD

Other United States Soluble Coffee Plants
1. Savarin, Palisades Park, N.J.
2. Bordens, Newport, N.Y.
3. Chase & Sanborn, Standard Brands, New Orleans, La.
4. Wm. B. Reilly, New Orleans, La.
5. Butternut-Penndale (Duncan still getting instant at Tenco)
6. Hills Bros., San Francisco, Calif.
7. Kwik-Cafe, Hatboro, Pa. (extract)
8. J.F.G., Knoxville, Tenn.
9. East Coast Coffee Corp., N.Y.C. (formerly Geo. Harrison's plant)

Soluble Coffee Plants in Europe—Other Than G.F. and Nescafé
1. Deutsche Extract Kaffee, Hamburg, West Germany
2. de Gruyter en Zoon N.V., 's-Hertogenbosch, Netherlands
3. Douwe-Egbert, Joure, Holland
4. Albert Heyn N.V., Zaandam
5. Le Cafe Martin, Paris, France
6. Chat Noit, Liege, Belgium
7. Kaffee Hag, Bremen, West Germany
8. Konsum, Mannheim, West Germany (1962)
9. Kafix-Rapid, Augsburg, West Germany (near Munich)
10. Franz-Kathreiners, Munich, West Germany
11. J. Lyons & Co., London, England
12. Brooke Bond & Co., London, England
13. Brooke Bond & Co., Johannesburg, South Africa (chicory)
14. USEGO, Olten, Switzerland
15. Thomi & Franck, Basel, Switzerland
16. Haco, Gumligen, Switzerland
17. Julius Mienl, Vienna, Asutria
18. Franz & Kathreiner, Linz, Austria
19. Moscow, U.S.S.R. (1962)
20. COGESOL (Niro) Monky, Madrid. 17 Spain 1963

Latin America—Soluble Coffee Plants Except Nescafé and G.F.
1. Caracas, Venezuela (Niro) 1961
2. Industria Colombiana de Cafe, Medellin, Colombia 1960
3. Coffee Company of Jamaica, Ltd., Kingston, Jamaica (Bowen)
4. Cafe Solubles Monterrey S.A., Monterrey, Mexico
5. Industrias de Cafes S.A., Guatemala City, (Cafetenango) Guatemala
6. Productos de Cafe, S.A., San Salvador, El Salvador, C.A.
7. Salvadorean del Cafe, San Salvador, El Salvador, (1961)
8. Cafe Soluble, S.A., Managua, Nicaragua (1961-Jan) (M.J.B.)
9. Cafe Presto de Costa Rica, S.A., San Jose, Costa Rica
10. Companhia Cacique de Cafe Soluvel, Londrinas, Parana, Brazil
11. Several new plants underway in 1962 in Brazil
12. Chile, Valparaiso, Tres Montes
13. Argentina, Buenos Aires—Arlistan, S.A. and Saint Hnos. S.A.

Canada
1. Nabob (Douglas-Kelly) Vancouver, B. C. 1962

Soluble Coffee Plants Outside Western Hemisphere and Europe
1. Australia, Bushell's Ltd., Sydney, Niro-1957, Bowen-1961
2. New Zealand, Dunedin, W. Gregg & Co.
3. Israel, Ramat Gan (Safed)—by Sol Cafe—Elite Food Ind. Ltd.
4. Commonwealth Foods, Inc., Makati, Rizal. Phillipines (Heyman)
5. Meiji Confectionary Co., Chuo-ku, Tokyo (new plant 1962)
6. Commonwealth Foods Int'l, Ltd., Hong Kong (Br.) China (1962)
7. Morinaga Confectionary Co. Ltd., Tokyo, Japan
8. India has interest currently in small soluble coffee plant
9. Serg Products, Quezon City, Philippine Islands

Index

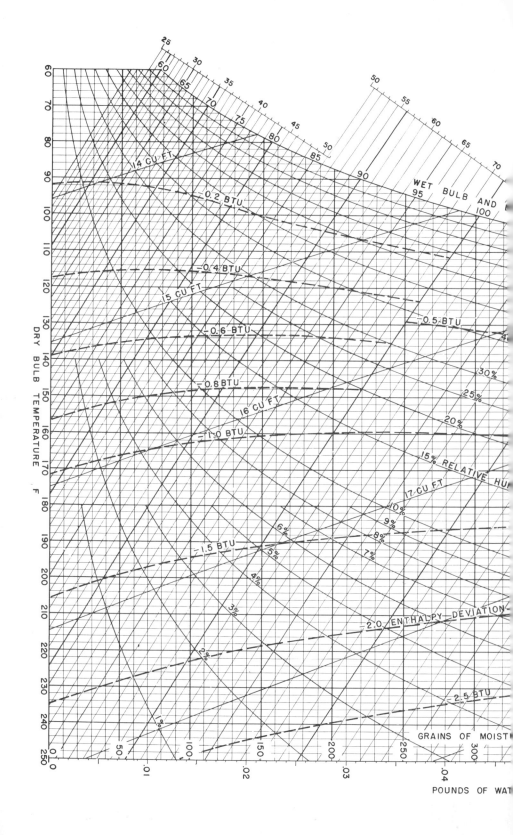